P9-EKE-847

D0037585

Bioethical Dilemmas
A Jewish Perspective
Volume II

Other Books by the Same Author

Providence in the Philosophy of Gersonides
Contemporary Halakhic Problems, Vols. I–V
Jewish Bioethics: A Reader (ed. with Fred Rosner)
Judaism and Healing
Bircas ha-Chammah
With Perfect Faith: Foundations of Jewish Belief (ed.)
Time of Death in Jewish Law
Be-Netivot ha-Halakhah, Vols. I–III
Bioethical Dilemmas: A Jewish Perspective, Vol. I

Bioethical Dilemmas
A Jewish Perspective
Volume II

J. David Bleich

A TARGUM PRESS Book

First published 2006

ISBN 1-56871-408-4

Published by:
TARGUM PRESS, INC.
22700 W. Eleven Mile Rd.
Southfield, MI 48034
E-mail: targum@netvision.net.il
Fax: 888-298-9992
www.targum.com

Distributed by:
FELDHEIM PUBLISHERS
208 Airport Executive Park
Nanuet, NY 10954

Printing plates by Frank, Jerusalem
Printed in Israel by Chish

ועל דא אצטריך לאסיא חכים לאשתדלא עליה אי יכיל למיתב ליה אסוותא מן גופא יאות ואי לאו יתן ליה אסוותא לנשמתיה, ודא הוא אסיא דקב"ה ישתדל עליה בהאי עלמא ובעלמא דאתי.

זהר, דברים דף רצ"ט.

A person needs a wise physician to endeavor on his behalf. If he can prescribe a remedy for the body, good! If not, he should provide a remedy for his soul. It is on behalf of such a physician that the Holy One, blessed be He, endeavors in this world and in the world to come.

Zohar, Deuteronomy *299a*

Contents

Preface

The major portion of the material presented in this volume is culled from articles that were originally published in *Tradition*. Some of the material was originally presented in the form of papers delivered at various bioethical conferences. A number of those papers were designed to present a comprehensive halakhic perspective for the benefit of committed and erudite students of Jewish law; others were designed simply to present a concise view of Jewish teaching to general audiences. Thus, as was the case with regard to the first volume of *Bioethical Dilemmas*, the reader should not be surprised at the absence of a uniform style in the various chapters. In particular, the final chapter, based upon a paper delivered at a law school conference, was first published in a law review and the unique style of citation and annotation common to law journals has been preserved.

In two instances some repetition of material occurs. Analyses of the propriety of hazardous medical procedures and palliation of pain both require discussion of potential foreshortening of natural longevity; both cloning and genetic engineering represent human intervention in the natural order, a matter of profound theological import. The need to assure that each chapter retain its character as a self-contained entity requires parallel discussion of those issues.

I wish to express my thanks to my brother-in-law, Rabbi Mordecai Ochs, for his painstaking reading of the manuscript; to my son, Rabbi Dr. Moshe Bleich, for drawing my attention to sources that otherwise would have eluded me and for his many valuable insights; to Rabbi Moshe Shapiro of the Mendel Gottesman Library of Yeshiva University for his unstinting aid, far beyond the call of duty; to Mr. Zalman Alpert and Mr. Zvi Erenyi for their constant helpfulness and assistance; to Mrs. Racheline Habousha of the library of the Albert Einstein College of Medicine for her unfailing graciousness in expediting my many requests; and to Dr. Gerold Borodach for making pertinent medical sources available to me.

My gratitude also to the publisher of the first volume of this work, Mr. Bernard Scharfstein of Ktav Publishing House, for his warm friendship and generous cooperation. That volume remains available from Ktav Publishing House, Jersey City, New Jersey.

Particular thanks are due to Mrs. Chaya Baila Gavant for her painstaking efforts and meticulous concern in shepherding the manuscript through the various stages of publication. Unfortunately, the untimely demise of the publisher of this volume, Rabbi Moshe Dombey, founder and managing director of Targum Press, occurred while this work was still in press. His warm friendship, unfailing indulgence and ongoing patience will never be forgotten.

Above all, I am grateful to the Almighty for my cherished collaborators—the members of my family. It is our fervent prayer that this endeavor, as our earlier efforts, serve to promote Torah study and to enhance the moral climate in which we live.

Introduction

As recently as a few decades ago, bioethics did not exist as an independent area of intellectual inquiry. Previously unfathomed advances in medical science and technology have transformed the science fiction of yesterday into the reality of today. As a result of this changing reality, contemporary society is confronted by previously unconsidered, and hence unexamined, dilemmas.

Committed Jews recognize full well that every facet of human endeavor is regulated by eternal norms enunciated at Sinai. For them, the challenge lies in teasing out the halakhic issues, uncovering relevant sources and precedents, and reaching normative determinations through the application of halakhic dialectic. Others, particularly those who are not members of the Jewish faith-community, thirst for guidance in navigating uncharted waters. At the minimum, challenges presented by a time-honored tradition serve to give pause and to spur further reflection; confirmation that one is on course, when forthcoming, serves as a form of intellectual reinforcement.

Thus it is not surprising that Jewish scholars and spokesmen are peppered with inquiries regarding these matters by

Jews and non-Jews alike. That is indeed a welcome phenomenon. Distressing is the fact that, as Rambam writes with regard to an entirely different matter: "Students are many, but the knowledgeable are few." Bioethics is but a particular and specialized facet of Halakhah. Halakhic decision-making requires extensive training, proficiency in texts and finely-honed analytic skills.

This is not to say that Jewish law is monolithic. There exist legitimate differences of opinion, often leading to conflicting conclusions, in all areas of Halakhah—and bioethics is no exception. By the same token, there are canons of decision-making that must be applied in adjudicating between conflicting views. That is the sacred duty of proficient halakhic decisors, not of self-annointed experts. One should certainly not assume that Jewish teaching will always be consonant with contemporary mores or that it will echo values currently in vogue.

This volume is not designed to provide a definitive ruling with regard to every question posed. It is designed to clarify the issues that must be raised, to explore halakhic sources pertaining to those questions, and, when appropriate, to indicate the halakhic consensus.

Even that limited task cannot be undertaken without trepidation. An exponent of Jewish law must be ever vigilant lest he err. To paraphrase the words of the ancient prayer of R. Neḥunya ben Hakanah: "May it be the Divine will that misfortune not occur through me, that I not stumble in a matter of Halakhah...that I do not declare the permissible forbidden, nor the forbidden permissible."

1

Cloning: Homologous Reproduction and Jewish Law

In the year six hundred of the sixth millennium the gates of wisdom will open on high and the fountains of wisdom [will open] below and the world will be readied to enter the seventh millennium. As a person who readies himself to enter the Sabbath on the sixth day, from the time the sun [begins to] decline, so with this as well. An allusion: "In the six hundredth year of the life of Noah . . . all the fountains of the great deep were split and the windows of the heavens were opened" (Genesis 7:11).

ZOHAR, BEREISHIT 117a

There is no gainsaying the fact that the world has witnessed quantum leaps in scientific and technological advances since the mid-nineteenth century or, according to Jewish reckoning, since 5600, i.e., the year six hundred in the sixth millennium. As foretold by the *Zohar*, the benefits are not merely pragmatic; the explosion of human knowledge is categorized by the *Zohar* as the direct result of heavenly inspiration and serves to herald the advent of the eschatological era of the seventh millennium.

God reveals Himself in the processes of nature with the result that insightful understanding of the laws of nature is, in at least some minuscule way, tantamount to apprehension of the Deity. Thus Rambam, *Hilkhot Yesodei ha-Torah* 2:2, writes that love of God is acquired by reflection upon His wondrous created works in which His wisdom can be discerned and, in *Hilkhot Yesodei ha-Torah* 4:12, Rambam declares that increased understanding of the nature of created entities carries with it enhanced love of God. Accordingly, the *tikkun*, or perfection, of which the *Zohar* speaks in describing the burgeoning of knowledge as the harbinger of the eschatological era is at one and the same time both preparation in the physical sense and preparation in the intellectual sense. In the physical sense it is comparable to Sabbath preparations carried out on the preceding day, so that, with the coming of the Messiah, man may enjoy undisturbed leisure to engage in spiritual pursuits; it is also perfection in the sense of intellectual preparation and development in the form of appreciation of the grandeur of creation, and hence of the Creator, so that man will be equipped for the more profound understanding of the nature of God that will be attainable in the eschatological era.

There can be no doubt that unraveling the mysteries of procreation and the genesis of human life are integral to this process. Attempts to fathom those mysteries are entirely laudatory. Whether or not those endeavors yield any licit practical benefit is secondary; their major value, as well as that of all aspects of theoretical science, lies in qualitatively enhanced fulfillment of the commandment "And you shall love the Lord, your God" (Deuteronomy 6:5). The legitimacy of acting upon such scientific information is another matter entirely. Surely every thinking person recognizes that not everything that can be done should be done; that which is possible is not for that reason moral.[1]

I. SCIENTIFIC BREAKTHROUGH AND POTENTIAL

Not everything that *can* be done *should* be done. But it is a truism that, in the usual course of human events, that which *can* be done *will* be done.

Since the early 1970s ethicists have grappled with the implications of human cloning.[2] What was then a vague specter now looms as an imminent reality. With the most recent breakthrough in the cloning of fetal mice in Hawaii it is evident that "advances in science are coming faster than even the most confident scientists had imagined."[3] Dr. Lee Silver, a mouse geneticist and reproductive biologist at Princeton University, described the speed at which cloning has progressed as "breathtaking" and added, "Absolutely, we are going to have cloning of humans."[4] The protestation of scientists such as Dr. Ryuzo Yanagimachi, whose cloning experiments have electrified the scientific world, that "we should stick to reproduction the way that Mother Nature did for us"[5] notwithstanding, it is now conjectured that in vitro fertilization clinics will add human cloning to their repertoires within the next five to ten years.[6]

The new era of reproductive technology was ushered in with the birth of Dolly on July 5, 1996, at the Roslin Institute in Roslin, Scotland.[7] The birth of a cloned sheep was the culmination of research undertaken by Dr. Ian Wilmut on behalf of PPL Therapeutics Ltd., a small biotechnology company with headquarters in Edinburgh. The purpose was to use sheep to generate drugs for use in treating human diseases such as hemophilia and cystic fibrosis. Genetic engineering had already been employed to produce sheep whose milk contains a drug, alpha-1 antitrypsin, that is used in treatment of cystic fibrosis. The purpose of cloning sheep was to avoid the laborious and expensive process of genetically engineering large numbers of animals individually. With cloning, once an animal has been genetically adapted, the process need not be repeated; the animal can simply be cloned and, since all its clones will have identical genetic characteristics, the clones will also produce the same drug.[8]

The research was certainly not conducted in a vacuum. Scientists have long been able to use skin cells from a frog to clone embryos that grow to the tadpole stage before dying. Much more successful is a process known as twin splitting. In 1993 Dr. Jerry Hall and Robert Stillmann of George Washington University separated as yet undifferentiated fetal cells of embryos to the two, four and eight cell stages of development and allowed each cell to develop as a separate embryo. The immediate precursor of the Roslin experiment was the work of Dr. Steen Willadsen, who was the first to successfully clone a sheep[9] from an embryo cell. Willadsen took cell nuclei, which contain the genetic blueprint encoded in DNA, and added them to animal ova whose own nuclei he had removed.[10]

However, cells derived from early embryos are not suitable for genetic engineering. Manipulation of embryo cells leads to their death with the result that they cannot be grown in a laboratory so that genes can be added in order to cause the organism to produce pharmaceutical agents. Moreover, vast numbers of cells must be grown in order to assure that at least a few will become genetically modified. Wilmut and his associate, Dr. Keith Campbell, successfully took the nucleus of a cell removed from the udder of a mature sheep and inserted it into the ovum of a ewe from which they had previously removed the existing nucleus. The egg was then jolted with a burst of electricity causing it to behave as if it was newly fertilized. The difficulty of the procedure is evidenced by the fact that it successfully culminated in the birth of a lamb only after 277 attempts.

Some time after the birth of Dolly, ABS Global Inc., a company in De Forest, Wisconsin, announced the birth of Gene, a calf that was cloned from a genetically altered fetal cell.[11] Less than two years after the cloning of a sheep from an adult cell, Dr. James Robl of the University of Massachusetts at Amherst and Dr. Steven L. Stice, a scientist employed by

Advanced Cell Technology, a commercial firm, reported the cloning of Holstein calves from genetically engineered fetal cells taken from a fifty-five-day-old male Holstein embryo.[12] Two hundred seventy-six fetal cells were inserted into an equal number of unfertilized cow eggs whose own genetic material had been removed. At the end of a week only thirty-three embryos remained alive. Twenty-eight of those were transferred to eleven cows that served as surrogate mothers. Four calves survived to parturition, but one of the calves died five days after birth as the result of a congenital heart defect. Robl and Stice had previously attempted to clone calves from adult cells but none of the fetuses survived. There have been other unpublished reports of cows pregnant with fetuses cloned from adult cells[13] but there have been no reports of the birth of other cows or sheep cloned from adult cells.

More recently and more dramatically, biologists at the University of Hawaii have reported the cloning of over fifty mice, including clones of clones, from the cells of adult mice.[14]

These experiments have implications far beyond the goal of facilitating the manufacture of pharmaceutical products from genetically altered cells, which itself is potentially of far-reaching benefit in the treatment of numerous diseases and disorders. Cells of mature organs are capable of reproducing themselves but cannot be altered to form the cells of different organs. In effect, the DNA of differentiated cells is programmed to reproduce cells of one specialized type and of no other. Thus, for example, if a pancreas is destroyed, a new pancreas cannot be generated by other cells in the body. Successful cloning of adult cells demonstrates that, when inserted into an ovum, the program of a cell's DNA can be reversed, thereby allowing the cell to reproduce and develop into cells of other bodily organs. When the process is more fully understood, it may become possible to create particular organs to replace those that become diseased or destroyed.

As noted, subsequent to the successful cloning of Dolly, the prospect of human cloning became much more than a theoretical conjecture. The initial reaction of both ethicists and scientists was that human cloning is morally unacceptable. President Clinton, following the recommendation of the National Bioethics Advisory Commission, banned the use of federal money to conduct human cloning experiments and requested that privately funded enterprises adhere to a voluntary ban on human cloning. Nevertheless, at present, other than in California,[15] the cloning of a human being is perfectly legal in the United States, although it is prohibited by law in Britain, Spain, Denmark, Germany and Australia.[16]

Despite the generally negative view with regard to cloning humans, G. Richard Seed, a Chicago physicist who has been involved in various forms of fertility research since the early 1970s, has announced that he has assembled a team of scientists for the purpose of cloning a human being before the procedure is banned and is seeking venture capital for the project.[17] Moreover, the climate of opinion has changed rapidly. Three decades ago, two fertility experts, Sophia J. Kleegman and Sherwin A. Kaufman, wrote that reproductive breakthroughs pass through several predictable stages. Reactions proceed from "horrified negation" to "negation without horror" to "slow and gradual curiosity, study, evaluation" and, finally, to "a very slow but steady acceptance."[18] The volte-face that has occurred with regard to the prospect of human cloning is best expressed in a headline that appeared in the *New York Times*: "On Cloning Humans, 'Never' Turns Swiftly into 'Why Not.'"[19] In that article Dr. Steen Willadsen, the cloning pioneer who developed the fundamental methods for cloning animals, is quoted as saying that it is just a matter of time before the first human is cloned. Earlier, John Paris, a Jesuit ethicist, remarked that he is certain that humans will be cloned: "I can't imagine a world in which someone won't try it. There are two things that drive man—power and money.

And fame leads to fortune. Someone will try it."[20]

The present climate of opinion makes analysis of the moral and ethical issues involved in cloning an imperative. But the enterprise must be undertaken honestly and objectively. To quote the late Professor Paul Ramsey, it is imperative that we

> raise the ethical questions with a serious and not a frivolous conscience. A man of frivolous conscience announces that there are ethical quandaries ahead that we must urgently consider before the future catches up with us. By this he often means that we need to devise a new ethics that will provide the rationalization for doing in the future what men are bound to do because of the new actions and interventions science will have made possible. In contrast, a man of serious conscience means to say in raising urgent ethical questions that there may be some things that men should never do. The good things that men do can be made complete only by the things they refuse to do.[21]

II. HUMAN INTERVENTION IN THE NATURAL ORDER

Faith communities that base their moral teaching upon natural law theory regard various forms of artificial procreation as immoral. The immorality of such acts lies not in their artificiality per se but in the fact that they thwart the natural character of transmission of human life. In its Thomistic formulation, the essence of natural law is a divinely ordained teleological system and the notion that divine wisdom, in guiding all creatures to their proper ends, imparts moral law to man through the medium of his intellect. As a rational creature, man's intellect inclines him toward the actions and goals proper to his nature. Thus, according to natural law theorists, among other things, lying, gluttony, drunkenness and contraception are all immoral for essentially the same reason. Such acts are performed by a human faculty created for a readily discernible purpose. The evil in the immoral form of conduct described lies in the abuse of a natural faculty by its use in an unnatural manner.

These natural law theorists further assert that it is in the nature of man to transmit life through conjugal union. Use of body fluids or tissue for generation of life in some other manner, they contend, constitutes a subversion of man's teleological function and purpose. They maintain that it is the conjugal act by which the spouses become one flesh, and only the conjugal act, that is designed for the purpose of generating human life. In effect, the phrase ". . . and they shall be one flesh" (Genesis 2:24) is understood by these theorists as having a double meaning: (1) A man "shall cleave to his wife" in order that they "shall be one flesh," i.e., that they may jointly produce a single flesh, namely, a child. Hence the announced *telos* of the conjugal act is procreation. (2) The generation of a child reflexively causes the parents themselves to become "one flesh." Thus generation of new life has as its *telos* solidification of the marital bonds.[22] Generation of a human life in some other manner and for some other purpose violates the divinely ordained *telos* for which the human body was created. On that analysis, homologous artificial fertilization is unacceptable because it separates the unitive and procreative aspects of propagation of the human species. Thus it has been stated that:

> By comparison with the transmission of other forms of life in the universe, the transmission of human life has a special character of its own, which derives from the special nature of the human person. "The transmission of human life is entrusted by nature to a personal and conscious act and as such is subject to the all-holy laws of God: immutable and inviolable laws which must be recognized and observed. For this reason one cannot use

> means and follow methods which could be licit in the transmission of the life of plants and animals."[23]

With regard to cloning specifically, the same source declares:

> . . . attempts or hypotheses for obtaining a human being without any connection with sexuality through "twin fission," cloning or parthenogenesis are to be considered contrary to the moral law, since they are in opposition to the dignity both of human procreation and of the conjugal union.[24]

There is no reflection in Jewish tradition of a doctrine that establishes a global prohibition forbidding man to tamper with known or presumed *teloi* of creation. There are indeed individual thinkers who have explained the rationale underlying particular *miẓvot* in a manner echoing such a concept. Biblical commandments prohibiting interbreeding of species and the mingling of diverse agricultural species certainly lend themselves to such an interpretation. Although Rashi, in his commentary to Leviticus 19:19, regards those restrictions as *ḥukkim*, i.e., arational statutes not subject to human inquiry, Ramban, *loc. cit.*, takes sharp issue with Rashi and opines that interbreeding and prohibited mingling of species are forbidden as constituting illicit tampering with creation. Ramban states that every creature and every plant is endowed by God with cosmically arranged distinctive features and qualities and is designed to reproduce itself so long as the universe endures. Crossbreeding and cross-fertilization produce a reconfiguration of those distinctive qualities and also compromise reproductive potential. By engaging in such activities man usurps the divine prerogative in producing a new species or entity with its own novel set of attributes and, presumably, less than optimally suited to fulfill the divinely ordained *telos* associated with the original species.

Ibn Ezra has been understood as presenting the matter in

a somewhat different light. He has been understood as declaring that the Torah prohibits crossbreeding of species because the act thwarts propagation of the species and hence represents an injustice to the animals who are prevented from fulfilling the divine purpose of propagating their respective species,[25] and as explaining the prohibitions against the mixture of agricultural species as well as against the combination of linen and wool in the cloth of a garment as violative of the natural order decreed by the Creator.[26] R. Samson Raphael Hirsch had no difficulty in explaining the prohibition regarding *sha'atnez* (the mixing of linen and wool) in similar terms. Indeed, R. Hirsch understood all *ḥukkim* as being reflective of the principle that man should not interfere with the order and harmony—and hence the *telos*—of creation.[27] According to R. Hirsch, such laws are distinguished from *mishpatim* or so-called rational commandments only because our duties toward fellow men are more intelligible to us by virtue of our recognition of our own needs and aspirations. That particular purposes are similarly assigned to animals and even to inanimate objects is not immediately grasped by the human intellect and hence *ḥukkim* are depicted as arational. It is noteworthy that, although R. Hirsch regards these commandments as designed to prevent interference with divinely ordained *teloi*, unlike natural law theologians, he regards the *teloi* themselves as not being immediately available to human reason. That is certainly confirmed by the fact that no natural law philosopher has ever asserted that the manufacture of linsey-woolsey or even agricultural hybridization is intuitively perceived as violative of the divine plan for creation.

Were it to be assumed that tampering with the ostensive or presumed nature of animal species is always forbidden, most forms of genetic engineering would be illicit. No bacterium is designed by nature to clean up oil spills by metabolizing petroleum or to excrete human insulin for use by diabetics. In the absence of evidence in rabbinic sources to the contrary, it must be assumed that, even accepting Ramban's explanation of the prohibition against interbreeding or R. Hirsch's broader analysis of the rationale underlying *ḥukkim* in general, such strictures must be understood as limited to those matters explicitly prohibited.[28]

Indeed, there is a perceptible tension between the concepts enunciated by Ramban and R. Samson Raphael Hirsch and the many midrashic sources indicating that man is an active partner in the process of creation and, as such, is charged with bringing creative processes to completion. Indeed, the biblical charge to Adam exhorting him to "fill the earth and conquer it" (Genesis 1:28) seems to give Adam *carte blanche* to engage in any form of conduct that is not specifically proscribed. The problem is readily resolved if it is understood that, in general, the functions and *teloi* of the products of creation are not immutable; that the Creator did not intend to bar man from applying his ingenuity in finding new uses and purposes for the objects of creation;[29] and that there is no injustice to animal species or inanimate objects in doing so. Immutability of function and *telos* is the exception, not the rule. Thus, for example, it has never been suggested that manufacture and use of synthetic fibers in the making of clothes is in any way a contravention of either the letter or spirit of the law.[30] The exceptions were announced by the Creator as formal prohibitions.[31] It is precisely because human reason cannot intuit, or even comprehend, when and under what circumstances contravention of the natural order is inappropriate that these commandments are in the nature of *ḥukkim*.

More generally, man's creative power, at least to the extent that it does not involve creation of novel species, is extolled in rabbinic sources. The divine appellation "*Shaddai*" is understood in rabbinic exegesis as an acronym: *she-amarti le-olami "dai"*—Who said to My universe, "Enough!" Thus the verse, "I, the Lord *Shaddai*" (Genesis 17:1) is rendered by

Midrash Rabbah 46:2, "I am the Lord who said to the universe 'Enough!' "[32] R. Jonathan Eibeschutz, *Tiferet Yonatan, ad locum*, followed by R. Joseph Dov Soloveitchik, *Bet ha-Levi, ad locum*, explains that, in His creation of various artifacts, God arrested their development before completion. Man plants a seed, the seed germinates, a stalk grows and kernels of wheat develop. The Creator could well have made it possible for the kernels to crumble into flour, for the flour to absorb rain or moisture from the atmosphere, for the wind to churn the water-drenched flour so that dough be formed and for the heat of the sun to bake the mixture in order to yield a product that might literally be termed a "breadfruit." Instead, the Creator arrested the process long before its completion and ordained that grinding of the wheat, mixing the flour with water, kneading the dough and baking the bread be performed by man. Similarly, the flax plant could have been endowed with properties causing strands of flax to separate and intertwine themselves in a cloth which might grow in the shape of a cloak. Instead, the process is arrested and brought to completion by man. Indeed, the Gemara, *Shabbat* 30b, declares that in the eschatological era the Land of Israel will yield "cakes" and "linen garments." *Bet ha-Levi* explains that the import of that statement is simply that, in the end of days, God will allow the processes of creation to be culminated by modifying the natural order in a manner that will permit the creative process to become complete and thus spare man any travail. In the interim, however, He has declared, "Enough!" i.e., He has precipitously interrupted the process of creation and coopted man, who must complete the process, as a collaborator in fashioning the universe.

The concept of man as an active partner in bringing the process of creation to completion as portrayed in the aggadic statement of the Gemara reappears much later in rabbinic writings as an explanation of the nature of the forms of "labor" that are prohibited on the Sabbath. In the nineteenth century, R. Jacob Zevi Mecklenberg, *Ha-Ketav ve-ha-Kabbalah*, Exodus 20:10, and R. Samson Raphael Hirsch,[33] each writing independently, take note of the fact that the "labor" prohibited on *Shabbat* is not a correlative of physical exertion. For example, carrying or stacking heavy objects, so long as performed within the confines of a private domain, entails no violation of any biblical prohibition, while placing even a small quantity of food over an already existing flame constitutes a capital transgression. These scholars develop the thesis that, on the Sabbath, the Jew is commanded to emulate God, who desisted from creative endeavors on the seventh day. The notion of exertion or expenditure of physical energy in association with the Deity is entirely noncognitive. God "rested" on the seventh day "from all His work that He created" (Genesis 2:2) solely in the sense that He ceased to bring novel entities into being. Man, too, assert these writers, is commanded to rest on the seventh day, not from physical labor, but from activities that serve to complete the creative process and bring it to fruition. Thus God created foodstuffs, but many are inedible until cooked; man initiates the process of cooking which serves to render those products edible and in doing so completes the creation of food. God arrested the creative process by saying "Enough!" and left it for man to bring the process to final culmination. It is precisely such activity, *viz.*, completion of the creative process, that is prohibited to man on the Sabbath regardless of how effortless and physically undemanding the task may be. To rephrase the concept, six days a week man engages in completing the tasks left uncompleted by the Creator and by doing so becomes an active partner in the process of creation; on the seventh, the Jew emulates the Creator by ceasing and desisting from all such creative endeavors.

It is abundantly clear that human intervention in the natural order is normatively interdicted only to the extent that there are explicit prohibitions limiting such intervention.

Moreover, there is no evidence either from Scripture or from rabbinic writings that forms of intervention or manipulation not expressly banned are contrary to the spirit of the law. Quite to the contrary, Jewish tradition, although it certainly recognizes divine proprietorship of the universe, nevertheless, gratefully acknowledges that while "The heavens are the heavens of God" yet "the earth has He given to the sons of man" (Psalms 115:16). In bestowing that gift upon mankind, the Creator has granted man dominion over the world in which he lives and over the living species that are coinhabitants of that world. Man has been given license to apply his intellect, ingenuity and physical prowess in developing the world in which he has been placed subject only to limitations imposed by the laws of the Torah, including the general admonition not to do harm to others, as well as by the constraints imposed by good sense and considerations of prudence.

There is ample reason to assume that Jewish teaching would not frown upon cloning of either animals or humans simply because it is a form of asexual, and hence "unnatural," reproduction. The Gemara, *Sanhedrin* 65b, relates that R. Ḥanina and R. Oshia met every Friday for the purpose of perusing *Sefer Yeẓirah* in order to create a calf for their Sabbath meal. This anecdote is recounted by the Gemara without the slightest hint of censure. The text incontrovertibly yields two principles: 1) asexual husbandry, at least with regard to animal species, is morally innocuous; and 2) harnessing metaphysical forces, or "white magic," at least when practiced by masters of the Kabbalah, is acceptable. Although there is nothing in this narrative that may be cited as providing an explicit basis for extending such sanction to creation of a hybrid, interbreed or genetically engineered animal, the report certainly reflects acceptance of the legitimacy of asexual, and hence homologous, reproduction of animals.

Me'iri, *Sanhedrin* 67b, finds asexual reproduction, at least of animals, to be not only permissible but even empirically possible. He asserts that creation of "beautiful creatures other than from a sexual union" is known "from scientific books" to be a phenomenon that is "not in the realm of the impossible." Me'iri declares that employment of natural causes for purposes of asexual reproduction is not to be regarded as a form of magic or sorcery and hence is entirely permissible.

III. MAN AS CREATOR OF MAN

The notion that man is an active partner of the Deity in the process of creation extends to the creation of members of the human species as well. This is poignantly reflected in the words of the Sages recorded in *Kiddushin* 30b: "There are three partners in [the conception of] a person: his father, his mother and God." Thus man, in engaging in procreative activity in order to promulgate the human species, is depicted as an active participant in the ongoing process of creation. The question is whether procreative license is limited to sexual reproduction or whether it encompasses asexual or homologous reproduction as well.

There may well be cogent reason to distinguish between various forms of asexual reproduction with the result that approbation expressed with regard to a particular mode of reproduction may not necessarily be transposed to endorsement of all. Thus, for example, parthenogenesis, although homologous in nature, is more closely akin to natural reproduction with the result that it is less likely than cloning to be found objectionable. Similarly, artificial splitting of an embryo in the earliest stages of cell division represents a relatively minimal level of human intervention. Cloning involves a much higher degree of manipulation and interference with the natural order. Least natural is the creation of a *golem* or anthropoid in whom replication of already existing human genetic material is completely lacking. For reasons that require no elaboration, creation of a *golem* is the only form of asexual reproduction heretofore addressed in rabbinic literature. Although cloning may present an array of halakhic and moral issues significantly different from those posed in the fashioning of a *golem*, examination of extant *golem* literature is instructive for purposes of establishing an attitudinal framework in which the contemporary problem can be examined.

The most significant source by far is the narrative recorded by the Gemara, *Sanhedrin* 65b. According to Rashi's understanding, the Gemara cites the verse "Your iniquities have been a barrier between you and your God" (Isaiah 59:2) as establishing that, but for their supposedly minor transgressions, the righteous would find it within their power to emulate God and create a universe.[34] Presumably in illustration of that point, the Gemara reports that Rava created a man and sent him to R. Zeira. R. Zeira spoke to the man but he did not answer. Thereupon R. Zeira said to him, "You stem from [our] colleagues.[35] Return to your dust."

R. Zeira must have been aware that the creature appearing before him was an anthropoid before he attempted to engaged him in conversation; otherwise, it would have been impossible for R. Zeira to have known that he was not simply confronting a mute person. R. Zeira then proceeded to destroy the creature because as an artificial creature he regarded it as defective or undesirable.[36] Had the anthropoid been capable of speech R. Zeira would presumably have had no problem with its continued existence.

Maharsha's comments *ad locum* are most revealing in this regard. Maharsha comments that speech is the "power of the soul." The anthropoid could not speak, declares Maharsha, because Rava lacked the ability to create a soul and R. Zeira proceeded to destroy it precisely because it was not endowed with a human soul. It follows from Maharsha's analysis that had Rava, either by harnessing the teachings of *Sefer Yeẓirah* or otherwise, been capable of creating an anthropoid endowed with a soul, R. Zeira would have had no objection.[37]

Maharsha's analysis serves to underscore the import of the

Gemara's original statement declaring that, in the total absence of transgression, the righteous are capable of creating not merely an anthropoid but even an entire universe and to resolve the tension between that statement and R. Zeira's destruction of the anthropoid actually created by Rava. The Gemara ascribes the power of creation to the righteous in terminology that is entirely matter of fact. There is no hint that such power should not be utilized just as there is no censure of R. Ḥanina and R. Oshia for having created a calf. R. Zeira did not destroy the *golem* created by Rava because he disapproved of Rava's attempt to engage in such an enterprise but because the result was not satisfactory. Rava, presumably because of the "inequities" that constitute a barrier between man and God, was incapable of creating a man endowed with a soul. Had it indeed been within Rava's power to do so, R. Zeira would not have interfered. However, upon discovering the inherent deficiency of the anthropoid, R. Zeira destroyed the creature.[38] Although the considerations that prompted R. Zeira to act in that manner are not spelled out, R. Zeira undoubtedly had reason to fear that the imperfect anthropoid arising from a failed attempt to create a human would prove to be a source of grief. Indeed, as will be noted later,[39] this indeed proved to be the case with regard to the *golem* purportedly created by R. Elijah of Helm.

Nevertheless, even if man has the power to create a clone endowed with a human soul, there may well be reason to question whether that power should be used. Lurking beneath the surface of theological opposition to cloning is not simply that artificial creation of human beings represents an illicit mode of *imitatio Dei* but that success in such an endeavor would have a profound psychological effect upon the perceiver, *viz.*, perception of the uniqueness of the Deity as compromised by human emulation of creative function would lead to denial of divine creation of the universe and even to denial of the existence of God.

That concern is indeed echoed in one kabbalistic source. One of the earliest medieval references to creation of a *golem* is found in a thirteenth-century work, *Sefer ha-Gematri'ot*, authored by disciples of R. Judah the Pious.[40] That source reports:

> Ben Sira wanted to study *Sefer Yeẓirah*. A voice [*bat kol*] came out and said, "You cannot do it alone." He went to Jeremiah his father. Ben Sira is [numerically equivalent to] Ben Yermiyahu [the son of Jeremiah], and they studied it and after three years, a man was created to them, upon whose forehead it was written *Emet*, as on the forehead of Adam. And the created one said to them: "If the Unique One, the Holy One, Blessed be He, [who] created Adam, when He wanted to kill [*le-hamit*] Adam, He erased a letter from *emet* and what remained is *MeT* [dead], even more so I would like to do it and you shall no longer create a man, so that people shall not err concerning him, as it happened in the generation of Enosh."[41] This is why Jeremiah said: "Cursed is the man who relies on Adam." The created man said to them: "Reverse the combination of the letters backwards." And they erased the *alef* from his forehead and he immediately turned into ashes.[42]

As expressed in *Sefer ha-Gematri'ot* the concern to which the *golem* gives voice is that he might be deified as, according to the midrashic tradition cited in this narrative, had previously occurred in the generation of Enosh when people prostrated themselves before Adam, believing that he was God because of his gargantuan height.

However, the same narrative is presented in a somewhat different manner by the anonymous author of a manuscript treatise titled *The Secret of the Name of 42 Letters*:

> We found in *Sefer ha-Bitaḥon* written by R. Yehudah (ben Bateirah) that Jeremiah, of blessed memory, was

studying *Sefer Yeẓirah* alone. A voice came out and said to him: "Take a companion." He went to Sira his son and they studied [together] for three years in order to accomplish what was written. Then they that feared the Lord spoke one with the other. At the end of three years, when they wanted to combine the alphabets, according to the *Ẓeruf* [combination], the *Mikhlol* and the *Ma'amar,* a man was created, and on his forehead it was written, *YHVH Elohim Emet.* In the hand of that man there was a knife, and he was erasing the *alef* of the word *emet* and there remained *met.* Jeremiah rent his garment and said to him, "Why did you erase the *alef* of *emet*?" He answered him, "I will tell you a parable . . . . Thus is God, when He created you in the image, likeness and form. Now, when you created a man like Him, the people will say that there is no God in the world but you." Jeremiah told him, "If so, how can we repair it [*mai takanteh*]?" He answered them, "Write the letters backwards on the dust that was thrown, by the intention of your heart, and do not think about the way of [its] honor or of its order [*tikkuno*] but do all this backwards." And they also did so and that man became before their eyes dust and ashes. Then Jeremiah said, "Indeed it is worthwhile to study these matters for the sake of knowing the power and dynamis of the creator of the world, but not in order to do [them]. You shall study them in order to comprehend and teach."[43]

Whether or not successful cloning of a human being in the early years of the twenty-first century would have the same profound psychological impact as the creation of an awesome anthropoid in the days of Jeremiah or even in the thirteenth century is speculative. Neither polytheistic confusion nor deification of man appears to be likely in our day, although belief in the Deity's role as Creator of the universe, and of man in particular, may be weakened in the minds of some. Moreover, the concern voiced in this anonymous kabbalistic treatise is not reflected in authoritative halakhic sources. Nevertheless, there is a widespread perception that any attempt at human cloning would constitute an act of extreme hubris on the part of man.

IV. IMPORT OF THE *GOLEM* LITERATURE

The rabbinic literature devoted to the *golem* is of importance with regard to another matter pertaining to cloning as well, *viz.*, the halakhic status of a cloned individual. In its broadest terms, the question is whether or not an anthropoid enjoys the halakhic status of a human being. Particular issues that have been addressed explicitly are whether destruction of an anthropoid is tantamount to homicide, whether an anthropoid can be counted in a *minyan* and whether its corpse defiles in the manner of a human cadaver. Analogous questions have also been raised with regard to animals created in a similar manner, e.g., may the meat of such an animal be cooked in milk and may the animal be offered as a sacrifice. The discussion of these questions with regard to anthropoids is only the first step in an analysis of the relevant halakhic issues since generation from human gametes, gestation in vitro as well as normal parturition, as will be shown, may indeed significantly alter the conclusions. These discussions are, however, entirely relevant to the analogous situation of a cloned embryo or an embryo fertilized in vitro that is also subsequently artificially incubated outside the mother's womb, as described by Aldous Huxley in his *Brave New World*.

In the course of Jewish history there have been numerous reports concerning the creation of a *golem* by various individuals.[44] In the annals of Halakhah, most significant by far is the narrative of R. Zevi Ashkenazi. R. Zevi Ashkenazi, *Teshuvot Ḥakham Ẓevi*, no. 93, reports that his grandfather,[45] R. Elijah Ba'al Shem of Helm, had created a *golem*.[46] *Ḥakham Ẓevi*'s son, R. Jacob Emden, *She'ilat Ya'aveẓ*, II, no. 82, adds that when the *golem* "grew stronger and greater because of the Divine Name written on a paper attached to his forehead," R. Elijah became afraid that the *golem* would wax harmful and destructive. R. Elijah therefore destroyed the creature by tearing the paper from the *golem*'s forehead, whereupon the *golem* fell to the ground as a lump of dust.[47]

Although the discussion is directed to an entirely different issue, *Ḥakham Ẓevi*, perhaps prompted by the fact that his grandfather subsequently destroyed the *golem* that he himself had created, remarks, *en passant*, that even if the *golem* is deemed to be human for other purposes, its destruction is not a violation of the prohibition against homicide. The basic assumption, *viz.*, that there is no attendant prohibition, is amply evidenced by R. Zeira's conduct with regard to the anthropoid created by Rava. The simplest explanation for R. Zeira's lack of concern in taking the life of the anthropoid is that such a creature is not at all deemed to be human—and perhaps not even an animal[48]—and hence can be destroyed with impunity. [As will be noted later, this is indeed the position of the sixteenth century kabbalist, R. Moses Cordovero, *Pardes Rimmonim*, chap. 24, sec. 10, as well as of the early seventeenth century authority (and ancestor of *Ḥida*), R. Abraham Azulai, *Ḥesed le-Avraham, Ma'ayan Revi'i, nahar* 30. *Ḥesed le-Avraham* asserts that the vitality of a creature created by means of *Sefer Yeẓirah* is comparable to the "vitality of an animal" and that, since anthropoids do not enjoy the status of human beings,[49] their destruction entails no transgression. *Ḥesed le-Avraham* was followed in this position by his descendant, R. Chaim Joseph David Azulai (*Ḥida*), *Maḥazik Berakhah, Oraḥ Ḥayyim* 55:1, and later in his *Mar'it he-Ayin, Sanhedrin* 65b.]

However, *Ḥakham Ẓevi*, at least for the purpose of his initial discussion, assumes that an anthropoid does enjoy the status of a human being and hence was constrained to find an alternative justification for R. Zeira's conduct. *Ḥakham Ẓevi* cites the discussion of the Gemara, *Sanhedrin* 57b, with regard to feticide. The Gemara adduces Genesis 9:6, which is conventionally rendered "Whosoever sheds the blood of a man, by man shall his blood be shed." The Hebrew phrase "*ba-adam damo yishafekh*" in the verse "*shofekh dam ha-adam ba-adam damo yishafekh*" is readily translated in that manner, i.e., "by man shall his blood be shed." However, since the biblical text contains no commas and the word "*ba-adam*" can equally well be understood as meaning "within man," the verse can also be rendered "Whosoever sheds the blood of a man within a man, his blood shall be shed." For purposes of talmudic exegesis the verse is indeed understood as having the latter meaning. Hence the ensuing talmudic query: "Who is a 'man within a man?' " And the immediate response: "One must say this is a fetus in the mother's womb." That interpretation forms the basis for the Gemara's determination that feticide is a capital offense in the Noahide Code. *Ḥakham Ẓevi* alludes to that discussion in declaring that since an anthropoid is not formed in a woman's womb its destruction cannot constitute an act of homicide.

Ḥakham Ẓevi's opinion regarding destruction of an anthropoid was challenged by R. Gershon Leiner, popularly known as the *Radzyner Rebbe*, in his *Sidrei Taharot*, *Oholot* 5a. Acceptance of *Ḥakham Ẓevi*'s thesis would logically lead to the conclusion that, since Adam was not born of a human mother, Adam might have been murdered with impunity—a conclusion *Sidrei Taharot* regards as absurd particularly since Adam was created by God as a human *par excellence*.

The major problem, however, is that the talmudic interpretation is not at all intended to be a literal reading of the scriptural passage but expresses an additional level of meaning reflecting the notion that the particular language in which the commandment is couched is designed to incorporate feticide within the parameters of the prohibition against homicide. The rabbinic interpretation may well be understood as inclusive rather than exclusive. As such, the rabbinic interpretation of the verse should be understood as having the effect of rendering its meaning: "Whosoever shall shed the blood of *even* a man within a man, his blood shall be shed." Or to put the matter somewhat differently, the exegetical interpretation is designed to expand the ambit of the prohibition to include "a man within a man" but does not ordain that characteristic as a necessary condition of applicability.

More significantly, the verse in question was addressed to Noah and forms part of the Noahide Code. The verse serves to elucidate the crime of homicide as integral to the Seven Commandments of the Sons of Noah. Murder as one of the 613 commandments of the Sinaitic code binding upon Jews is prohibited on the basis of entirely different verses. Indeed, albeit with a number of highly significant exceptions, there is a plethora of authorities who maintain that, for Jews, feticide, although forbidden on other grounds, is not a form of homicide.[50] Those authorities clearly regard extension of the prohibition to encompass feticide as limited solely to the prohibitions which form part of the Noahide Code. Similarly, even if the verse is regarded as limiting the prohibition to the killing of a person born of a woman's womb, such limitation should also be regarded as applicable only to the Noahide Code.

The particular issue addressed by *Ḥakham Ẓevi* is whether the *golem* may be counted as one of the ten people necessary to constitute a *minyan*, i.e., a quorum for public prayer. In effect, the issue addressed by *Ḥakham Ẓevi* is not the anthropoid's status as a human being but his status as a Jew. Indeed, although *Ḥakham Ẓevi*'s final position is somewhat ambiguous, the anthropoid's status as a human is taken for granted as evidenced by the argument presented. *Ḥakham Ẓevi* cites the dictum recorded in *Sanhedrin* 19a: "He who rears an orphan in his home, Scripture considers it as if he had begotten him" and, without further elaboration, astonishingly concludes, "Likewise since [the *golem*] is the handiwork of the righteous he is included among the sons of Israel for the handiwork[51] of the righteous are their progeny." However, *Ḥakham Ẓevi* dismisses his own argument on the grounds that, were the anthropoid capable of providing any benefit (*to'elet*), e.g., were he qualified to serve as a member of a *minyan*, R. Zeira would not have been justified in destroying him.[52] The implication is that the *golem* was ineligible to serve as a member of a *minyan* because the *golem* shares neither the responsibilities nor the prerogatives of members of the Jewish community and hence that *Ḥakham Ẓevi* does not regard a *golem* as Jewish.[53] Whether or not his concluding comment indicates that the *golem* is also not to be regarded as human is unclear.[54]

In his earlier cited responsum, *Ḥakham Ẓevi*'s son, R. Jacob Emden, questions his father's conclusion regarding the anthropoid's eligibility to be counted as a member of a *minyan*. *She'ilat Ya'aveẓ* sees no reason why a *golem* endowed with auditory perception and capable of understanding words addressed to him should not be capable of speech as well and hence assumes that the anthropoid created by Rava was not only incapable of speech but was deaf as well. But, notes *She'ilat Ya'aveẓ*, a deaf-mute cannot be included in a *minyan*. Accordingly, argues *She'ilat Ya'aveẓ*, adjudication of the status of an anthropoid in that context is superfluous. The identical observation is made by R. Chaim Joseph David Azulai, *Birkei Yosef, Oraḥ Ḥayyim* 55:4. It would follow from these comments that there is no evidence to rebut *Ḥakham Ẓevi*'s original argument—assuming it is regarded as cogent in the first instance—establishing the *golem*'s status as a Jew. *She'ilat Ya'aveẓ*, however, concludes his responsum by citing an earlier authority, *Ḥesed le-Avraham, Ein Ya'akov, Ma'ayan Revi'i, nahar* 30, who comments that the vitality of a *golem* is that of an animal and hence the *golem* is to be regarded as "an animal in the form of man" whose destruction entails no transgression.[55] *Ḥesed le-Avraham*, and apparently *She'ilat Ya'aveẓ* as well, maintain that a *golem* is not at all human.

Writing in the latter part of the nineteenth century, R. Judah Asad, *Teshuvot Maharya*, I, no. 26, asserts that *Ḥakham Ẓevi*'s original quandary with regard to including an anthropoid as a member of a *minyan* must be understood as a question according to only one school of rabbinic thought. *Shulḥan Arukh, Oraḥ Ḥayyim* 55:6, rules that a person who is asleep may be counted as a member of the quorum of ten. *Bet Yosef*, in his commentary on the Tur, *ad locum*, attributes that view to his teacher, Mahari bei Rav. *Taz, Oraḥ Ḥayyim* 55:4, takes sharp issue with that view and argues that the status of a sleeping person is inferior even to that of a minor. Referring to *Bet Yosef*'s own citation of a comment of the *Zohar, Taz* declares that the soul departs from a person during sleep with the result that a sleeping person is in a state of quasi-death and devoid of sanctity. In defense of the ruling of *Shulḥan Arukh*, *Mahari Asad* declares that the comment of the *Zohar* must be understood as applying only to a person sleeping alone. When, however, there is a group of ten and the *Shekhinah* rests upon them the *Shekhinah* does not depart simply because one member of the group has fallen asleep. Under such circumstances, declares *Mahari Asad*, the soul of the sleeping person remains in his body.

Mahari Asad observes that, if a sleeping person cannot be counted as a member of a *minyan* because his soul has temporarily taken leave of his body as maintained by *Taz*, *a fortiori*, an anthropoid "in whom there is no soul at all, only an animating spirit" cannot be counted toward a *minyan*. Thus, he observes, *Ḥakham Ẓevi*, in formulating his question, must have assumed with conviction that the normative view is that of *Shulḥan Arukh*, i.e., that a person may be counted toward a *minyan* even while asleep.

The ruling of *Ḥakham Ẓevi* and *She'ilat Ya'aveẓ* disqualifying an anthropoid from being counted in a *minyan* and *She'ilat Ya'aveẓ*' view that an anthropoid is not deemed to be a human being for purposes of Halakhah was challenged by

R. Ẓadok ha-Kohen of Lublin, *Kuntres Divrei Ḥalomot,* sec. 6.[56] As reflected in the title of the work, R. Ẓadok reports that the argument in its entirety occurred to him in a dream. The position espoused by *Ḥakham Ẓevi* and *She'ilat Ya'aveẓ* is based entirely upon the fact that R. Zeira destroyed the *golem* sent to him by Rava, an action those authorities deemed unthinkable were the *golem* to have been able to serve a worthwhile purpose such as being included in a *minyan.* R. Ẓadok, however, notes that it is in the nature of a *golem* continuously to grow and expand, as *She'ilat Ya'aveẓ* reports was the case with regard to the *golem* created by R. Elijah of Helm.[57] Interestingly, R. Ẓadok notes that the Gemara reports that R. Ḥanina and R. Oshia created their calf only on the eve of the Sabbath. Had they created it earlier in the week, conjectures R. Ẓadok, by *Shabbat* it would have grown much too large.[58] R. Ẓadok maintains that the *golem* created by Rava must have been created for some specific purpose not disclosed by the Gemara and was destroyed by R. Zeira because of the fear that as it continued to grow it would wreak havoc. It will be remembered that it was for that reason that R. Elijah of Helm destroyed the *golem* that he had created. Hence, argues R. Ẓadok, there is no evidence that an anthropoid should not be considered human.

Curiously, R. Ẓadok seems to accept *Ḥakham Ẓevi*'s original contention that the anthropoid is not only human but also a Jew because the anthropoid was created by a righteous Jew. Nevertheless, R. Ẓadok maintains the anthropoid is not endowed with a soul and hence is neither rewarded nor punished in the afterlife. Accordingly, he argues, when Moses is directed to transmit a commandment and addressed in the words "speak to the children of Israel," such admonition does not include an anthropoid.

It is remarkable that R. Ẓadok adopts this position while simultaneously asserting that we must assume that a *golem* is endowed with reason.[59] Consistent with that view he disputes *She'ilat Ya'avez̧'* contention that an anthropoid cannot be considered for inclusion in a *minyan* by virtue of the fact that he is a deaf-mute. Developing a thesis that is more fully articulated in other sources,[60] R. Z̧adok declares that disqualification of a deaf-mute is not absolute. R. Z̧adok adopts the view that a deaf-mute lacks legal capacity solely because, since he is deprived of the ability to communicate, he cannot develop intellectually. The anthropoid, however, contends R. Z̧adok, is created "as a mature man," and therefore it should be assumed that he is endowed with reason in a manner comparable to an adult.[61] In the case of an anthropoid, lack of speech, asserts R. Z̧adok, is to be attributed to the fact that it lacks "a portion of God from above." R. Z̧adok attributes the source of speech to the divine power breathed into Adam as recounted in the verse "and He breathed into his nostrils the breath of life" (Genesis 2:7) in accordance with Targum Onkelos' translation of "the breath of life" as "the speaking spirit (*ruaḥ memallela*)." But, according to R. Z̧adok, since the anthropoid is fully developed in every other way there is no reason to assume that his rational faculty is defective.

Various other halakhic aspects of the status of an artificial animal created by means of *Sefer Yez̧irah* are discussed by rabbinic writers. *Shelah, Parashat Va-Yeshev*, declares that an animal created in such a manner does not require ritual slaughter and, moreover, its *ḥelev* (fat from certain portions of the body that in the case of sacrificial animals is offered on the altar) and blood is permissible.[62] R. Meir Leibush Malbim, in his commentary on Genesis 18:18, indicates that the meat of such a creature may be cooked and eaten with milk. Malbim employs that halakhic observation in explaining how it was possible for Abraham to serve the angels who visited him dairy foods together with the meat of a calf. According to Malbim, the calf that was served was created by Abraham by means of *Sefer Yez̧irah*, with the result that eating its meat together with milk was entirely permissible.[63] R. Z̧adok asserts that such an animal cannot be offered as a sacrifice since the biblical section defining the suitability of animals for sacrificial purposes begins with the phrase "When a bull or a sheep or a goat will be born" (Leviticus 22:27).[64]

It is rather evident that there are four[65] distinct views with regard to the status of a *golem*: *Ḥesed le-Avraham*, *She'ilat Ya'aveẓ*, and possibly *Ḥakham Ẓevi* maintain that its status is identical to that of a brute animal; R. Ẓadok ha-Kohen maintains that it is human in every sense; Maharsha and R. Gershon Leiner maintain that only an anthropoid endowed with speech is human; *Ẓofnat Pa'aneaḥ* maintains that an anthropoid does not at all have the status of a living creature.

V. CLONING AND SPECIES IDENTITY

As stated at the outset, discussion of the halakhic status of a *golem* may appear to be esoteric and irrelevant to the status of a cloned animal or person. That presumption, however, is incorrect. The *golem* literature serves to demonstrate the unassailability of the status of a cloned human as a human being according to the view of Maharsha, R. Ẓadok ha-Kohen and R. Gershon Leiner.[66] In order to establish the humanity of a human clone according to the authorities who espouse a conflicting view with regard to the status of an anthropoid it is necessary to distinguish between a clone and a *golem*.[67]

The crucial distinction between a *golem* and a clone is that a *golem* is created, if not *ex nihilo*, then from mere dust, but clearly lacks a human progenitor. A human clone, although the product of asexual reproduction, does have a human progenitor. There is no evidence that Halakhah assigns a living creature membership in a particular species solely on the basis of sexual reproduction or on the basis of the identity of both parents as members of a common species. On the contrary, Halakhah is cognizant of the existence of interspecies and attributes to the progeny the identity of the species of the mother. Whether the identity of the father, and with it membership in the father's species as well, is to be attributed to offspring produced by interbreeding is a matter of talmudic controversy.

The matter of identification as a member of a species is best summed up in a pithy comment attributed to R. Chaim Soleveitchik. It is reported that R. Chaim explained a certain halakhic concept by posing the following query: Why is a horse a horse? Is it a horse because it manifests certain characteristics which are necessary conditions of being a horse, or is a horse a horse because its mother was a horse? The answer is that a horse is a horse because its mother was of that species. For that reason the Mishnah, *Bekhorot* 5b, declares that the offspring of a kosher animal is kosher even if it has the appearance and physical attributes of a non-kosher animal and, conversely, the offspring of a non-kosher animal is non-kosher even if it has the appearance and physical attributes of a kosher animal. Thus identity as a member of a particular species is determined not by distinguishing characteristics, but by birth.

Applied to the human species, it may well be the case that humans differ from other members of the animal kingdom by virtue of defining characteristics such as being featherless bipeds or by virtue of being endowed with reason, yet the progeny of beings categorized as humans by virtue of having been endowed with those attributes at the time of Creation are also human even if such progeny lack those characteristics.

Similarly, R. Elchanan Wasserman remarks several times in his writings that, although the concept of *yoẓei* is generally associated with the status of food products, it does not represent a novel rule limited to determining the permitted or prohibited nature of a foodstuff for purposes of the dietary code. Rather, asserts R. Elchanan, any thing that is emitted by, or proceeds from, a particular entity has the status of the entity that produced it. Thus, the concept of *yoẓei* serves as the principle to be employed in determining identity as a member of a species with such determination of identity having consequential effect in determining issues of religious law.[68]

The term *yoẓei* used in the foregoing is not to be understood in its narrow halakhic sense according to which, for example, the milk of a non-kosher animal is forbidden as *yoẓei*. Halakhah distinguishes between the prohibition against eating the meat of the non-kosher animal and its milk which is prohibited on the basis of an independent and less severe prohibition. The concept as employed herein is best reflected in a comment of Rashi, *Ḥullin* 90a, s.v. *alma*, in which Rashi notes that a prohibition that is attendant upon an embryo in an early stage of gestation is temporally prior to the actualization of the prohibition against eating the sciatic sinew that is triggered only during a later stage of gestation (*viz.*, upon development of the sciatic sinew) and explains that the first prohibition is regarded as having temporal priority even with regard to fetal tissue produced later in the gestational period. Thus Rashi asserts that the prohibition against partaking of the flesh of sacrificial animals devolves upon an embryo within the womb of a sacrificial animal and is regarded as preempting the further prohibition attendant upon the subsequently developing sciatic sinew. That priority carries over even to tissue that clearly develops subsequently.[69] Rashi's comment reflects the notion that, for purposes of halakhic status, tissue produced as a result of natural growth and maturation is regarded as having the selfsame identity as the tissue from which it is generated.

The concept underlying Rashi's comment is readily discernible in the very nature of the prohibition concerning eating the flesh of forbidden species. An adult animal is much larger and heavier than it was at the time of birth. Yet a person who consumes any part of the flesh of the adult animal is subject to the penalty of lashes. Were the additional weight acquired by the animal regarded as mere *yoẓei* comparable to its milk the penalty of lashes would be inappropriate. The conclusion to be deduced is that any part of the animal resulting from natural growth and development of the animal itself is endowed with the selfsame halakhic identity as the nascent animal from which it developed.[70] The same principle serves to explain why the progeny of an animal is endowed with the halakhic status of its progenitor rather than as mere *yoẓei*.[71]

Thus, there can be no question that, for example, a sheep cloned from a cell of another sheep and gestated within the womb of a ewe has the halakhic status of a sheep. Similarly, a human cloned from the cell of another human and gestated within the womb of a human female is a human being. It appears to this writer that the same conclusions with regard to species identity would apply to a cloned animal or to a person that develops artificially in a laboratory incubator, with a possible exception in the latter case with regard to the punishment of the perpetrator of an act of homicide directed against such a person.[72]

The question that must be addressed is the status of an animal cloned from a cell of an animal of one species but nurtured in the womb of a female of another species. For example, what is the status of an animal cloned from the cell of a pig but gestated in the womb of a cow or a ewe? Is the offspring, in effect, a kosher pig?

Elsewhere,[73] it has been argued that Halakhah recognizes parturition as generating a maternal relationship. Presumably, that is the case not only with regard to an individual maternal-filial relationship but with regard to species identification as well since, as has been shown, species identity is a concomitant of maternal identity.

Nevertheless, if the position that *ḥosheshin le-zera ha-av*, i.e., that consideration is given to the seed of the father, is accepted, the offspring must be regarded as a member of the two separate species, i.e., in the example given, part pig, part cow or part sheep. Thus, *Shulḥan Arukh, Yoreh De'ah* 28:3, as amplified by *Shakh, Yoreh De'ah* 28:7, rules that the progeny of a stag and a ewe has doubtful status as a "part deer" because the question of *ḥosheshin le-zera ha-av* is an unresolved halakhic issue.

It seems to this writer that the principle of *ḥosheshin le-zera ha-av* is not founded on the fact that the father contributes *zera* or sperm in a literal sense but upon whether the father's donation of chromosomes or perhaps even of cytoplasm is of sufficient halakhic significance to cause the developing embryo to be regarded as the "*yoẓei*" or "outgrowth" of the father. If so, the principle of *ḥosheshin le-zera ha-av* is applicable to any and all sources of genetic material that contribute to the development of an animal. Accordingly, from the viewpoint of Halakhah, the animal, male or female, from which the cloned cell is taken is regarded as the "father" regardless of the organ from which the cell is taken.[74] In the case of human cloning, *ḥosheshin le-zera ha-av* would render the person from whom the nucleus is taken a "parent"[75] regardless of whether that individual is a male or a female.

Although at present the matter is in the realm of science fiction, it must be freely conceded that this analysis yields a number of conclusions that may be counterintuitive. Offspring produced from a cloned cell of a monkey or chimpanzee implanted in a human womb, although having both the genotype and phenotype of an animal, would be regarded as human for purposes of Jewish law. It is indeed evident from the discussion of the Gemara, *Niddah* 23b, that an animal-like creature born of a human mother is regarded as a human being.[76] Conversely, a cell cloned from a human and gestated within the womb of a primate, despite being endowed with both the genotype and phenotype of a human, would, on the basis of the halakhic principle of *ḥosheshin le-zera ha-av*, have the halakhic status of a doubtful human being.

One additional point should be made regarding the status

of a cloned human being. A clone acquires human status by virtue of the fact that it is a *yoẓei* of a human being, i.e., by virtue of its generation from human tissue. Nevertheless, it seems quite evident to this writer that, if a clone is produced from a cell of a male, the male does not thereby fulfill the biblical commandment with regard to procreation. Stated in somewhat different terms, a male cannot fulfill his obligation with regard to procreation by siring a clone. Elsewhere,[77] this writer has discussed the birth of a child *sine concubito* as exempting the father from further biblical obligation with regard to procreation. Although some authorities disagree, the majority of rabbinic decisors rule that a male is discharged from further obligation even if the child is not conceived as a result of intercourse. Nevertheless, it would seem quite strange to extend that notion to the case of a childless person who creates an anthropoid by means of metaphysical methods gleaned from *Sefer Yeẓirah*.[78] It seems cogent to assume that, even if a sexual act is not required, nevertheless, the children whose birth is the subject of the commandment are those produced from male semen.[79] In context, the command "be fruitful and multiply" is formulated in the plural in the Hebrew text even though it is binding only upon the male and is also immediately preceded by the phrase "male and female did He create them."[80] It would thus seem that, even if actual cohabitation is not required, the commandment is nevertheless fulfilled only if the child is the product of gametes contributed by both the male and the female.[81] If so, for example, birth of a child cloned from a cell taken from the cheek would not release the donor of the cell from further biblical obligation.

VI. POTENTIAL HARM TO THE CLONE

Although, from the vantage point of Jewish tradition, animal cloning presents no ideological or halakhic problem, the same cannot be said with regard to the cloning of a human being.

The ethical implications of fetal experimentation which, by its very nature, may result in the birth of a defective neonate were analyzed some time ago by the late Professor Paul Ramsey.[82] In the early days of in vitro fertilization Professor Ramsey argued that such a procedure represented an immoral experiment upon a possible future life since no researcher can exclude the possibility that he may do irreparable damage to the child-to-be. In the words of Professor Ramsey: "We ought not to choose for another the hazards he must bear, while choosing at the same time to give him life in which to bear them and to suffer our chosen experimentations."[83]

This argument is no less applicable to homologous reproduction than to artificial conception and is entirely consistent with the norms of Torah ethics. Jewish law does not sanction abortion motivated solely by a desire to eliminate a defective fetus, nor does it sanction sterile marriage as a means of preventing transmission of hereditary disorders. However, it does discourage marriages which would lead to the conception of such children. The Gemara, *Yevamot* 64b, states that a man should not marry into an epileptic or leprous family, i.e., a family in which three members have suffered from those diseases. This declaration obviously represents a eugenic measure designed to prevent the birth of defective children. It follows, *a fortiori*, that overt intervention in natural processes which might cause defects in the fetus would be viewed with opprobrium by Judaism.

There is some question with regard to whether the Gemara's negative statement regarding entering into a marital relationship with a woman whose family has a history of leprosy or of epilepsy represents a formal interdiction or simply constitutes sound eugenic advice. The talmudic dictum is presented in the ambiguous form "*lo yisa adam*" which may be understood either as an imperative, *viz.*, "a person dare not" or as having a much weaker prudential meaning, *viz.*, "a person ought not." The dictum is recorded in the same language by Rambam, *Hilkhot Isurei Bi'ah* 21:30, and by *Shulḥan Arukh, Even ha-Ezer* 2:7. Unfortunately, there is scant discussion of this statement either in the talmudic commentaries or in commentaries upon Rambam or *Shulḥan Arukh*. However, the formulation employed by *Tur Shulḥan Arukh, ad locum*, may be instructive. The Gemara defines a family of epileptics or of lepers as a family in which there have been three occurrences of the disease. In recording that provision *Tur* adds that if there have been only two such occurrences "it is permissible [to marry]." Employment in this context of the term "*shari*" or "it is permissible" would seem to indicate that in a situation involving a family in which there have been three such occurrences the marriage is not merely imprudent but impermissible.[84]

It should also be noted that the Gemara, on the very same page on which this statement is presented, employs almost identical language in declaring that a twice-widowed woman should not marry a third time for fear that her third husband will meet an untimely death as well. The consensus of opinion among early-day authorities is that such a marriage is not merely ill-advised but is prohibited.[85] It would be cogent to assume that the Gemara has herein recorded two separate but parallel rabbinic edicts, one based upon concern for the life of the prospective husband, the other based upon concern for the well-being of prospective issue of the marriage. R. Isaac Schmelkes, *Teshuvot Bet Yiẓḥak, Even ha-Ezer*, I, no. 46, sec. 3, strives to show that the prohibition against marrying a woman who has buried two husbands is rabbinic in nature. That is also the position of *Besamim Rosh*, no. 276.[86] However, numerous authorities, including *Teshuvot Ketav Sofer, Even ha-Ezer*, no. 13 and *Teshuvot Bet Shlomoh, Even ha-Ezer*, no. 18, maintain that, in light of the danger involved, the prohibition is biblical in nature.[87] Moreover, Ritva, in his commentary on the talmudic discussion, indicates that the prohibition against marrying a twice-widowed woman is subsumed under the prohibition against suicide. Since marrying a woman who stems from a family of epileptics or a family of lepers, even if formally prohibited, is presumably banned only by virtue of rabbinic decree,[88] no comparison can be drawn between the negative statement regarding such marriages and the statement decrying marriage to a twice-widowed woman if it is accepted that the latter prohibition is biblical in nature.

On the other hand, Rambam, *Teshuvot Pe'er ha-Dor*, no. 156, cited by *Kesef Mishneh*, *Hilkhot Isurei Bi'ah* 21:31, maintains not only that there is no prohibition against entering into marriage with a twice-widowed woman but that such a union does not even pose an intrinsic danger. Rambam understands the Gemara's negative attitude as based entirely upon the fear that people experience in such situations and the resultant harm that can be engendered even by psychological causes. Hence, if the parties are sanguine with regard to the matter, Rambam sees no reason to discourage, much less prohibit, the marriage. Nevertheless, Rambam does take the genetic danger of epilepsy and leprosy seriously as evidenced by his unqualified statement in *Hilkhot Isurei Bi'ah* 21:30. Accordingly, for Rambam as well, there is no theoretic parallelism between the Gemara's statement concerning twice-widowed women and women stemming from families having a history of epilepsy or leprosy.

Be this as it may, as noted earlier, the sole rabbinic source to offer a concrete basis for even an inferential conclusion is *Tur Shulḥan Arukh* and that conclusion is not challenged by evidence from any other source. Nevertheless, acceptance of the fact that the Sages promulgated a eugenic ordinance in order to prevent occurrences of epilepsy and leprosy does not entail the conclusion that they prohibited any and every marriage carrying a greater than normal risk of hereditary defects in potential progeny,[89] much less that they established a prohibition against artificial forms of reproduction that carry with them such risks. On the contrary, rabbinic ordinances in general are not paradigmatic; their ambit is limited to that which is explicitly proscribed.

Nevertheless, such prohibitions are reflective of underlying policy considerations. The concern in this case was clearly the prevention of congenital anomalies. There is little question that were the Sages legislating in response to contemporary circumstances and in possession of scientific information available to us they would have targeted other genetic anomalies. Given the values they so clearly espoused there is strong reason to suppose that they would have decried fetal experimentation and human cloning because of the inherent danger of producing congenital defects. It must also be recognized that birth outside of a family unit carries with it the potential for psychological burden. Clones are likely to suffer even greater psychological problems. Since serious psychological problems are as real and as burdensome as physical defects it is likely that the Sages would have viewed their imposition upon as yet unborn children with disfavor.

This consideration notwithstanding, the prohibition against causing harm to a fellow human being admits of some exceptions. Accordingly, there are conceivable situations in which an unborn life may be burdened with potential defects in order to achieve an overriding purpose.

It must be emphasized that, despite its tragic nature, overcoming infertility does not warrant causing harm to another. Elsewhere,[90] this writer had endeavored to show that the therapeutic exemption to the prohibition against "wounding" is not limited to "wounding" oneself or allowing a physician to perform a surgical procedure in order to benefit the subject of the procedure but includes even an act of "wounding" performed upon an individual who himself or herself derives no personal benefit from the assault. Nevertheless, in no way does that line of reasoning serve to justify the potential harm to a fetus that may occur in the course of cloning. Cloning is not restorative in nature. The process neither cures a malady nor restores a dysfunctional organ to its intended purpose. The effect of cloning is to provide a child for a couple to raise and thereby satisfy a deeply felt human need. Cloning, particularly since it does not serve as a fulfillment of the commandment to "be fruitful and multiply," is, from the vantage point of Jewish law, analogous to adoption. Adoption ameliorates the pain arising from infertility, but does not remedy the underlying physical cause. An adopted child may be loved and cherished, but adoption is not a "cure" for infertility. Neither adoption nor cloning can be accorded the halakhic status of a "cure." Hence it must be concluded that, if cloning is otherwise regarded by Jewish teaching as immoral, it cannot be sanctioned as means of alleviating the effects of infertility. It is almost superfluous to add that this is the case even if cloning is contemplated in order to preserve the family line of a Holocaust survivor who has no other living relatives.[91]

It has also been suggested in some quarters that cloning may be morally acceptable in situations in which the sole child of parents who have become infertile develops a terminal disease. By means of cloning, the parents could use a cell obtained from the child to create another child who would be an exact replica of the child they are about to lose. However, tragic as such cases may be, there is nothing in those circumstances halakhically to distinguish that situation from more usual situations of infertility.

VII. MORAL AND LAUDATORY PROCEDURES

Nevertheless, there are some very rare situations in which cloning, despite the attendant risks, may be regarded as moral and even laudatory. Despite the contrary view of some early-day authorities, the overwhelming consensus of rabbinic opinion is that restrictions governing interpersonal relationships, including the prohibitions against theft and "wounding," are treated no differently from purely religious prohibitions and are suspended in face of danger to human life.[92]

There have been unfortunate cases of children afflicted with leukemia whose only chance of survival is a bone marrow transplant. To be successful, a donor must be genetically compatible, otherwise the transplant will be rejected. When bone marrow of family members is incompatible, finding a suitable match is exceedingly difficult. There have been cases of the mother of such a child becoming pregnant in the hope that the newly-born child will be a suitable donor. However, the statistical probability that the child will be a compatible donor is only twenty-five percent. If cloning were available, parents, in such rare situations, could clone the ill child. The newly-born infant would be disease-free but would be genetically identical to its afflicted sibling. Medically, the child would be an ideal donor.

There may well be other forms of research requiring cloning designed to find a cure for disease that may benefit individuals who are in the category of a *ḥoleh le-faneinu*, i.e., individuals for whom the danger and potential benefit is regarded as actual rather than merely hypothetical. Under such limited circumstances—and only in such circumstances—human cloning, when scientifically prudent and undertaken with appropriate safeguards, may be deemed appropriate and halakhically sound.

More significantly, cloning technology may prove to be extremely beneficial in cell and tissue therapy. Embryonic stem cells have the ability to differentiate into any cell type and, in theory, could be produced from human blastocysts. Perfection of cloning procedures would make it possible for a person to provide the nucleus of his own cell to replace the nucleus of a donor egg. Stem cells could then be taken from the developing blastocyst and induced to differentiate in culture.[93] Those cells would be genetically identical to those of the person from whom the nucleus was taken with the result that cell and tissue replacement would be possible without the problems of rejection currently attendant upon transplantation. Rejection of transplants occurs because the body's immune system recognizes the transplanted tissue as foreign. Cloned tissue is genetically identical to the tissue from which it is cloned and hence will not be rejected. The goal of such technology would be the cloning of human tissues and organs rather than of human beings. Although the cloning of human beings is highly problematic, the cloning of tissues and organs for therapeutic purposes is entirely salutary.

There is one final lesson to be derived from the *golem* literature. Absence of a prohibition against creating an anthropoid does not mean that such endeavors were encouraged by rabbinic scholars. Thus, to cite but one source, R. Chaim Joseph David Azulai, *Birkei Yosef, Oraḥ Ḥayyim* 55:4, notes that, in order to complete a *minyan*, R. Eliezer chose to emancipate his slave rather than to create a *golem*. *Birkei Yosef* regards R. Eliezer as having been quite capable of that feat but comments that R. Eliezer refrained from creating a *golem* as an act of piety. Many scholars frowned upon engaging in *kabbalah ma'asit* or "white magic" because of fear that the procedure might go awry, because of fear of misuse for less than noble purposes or because of fear that this esoteric knowledge might fall into the hands of unworthy persons.[94] The identical concerns surround creation of the modern-day *golem* in the form of the product of homologous reproduction and similar restraint is in order.

Society certainly has reason to regard development of cloning technology with concern. Such concern is by no means limited to the exaggerated fear of the specter of mad scientists engaging in cloning for nefarious purposes *à la The Boys from Brazil*. Quite apart from the earlier discussion regarding concern for potential defects in the clonee, society has reason to fear that untrammeled cloning may result in a disproportionate number of clones of one gender, that a multiplicity of persons identical to one another may spell confusion and give rise to an assortment of social problems and that idiosyncratic preferences may create an imbalance in the distribution of physical attributes and human talents. These and other demographic concerns are quite real. Tampering with natural processes in a manner that would lead to social upheaval is not included in man's mandate "to fill the earth and conquer it" (Genesis 1:28). Assuredly, society is justified in preventing such a situation from arising. Accordingly, society has both the right and the obligation to regulate experimental endeavors designed to perfect techniques necessary for successful cloning of humans. The goal of such regulation should be assurance that those skills be utilized only for purposes that are beneficial to society.

NOTES

1. Cf. the statement ". . . what is technically possible is not for that reason morally admissible," Congregation for the Doctrine of the Faith, *Instruction on Respect for Human Life in Its Origin and on the Dignity of Procreation* (*Donum Vitae*) (February 22, 1987), introduction, sec. 3. Although that document is not an expression of Jewish teaching, the validity of the quoted axiom is self-evident.
2. See Willard Gaylin, "The Frankenstein Myth Becomes a Reality: We Have the Awful Knowledge to Make Exact Copies of Human Beings," *The New York Times Magazine*, March 5, 1972, pp. 12–13, 41–49.
3. *New York Times*, July 23, 1998, p. A1.
4. Ibid., p. A20.
5. *New York Times*, July 24, 1998, p. A12.
6. *New York Times*, July 23, 1998, p. A20. In an editorial accompanying the report of the cloning of Dolly, the editors of *Nature* voiced the opinion that "Cloning humans from adults' tissues is likely to be achievable any time from one to ten years from now." See *Nature*, vol. 385, no. 6619 (February 27, 1997), p. 753.
7. A full report of the methods employed in causing that event to occur was published by I. Wilmut *et al.*, "Viable Offspring Derived from Fetal and Adult Mammalian Cells," *Nature*, vol.

385, no. 6619 (February 27, 1997), pp. 810–813.

8. See Gina Kolata, *Clone: The Road to Dolly and the Path Ahead* (New York, 1998), p. 25.
9. Much earlier, in 1981, to the excitement of the scientific community, a prominent German researcher, Dr. Karl Illmensee, and a younger colleague, Dr. Peter Hoppe, reported the successful cloning of three mice from early embryo cells. However, a formal investigation of charges of scientific fraud culminated in a somewhat equivocal report and Illmensee's reported results were not duplicated. For an intriguing survey of the entire episode see *Clone,* pp. 120–156.
10. *New York Times*, June 3, 1997, p. C1; *Clone*, p. 129.
11. *New York Times*, December 2, 1997, p. A24.
12. See Jose B. Cibelli *et al.*, "Cloned Transgenic Calves Produced from Nonquiescent Fetal Fibroblasts," *Science*, vol. 280, no. 5367 (May 22, 1998), pp. 1256–1258.
13. *New York Times*, May 23, 1998, p. A11, col. 1.
14. See T. Wakayama, *et al.*, "Full-Term Development of Mice from Enucleated Ocytes Injected with Cumulus Cell Nuclei," *Nature*, vol. 394, no. 6691 (July 23, 1998), pp. 369–374.
15. *New York Times*, December 2, 1997, p. A24.
16. *Clone*, p. 32.
17. *Washington Post*, January 7, 1998, pp. A2–A3. A company named Clonaid has already been established in the Bahamas in contemplation of offering cloning for fees of $200,000 and higher. At that time the firm's scientific director stated that "Before the year 2000, there will be a human cloned on this planet." See John Carey, "Human Clones: It's Decision Time," *Business Week*, August 10, 1998, p. 37.
18. Sophia J. Kleegman and Sherwin A. Kaufman, *Infertility in Women: Diagnosis and Treatment* (Philadelphia, 1966), p. 178.
19. December 2, 1997, p. A1.
20. *Clone*, p. 39.
21. Paul Ramsey, *Fabricated Man: The Ethics of Genetic Control* (New Haven, 1970), p. 122.
22. Cf., the Yiddish folk saying, "*A shiddukh vert nisht geschlossen biz s'iz geboren a kind*—A match is not sealed until a child is born."
23. *Instruction on Respect for Human Life*, introduction, sec. 4 (cita-

tion omitted).

24. Ibid., chapter 1, sec. 6.

25. See R. Abraham ibn Ezra, *Commentary on the Bible*, Leviticus 19:19, and R. Judah Leib Krinsky, *Karnei Or, loc. cit.* See also R. Abraham Chill, *The Mitzvot: The Commandments and Their Rationale* (Jerusalem, 1974), p. 236.

26. See the supercommentary to Ibn Ezra of R. Shlomo Zalman Netter, Leviticus 19:19, published in the *Horeb* edition of the Pentateuch (Jerusalem, London, New York, 5711). A similar interpretation was earlier advanced by *Ohel Yosef* and *Mekor Ḥayyim* in their respective works on Ibn Ezra published in *Margoliyot Tovah* (Stanislav, 5687).
    Mekor Ḥayyim also understands Ibn Ezra's comments regarding interbreeding of animal species in a like manner. However, these scholars' understanding of the passage in question is less than compelling. Cf., R. Abraham Chill, *The Mitzvot*, p. 236.

27. See R. Samson Raphael Hirsch, *The Nineteen Letters of Ben Uziel*, Eleventh Letter; *idem*, *Horeb*, sec. 327.

28. Rambam, *Guide for the Perplexed*, Book III, chap. 37, regards the *ḥukkim* as prohibitions designed to stem idolatrous conduct. The actions in question, he asserts, were cultic practices associated with pagan worship and sacrifice. According to Rambam's understanding of these commandments, there is no hint of a negative attitude with regard to intervention by man in the natural order.

29. Cf., R. Joseph B. Soloveitchik, "Confrontation," *Tradition*, vol. VI, no. 2 (Spring-Summer, 1964), p. 20.

30. It is indeed the case that one finds occasional comments in rabbinic writings representing those prohibitions in phraseology that is general and unqualified; see, for example, the sources cited *supra*, note 26. Nevertheless, it seems to this writer that those comments must be understood in the manner herein indicated.

31. Maharal of Prague speaks about natural objects created during the six days of creation in juxtaposition to matters which are "above," or which transcend, nature. The latter were created only in potential but are actualized by man. The prime example of that phenomenon is fire that was produced by Adam. Thus man's role is "completion" (*hashlamah*) of the process of Creation. Insofar as "completion" of creation is concerned it is the divine plan that such development take place. Maharal

asserts that it is the divine will that even interspecies such as the mule come into being, although not in circumstances that involve violation of Torah law. Thus crossbreeding was permitted to Adam because emergence of interspecies is integral to "completion" of the universe. According to Maharal, crossbreeding by a person who is not commanded otherwise (or in situations in which the prohibition does not apply) does not constitute a violation of the divine will or of the divinely ordained *telos* because "the way of Torah is one thing and the way of completion is another matter entirely." See R. Judah Loew, *Be'er ha-Golah*, chap. 2, s.v. *be-Masekhet Pesaḥim*.

32. The Midrash includes "heaven" and "earth" as well as well as "universe" in this reference. A somewhat different version is presented by the Gemara *Ḥaggigah* 12a. In *Ḥaggigah* the reference is to containment of the portion of the earth covered by the waters of the sea. The comment "Enough!" with regard to the "earth" and "heaven" (despite contemporary theories of an expanding universe) should also be understood as connoting a similar concept. However, if so, the term "universe" appears to be redundant. Moreover, understood in this manner, the comment seems inappropriate in the context in which it appears, *viz.*, in conjunction with the commandment to Abraham concerning circumcision. It is that problem that led *Tiferet Yonatan* to understand the comment as having an additional connotation.
33. *Commentary on the Bible*, Genesis 2:2 and Exodus 20:10; *Horeb*, sec. 144; and *The Nineteen Letters*, Thirteenth Letter.
34. Cf., *Midrash Tehillim*, Psalm 3. *Midrash Tehillim* states: R. Eleazar said, "The sections of the Torah were not given in order for, had they been given in order, anyone who would read them would be able to create a universe, to resurrect the dead and to perform wonders. Therefore the order of the Torah was concealed."
35. Maharsha cites anonymous sources who regard the term "*ḥavraya*" used in this context as the plural form of the Aramaic equivalent of the Hebrew "*ḥaver*" that appears in Deuteronomy 18:11. If so, the term refers to animal charmers or magicians and is indeed employed in that manner by the Gemara, *Shabbat* 45a. See parallel occurrences cited by Marcus Jastrow, *Dictionary of Talmud Babli, Yerushalmi, Midrashic Literature and Targum*. See also Moshe Baer, "On the *Ḥavrayya*," *Bar Ilan: Annual of Bar Ilan University* (Ramat Gan, 1983), vol. XX–XXI, pp. 83–86

and Moshe Idel, *Golem* (Albany, 1990), pp. 27–28.

36. It should be noted that a fourteenth century commentator on the *aggadot* of the Talmud, R. Shem Tov ibn Shaprut, *Pardes Rimmonim* (Sabionetta, 5314), p.13a, asserts that the anthropoid was not veridical but an *aḥizat einayim*, i.e., an illusion in the form of man. According to *Pardes Rimmonim*, Rava produced an illusion in order to test R. Zeira; the latter perceived its real nature and, accordingly, commanded it to return to dust. See also Gershom G. Scholem, "The Idea of the *Golem*," *On the Kabbalah and Its Symbolism*, trans. Ralph Manheim (New York, 1965), p. 188.
37. For the relationship between speech and reason see this author's *Contemporary Halakhic Problems*, II (New York, 1983), pp. 368–370. See also R. Baḥya ben Asher, *Commentary on the Bible*, Genesis 2:7, and *idem*, *Kad ha-Kemaḥ*, II (Lvov, 5698), 103b. [For other kabbalistic sources disassociating speech from reason see Scholem, *On the Kabbalah*, pp. 193–194.] The human soul is an ontological entity and is either identical with, or the source of, man's rational faculty. The vital or animating force in living creatures, including man, is not uniquely human and hence even in man is referred to as the animal or animating soul.
38. See *infra*, note 53.
39. See *infra*, note 52 as well as notes 57–58 and accompanying text.
40. This work is published in Abraham Epstein, *Beitrage zur jüdischen Altertumskunde* (Vienna, 1887), pp. 122–123.
41. Cf., Rambam, *Hilkhot Avodah Zarah* 1:1. For an even more precise comparison with the generation of Enosh see Scholem, *On the Kabbalah*, p. 181.
42. Translated by Idel, *Golem*, p. 64. See also the translation published in Scholem, *On the Kabbalah*, p. 179. The Hebrew text appears in the Hebrew version of Scholem's work, *Pirkei Yesod be-Havanat ha-Kabbalah ve-Samalehah,* trans. Joseph Ben-Shlomoh (Jerusalem, 1976), p. 400.
43. Translated by Idel, *Golem*, p. 67. See also the translation published in Scholem, *On the Kabbalah*, p. 180. The Hebrew text appears in *Pirkei Yesod*, p. 401. The text of this work was published by David de Gunzburg, "La Cabale à la veille de l'apparition du *Zohar*," *Ha-Kedem*, I (1907), 115.
    See also Joseph Dan, *The Early Kabbalah* (New York, 1986),

pp. 54–55 and Idel, *Golem*, p. 67. Cf., Gershom Scholem, "The *Golem* of Prague and the *Golem* of Rehovoth," *Commentary*, January, 1966, p. 64.

44. See the various reports cited by Scholem, *On the Kabbalah*, pp. 158–204, and by Idel in his work, *Golem*. See also Byron L. Sherwin, *The Golem Legend: Origins and Implications* (New York, 1985). For accounts of the most widely known *golem* story, that of R. Judah Loew of Prague, see Yudl Rosenberg, *Nifla'ot Maharal* (Warsaw, 1909), trans. J. Neugroschel, *Yenne Velt: The Great Works of Jewish Fantasy and the Occult* (New York, 1976); Chaim Bloch, *Der Prager Golem* (Berlin, 1920), trans. H. Schneiderman, *The Golem of Prague* (Vienna, 1925); and Gershon Winkler, *The Golem of Prague* (New York, 1980).
45. Idel, *Golem*, p. 229, note 22, observes that it is unlikely that R. Elijah was the grandfather of *Ḥakham Ẓevi* since the latter was born in 1660 while R. Elijah died in 1583. Idel assumes that the reference is to a great-grandfather.
46. A similar report regarding the same figure appears in late seventeenth century Christian sources. See Scholem, *On the Kabbalah* pp. 200–203. See also Idel, *Golem*, pp. 207–211.
47. See also R. Jacob Emden's account of the *golem* created by R. Elijah as presented in his *Megillat Sefer* (Warsaw, 5656), p. 4 and in his *Mitpaḥat Sefarim* (Altona, 5529), p. 45a.
48. If an anthropoid is not deemed to be human solely because it lacks a human soul it might nevertheless have the status of an animal. If, however, it is not a human because it does not have human progenitors it should, for the same reason, not be considered to be an animal. For a discussion of whether painless, but purposeless, killing of an animal involves the prohibition of cruelty to animals (*ẓa'ar ba'alei ḥayyim*), see this author's *Contemporary Halakhic Problems*, III (New York, 1989), pp. 205–217.
49. R. Joseph Rosen, *Teshuvot Ẓofnat Pa'aneaḥ* (Jerusalem, 5728), II, no. 7, goes further in remarking that, for purposes of Halakhah, a creature produced by means of *Sefer Yeẓirah* has no cognizable existence and for that reason the anthropoid in question was commanded by R. Zeira to return to dust. If those comments are taken literally, it would follow, for example, that it would be permissible to cut the hair or pare the nails of a *golem* on *Shabbat*. Regarding creation of a *golem* on *Shabbat* see *infra*, note 64.

50. For a discussion of those sources see *Contemporary Halakhic Problems*, I (New York, 1977), pp. 326–339.
51. The phrase "*ma'aseh yedeihem*" is employed by *Ḥakham Ẓevi* in the sense of "handiwork" or "artifacts." The source for this comment is apparently *Bereishit Rabbah* 30:6 and is cited by Rashi, Genesis 6:9. However, in that source the phrase is "*ma'asim tovim*" meaning "good deeds."
52. R. Chaim Joseph David Azulai, *Mar'it ha-Ayin*, *Sanhedrin* 65b, dismisses this argument with the observation that R. Zeira would have been entirely justified in destroying the anthropoid because of a fear that he might wreak havoc. See also, *infra*, notes 57–58.
53. R. Chaim Joseph David Azulai, *Birkei Yosef*, *Oraḥ Ḥayyim* 55:4, cites a letter of R. Judah Leib Katz, a son of the *Sha'ar Efrayim*, who finds support for the view that an anthropoid cannot be included in a *minyan* in the talmudic report that R. Eliezer chose to emancipate his slave in order to complete a quorum. Why did R. Eliezer not simply create a *golem*, queries this scholar. Since he did not do so, Rabbi Katz infers that a *golem* would have been ineligible to serve in that capacity. *Birkei Yosef* dismisses that argument for three reasons: 1) R. Eliezer may have refrained from creating an anthropoid as an act of piety; 2) creation of a *golem* requires extensive preparation and cannot be undertaken at will; 3) emancipation of a slave is simpler and preferable because it involves no transgression whatsoever when undertaken for a valid purpose. *Birkei Yosef* notes conflicting authority with regard to the latter point. R. Chaim Pelaggi, *Ruaḥ Ḥayyim*, *Yoreh De'ah* 1:18, cites an earlier authority who asserts that a newly created anthropoid may have the status of a minor. Cf., *infra*, note 60 and accompanying text. *Ruaḥ Ḥayyim* observes that, according to that view, it follows that an animal created in a similar manner may not be offered as a sacrifice until the statutory eight-day period following birth has elapsed and cites an authority to whom that question was a matter of doubt.
54. R. Chaim Eleazar Shapira, *Darkei Teshuvah*, *Yorah De'ah* 7:11, raises the question of whether an animal slaughtered by a properly supervised anthropoid may be eaten and cogently relates that issue to the question of whether a *golem* is deemed to be a human being. *Darkei Teshuvah* asserts that, according to *Ḥakham Ẓevi*, the anthropoid is human and hence an act of slaughter performed by an anthropoid renders the meat of the

animal permissible. It is thus clear that *Darkei Teshuvah* assumes that *Ḥakham Ẓevi* regarded the anthropoid both as a human being and as a Jew. If so, it is unclear why the anthropoid cannot be counted in a *minyan*. If the reason is, as stated by R. Ẓadok ha-Kohen of Lublin, because the anthropoid is not included in "speak to the children of Israel" as cited later in the text, the anthropoid should for the same reason be excluded from the category of individuals competent to perform ritual slaughter.

55. *Ḥesed le-Avraham*'s view is followed by his descendant R. Chaim Joseph David Azulai, *Maḥazik Berakhah, Oraḥ Ḥayyim* 55:1, and *idem*, *Mar'it he-Ayin*, *Sanhedrin* 65b. See also R. Daniel Trani, *Ikkarei Dinim* (also cited as *Ikkarei ha-Dat*), *Oraḥ Ḥayyim* 3:15. It is of interest to note that with reference to counting a *golem* in a *minyan*, *Mishnah Berurah* 55:4 cites *Ikkarei Dinim* together with *Ḥakham Ẓevi*.
56. Published as an addendum to R. Ẓadok's *Resisei Lailah*. A translation of this material is provided by Idel, *Golem*, pp. 220–223.
57. Cf., *Bereishit Rabbah* 34:2 in which Adam is depicted as a *golem* "stretched out from one end of the world to the other" and *Bereishit Rabbah* 14:10 in which Adam is described as a *golem* extending in height from earth to heaven. It was only after Adam sinned that he was reduced to human proportions although, according to the earlier cited *Sefer ha-Gematri'ot*, he remained enormous in height.
58. Cf., *Teshuvot ha-Rashba*, I, no. 413, who opines that the feat can be performed only on the sixth day of the week, the day on which animals were created.
59. Cf., however, R. Chaim Joseph David Azulai, *Maḥazik Berakhah, Oraḥ Ḥayyim* 55:1 and *idem*, *Mar'it he-Ayin*, *Sanhedrin* 65b, who declares that under no circumstances is it possible for man to create an anthropoid who is endowed with reason and ascribes that position to Maharsha, *Sanhedrin* 65b, as well. In *Mar'it he-Ayin* he declares that only God has the power to breathe "into his nostrils the breath of life," i.e., of reason, as described in Genesis 2:7. This is actually the earlier cited view of *Ḥesed le-Avraham*, although *Ḥesed le-Avraham* less categorically confines his statement to a depiction of an anthropoid created on the basis of *Sefer Yeẓirah*.

    Scholem, *On the Kabbalah*, pp. 198–199, and Idel, *Golem*,

p. 55, cite sources that attribute this position to the early-day scholar, R. Shmuel he-Ḥasid, the father of R. Judah he-Ḥasid. Those sources associate that view with a hymnal phrase in the High Holy Day liturgy, namely, "Intelligence and speech are "[the prerogative] of the Life of the Worlds."

Maḥazik Berakhah's categorical declaration that "the Sages have no power to endow [the anthropoid] with reason" makes it more difficult to understand R. Zeira's attempt to converse with the anthropoid as described in *Sanhedrin* 65b. According to *Maḥazik Berakhah*'s view, it must be assumed that R. Zeira did not immediately perceive that man cannot create a rational anthropoid and hence he could not conclude that the anthropoid did not have the status of a human until it became clear that the anthropoid lacked the power of speech.

R. Moses Cordovero, *Pardes Rimmonim*, chap. 34, sec. 10, ascribes a vitality to the *golem* higher than that of the animal soul but nevertheless not human. According to *Pardes Rimmonim*, the parts of which the creature is formed strive upward toward their source in the upper world and come closer to their source in that world than does an animal. According to *Pardes Rimmonim*, the *golem* does not die as an animal does but simply returns to its element, the earth. Accordingly, causing a *golem* to return to dust is not an act of murder. See Scholem, *On the Kabbalah*, pp. 194-195. *Pardes Rimmonim*'s position seems to be similar to, but not identical with, that of *Ḥesed le-Avraham* who seems to equate the vitality of the *golem* with that of an animal. Cf., however, Scholem, *ibid.*, p. 194, note 4.

R. Judah Loew, *Ḥiddushei Aggadot Maharal me-Prague*, *Sanhedrin* 65b, similarly states that man cannot create an anthropoid capable of speech. Maharal makes this assertion on the basis of the curious argument that man cannot create his equal any more than God can create His equal.

On the other hand, a commentary on *Sefer Yeẓirah* of uncertain provenance but attributed to R. Sa'adya Ga'on speaks of the power to produce an anthropoid endowed with a soul. See Scholem, *On the Kabbalah*, p. 192. Probably of greater significance are the earlier cited sources that depict the *golem* created by Jeremiah and Ben Sira as endowed with speech. See *supra*, notes 40–43 and accompanying text. *Sefer ha-Bahir*, sec. 136, also indicates that, were it not for sins, man might create an anthropoid capable of speech.

60. For an analysis of the various views concerning this matter see *Contemporary Halakhic Problems*, II, 365–375.

61. With the exception of the source adduced by *Ruaḥ Ḥayyim* as cited *supra*, note 53, no rabbinic writer has suggested that the anthropoid, upon creation, has the status of a newly born infant and must wait thirteen years before attaining legal capacity as an adult.

62. This is also the position of *Teshuvot Sedei ha-Areẓ*, *Yoreh De'ah*, no. 1, and of *Ruaḥ Ḥayyim*, *Yoreh De'ah* 1:18. Cf., however, the anonymous interlocutor in *Teshuvot Sedei ha-Areẓ* and *Darkei Teshuvah*, *Yoreh De'ah* 7:11, who suggest that such an animal may require slaughter and its *ḥelev* and blood may be forbidden because of *mar'it ayin*, i.e., because an onlooker may suspect that a transgression is taking place. This is also the position of the author of *Darkei Teshuvah*, R. Chaim Eleazar Shapira, as expressed in his *Divrei Torah*, *mahadura revia'ah*, sec. 75. *Ikkarei Dinim*, *Yoreh De'ah* 1:22, remarks that "perhaps" the creature requires ritual slaughter because of *mar'it ayin*. See also *infra*, note 63.

63. Interestingly, Malbim observes that the onlooker would not have suspected a violation of the prohibition against milk and meat because it was commonly known that Abraham created animals in this manner. It should be remembered that the final section of *Sefer Yeẓirah* reports that Abraham mastered the methods therein described and succeeded in performing acts of creation. See Scholem, *On the Kabbalah*, pp. 169–172.

64. A Sephardic authority, R. Abraham Anakava, *Teshuvot Kerem Ḥemed*, I, *Oraḥ Ḥayyim*, no. 3, discusses in great detail the question of whether it is permissible to create a *golem* on *Shabbat*.

    See also R. Moshe Sternbuch, *Mo'adim u-Zemanim*, IV (Jerusalem, 5431), no. 319 as well as sources attributed to R. Yosef Shalom Eliashiv, *Moriah*, Elul 5758, p. 65. See also, *supra*, note 49.

65. As noted *supra*, note 59, *Pardes Rimmonim* actually represents a fifth view since he regards the *golem* as a loftier being than a brute animal. Nevertheless, insofar as the halakhic status of such a creature is concerned, there is no difference between his position and that of *Ḥesed le-Avraham*.

66. This seems to be true for R. Chaim Joseph David Azulai as well. *Ḥida* declares that a *golem* is not human because it is impos-

sible under any circumstances for man to create an anthropoid endowed with reason. A product of homologous reproduction would undoubtedly be endowed with reason. As such, it must be regarded as created by God—albeit with human cooperation, as is the case with regard to sexual reproduction—and hence, according to *Ḥida*, such a being would be entirely human in nature.

67. Since they make no specific mention of an anthropoid endowed with reason, it is possible, but not demonstrable, that those scholars would concede that a *golem* created by man and possessing reason is human.
68. See *Kovez̧ He'arot*, no. 33, sec. 8; ibid., no. 59, sec. 12; *Kovez̧ Inyanim*, *Ḥullin* 17a; and *Kovez̧ Shi'urim*, I, *Pesaḥim*, sec. 120.
69. *Tosafot*'s disagreement with Rashi should be regarded as limited in nature by virtue of the fact that the sinew, according to *Tosafot*, is regarded, not as another stage in the development of the flesh of the embryo, but as a totally novel structure arising, as it were, *sui generis*.
70. Philosophers have long struggled with the problem of identity reflected in the phenomenon of an infant who becomes a mature adult but is regarded as one and the same person despite the fact that the physical components of the adult are clearly not present in the infant. For a discussion of theories advanced to resolve this problem see "Personal Identity," *Encyclopedia of Philosophy* (New York, 1972), VI, 95–107.
71. The comments of *Avnei Nezer*, *Yoreh De'ah*, no. 75, secs. 7–8, in connection with the classification of a bird as a member of a particular species despite the fact that the egg from which it develops is halakhically considered to have become putrid are helpful in illuminating this concept.
72. See *supra*, note 50 and accompanying text and *Contemporary Halahkhic Problems*, IV (New York, 1995), 240, note 10.
73. For a discussion of the sources upon which this conclusion is predicated see *Contemporary Halakhic Problems*, II, 91-93.
74. More problematic is the status of a clone produced by removing the nucleus of a cell derived from an animal of one species and inserted in the cytoplasm of a cell of an animal of a second species and gestated by an animal that is a member of a third species. The halakhic issue is whether the principle of *ḥosheshin le-zera ha-av* extends to a "father" who contributes non-genetic material.

75. If the individual from whom the cell is taken is a male, his status is clearly that of a "father." If the individual is a female, it would be reasonable to assume that her status is that of a "mother" and that the clone, in effect, has two mothers. This assumption is based upon the premise that *ḥosheshin le-zera ha-av* is a principle with regard to parenthood rather that with regard to paternity specifically.

There are numerous halakhic differences attendant upon status as a "father" or as a "mother." The most obvious and also the most theoretical is whether the admonition required for capital punishment for "wounding" must be couched in language warning against wounding a father or wounding a mother. Even were we in a position to impose capital punishment the question would remain theoretical since *ḥosheshin le-zera ha-av* remains an unresolved halakhic issue.

The issue is more actual with regard to whether a paternal or a maternal sibling relationship exists between the clonee and other progeny of the clonor. Levirate obligations and the effectiveness of *ḥaliẓah* as a means of nullifying the levirate links are limited to brothers sharing a single father but not to brothers sharing a single mother. Thus, if a female donor of a nucleus were to be regarded as a "father" rather than a mother, levirate obligations would exist if two such male clones are produced and one of them dies without issue.

There are also differences with regard to consanguineous relationships. For example, a marital relationship with the mother of one's maternal grandfather is rabbinically forbidden but such a relationship with the grandmother of a maternal grandfather is permitted. However, maternal grandmothers in the female line are prohibited no matter how many generations they are removed. See *Shulḥan Arukh, Even ha-Ezer* 15:2–3. Hence the son of a woman cloned from the nucleus of a female would be permitted to marry the donor's grandmother if the donor is deemed to be a "father" but not if the donor is deemed to be a "mother."

R. Joseph Babad, *Minḥat Ḥinnukh*, no. 189, tentatively suggests that, if an androgynous male who sires a male child and then has a sexual relationship with the child involving the father's female organs, the parties may be liable for incest between a son and his "mother" and also suggests that if the androgynous father engages in a male homosexual relationship with the child they may be liable for incest as well as for homosexual activity. *Minḥat Ḥinnukh* certainly suggests that gender itself, rather than the male or female sexual act, may determine motherhood or fatherhood. However, in applying the principle of *ḥosheshin le-zera ha-av* it is not necessary to resort to *Minḥat Ḥinnukh*'s hypothesis. *Ḥosheshin le-zera ha-av* simply results in recognition of the non-gestational parent as a parent by virtue of application of the more general principle of *yoẓei*. It then seems reasonable to assume that, if the "parent" is a female, her status is that of a "mother" even if the result is that the child has two mothers. Unlike the case of the androgynous father who sires a child, there is no apparent reason to convey the status of a "father" upon the female donor. On the other hand, one might insist that a non-gestational parent is, by definition, a "father" rather than a "mother." That hypothesis is certainly contradicted by *Minḥat Ḥinnukh*'s speculative comments.

76. The Gemara clearly recognizes the theoretical possibility of a converse situation, *viz.*, of a human-like creature being born to an animal. If born to a member of a kosher species the Gemara questions whether or not the offspring may be slaughtered for food since, although it possesses a "hoof," it does not have the characteristic split hoof of a kosher species. From the very formulation of the question it is manifestly evident that the Gemara did not regard a creature of this nature as enjoying the status of a human being.

The principle that identity of the mother as a human determines the status of her progeny regardless of the physical characteristics of the offspring might appear to be contradicted by a discussion of the Palestinian Talmud, *Niddah* 3:2. Describing hypothetical human offspring, the Palestinian Talmud states:

> Suppose it is entirely human but its face is animal-like and it reads from the Torah. Can one say to it, "Come and be slaughtered"? Suppose it is entirely animal-like but its face is human and it plows the field. Can we say to it "Come and perform *ḥaliẓah* or levirate marriage"?

On the surface, the Palestinian Talmud seems to declare

that the human status, or absence thereof, of a creature having mixed physical characteristics should be determined on the basis of the creature's rational capacity. However, *Pnei Mosheh*, in his commentary *ad locum*, points out that the statement is made in an *ad absurdum* vein and its import is to assert that such questions could not arise because such a creature cannot survive for any period of time. The creature's lack of viability is of direct relevance to the purely technical question of whether the mother is subject to the impurity associated with childbirth. That issue is a matter of controversy between the Sages and R. Meir as is recorded in the Mishnah that serves as the focus of the discussion.

Notice must also be taken of the controversy recorded in the Mishnah, *Kelayim* 8:5, with regard to whether creatures known as *adnei ha-sadeh* defile as humans. It may be suggested that the crux of the controversy is whether the creatures in question are anomalous descendants of humans, presumably as a result of genetic mutation, or an independent animal species. However, Rabbenu Shimshon, in his commentary *ad locum*, cites a comment of the Palestinian Talmud indicating that *adnei ha-sadeh* are creatures tied to the ground by a structure resembling an umbilical cord and that, on the basis of rabbinic exegesis, R. Jose, whose opinion is recorded in the Mishnah, regards them as grouped together with humans solely for purposes of ritual defilement.

77. *Contemporary Halakhic Problems*, IV, 240, note 9 and *Bioethical Dilemmas: A Jewish Perspective*, I (New York, 1998), 251–253. Exemption from further obligation to procreate is a concomitant of recognition of a paternal relationship with regard to a child born *sine concubito*.
78. If, contrary to what is here stated, it is to be assumed that even creation of an anthropoid by means of *Sefer Yeẓirah* satisfies this requirement it should then follow that in cloning it is the physician or technician who performs the cloning procedure who fulfills the obligation of procreation rather than the passive donor of the cell.
79. R. Eliezer Waldenberg, *Ẓiẓ Eli'ezer*, XV, no. 45, has advanced a similar position with regard to in vitro fertilization. It is his contention that the many authorities who maintain that a sexual act is not necessary for fulfillment of the commandment

with regard to procreation maintain that position only because both production of the gametes and fertilization of the ovum are entirely natural. *Ẓiẓ Eli'ezer* contends that in vitro fertilization, which he describes as effecting a change "in the order of creation," is entirely different and that as an "unnatural" form of procreation it cannot lead to fulfillment of the *miẓvah*. That position is challenged by R. Avigdor Nebenzahl, *Assia*, no. 34 (Tishri 5743), cited by Abraham S. Abraham, *Nishmat Avraham, Even ha-Ezer* 1:6, note 5, sec. 3, on the grounds that, despite the "unnatural" externality of in vitro fertilization, the intrinsic physiological process involved in fertilization and conception are entirely natural. That certainly is not the case with regard to cloning.

80. In his tentative assertion that a *golem* may be counted toward a *minyan* because "He who receives an orphan in his home, Scripture considers it as if he had begotten him" and because "the deeds of the righteous are their progeny," *Ḥakham Ẓevi* certainly did not intend to intimate that the commandment of *peru u-revu* can be fulfilled by performing good deeds or even by raising an orphan in one's home.
81. An intriguing problem is presented in the hypothetical case in which the cloned cell is a male sperm. In such a situation the nucleus of the ovum would be replaced by the genetic material of the sperm but the remaining cytoplasm of the female gamete enters into the reproduction process. If such a procedure ever becomes possible, the child will not really be a clone since it would possess only half of a full complement of genes, but that is not a matter of halakhic relevance.
82. Paul Ramsey, "Shall We 'Reproduce'?" *Journal of the American Medical Association*, vol. 220, no. 10 (June 5, 1972), pp. 1346–1350, and vol. 220, no. 11 (June 12, 1972), pp. 1480–1485; and *idem, The Ethics of Fetal Research* (New Haven, 1975).
83. Paul Ramsey, *Journal of the American Medical Association*, vol. 220, no. 11, p. 135.
84. This also appears to be the understanding of R. Samuel Ehrenfeld, *Teshuvot Ḥatan Sofer*, no. 137.
85. See *Shulḥan Arukh, Even ha-Ezer* 9:1 and commentaries thereto; cf., however, *Oẓar ha-Poskim, Even ha-Ezer* 9:1, sec. 1.
86. For additional sources that subscribe to this view see *Oẓar ha-Poskim, Even ha-Ezer* 9:1, sec. 1.
87. For additional sources maintaining that the prohibition is bib-

lical in nature see *Oẓar ha-Poskim, Even ha-Ezer* 9:1, sec. 1.

88. Although "wounding" or causing harm to another person even indirectly must be regarded as biblically forbidden, it is unlikely that causing such harm to an unborn child who would otherwise not be born is included in the prohibition against harming a fellow man. Were that to be the case it would necessarily follow that all unions likely to result in progeny suffering from any genetic defect would be forbidden.
89. Cf., *Teshuvot Ḥatan Sofer*, no. 137, who appears to assert that such marriages are prohibited in all situations in which there have been three occurrences of any serious disease deemed to be hereditary.
90. *Contemporary Halakhic Problems*, IV, 302–309.
91. Cf., *Clone* p. 17.
92. The most frequent discussion of this issue in a medical context is in conjunction with post-mortem dissection of a corpse. For a survey of the conflicting positions regarding this matter see J. David Bleich, *Judaism and Healing* (New York, 1981), pp. 162–168.
93. For a discussion of the propriety of destroying nascent human life generated in this manner and at this very early stage of development see *Contemporary Halakhic Problems* IV, 24, note 10 and *Bioethical Dilemmas*, I, 209–211.
94. For a series of quotations from the writing of kabbalists enveighing against actual implementation of practical Kabbalah see R. Moshe Hillel's introduction to his edition of R. Elijah Ba'al Shem Tov's *Toldot Adam* (Jerusalem, 5754), pp. 38–39. See also Joshua Trachtenberg, *Jewish Magic and Superstition* (New York, 1939), p. 22.

2

Circumcision: The Current Controversy

[The Holy One, blessed be He] said to [Elijah], "By your life! [To] every place at which My children impress this holy mark upon their flesh you shall make your way. The same mouth that testified that Israel forsook the covenant will testify that Israel upholds the covenant."

ZOHAR, LEKH LEKHA 93a

For Jews, circumcision is first and foremost fulfillment of a divine command. But circumcision is unique among *mizvot* in that it represents the covenant established between God and Abraham and, through Abraham, with his progeny. Since the covenant represented by circumcision is shared by the entire people of Israel, circumcision also serves as a symbol of identification as a member of the community of Israel. As stated by *Sefer ha-Ḥinnukh*, no. 2, circumcision is designed "to separate [Israel] from other nations in the form of their body as in their souls." Thus, circumcision carries with it a nationalistic as well as a religious meaning. It is because of that consideration that Spinoza, in his *Tractatus Thelologico-Politicus* 3:53, writes that circumcision, in and of itself, is sufficient to guarantee survival of the Jewish people.[1]

Little wonder, then, that, as recorded in II Maccabees 6:10, when Antiochus Epiphanes sought to eradicate the people of Israel he prohibited them from practicing circumcision. Jews, however, knew precisely what was at stake and responded accordingly.[2]

Perhaps astonishingly and perhaps not, gentile oppressors were aided and abetted by Jews themselves. The Hellenists of antiquity accepted assimilation not only with equanimity but with enthusiasm. Many not only renounced circumcision, as is recorded in the Book of Jubilees 15:33–34, but sought to obliterate the sign of the covenant by undergoing a painful procedure designed to make them physically indistinguishable from their neighbors.[3]

Since circumcision is the hallmark of the Jew, when Jews became self-conscious of their identity as Jews they sought to forsake the sign of the covenant. In modern times, during the period of the French Revolution and its aftermath, circumcision increasingly came under attack by anti-Semites. Ridicule and accusations of primitivism or barbarism by non-Jews served as an impetus for renunciation of both the sign of the covenant and the covenant itself. The call for abolition of circumcision by the Frankfurt *Verein der Reformfreunde* is a case in point.

Those attacks upon circumcision abated over the course of time, in large measure, because circumcision came to be socially and culturally accepted among non-Jews because of its presumed medical benefits. With re-evaluation of the medical data in recent decades, circumcision again became ripe for attack. Many respected and well-meaning persons, particularly physicians, now discourage routine medical circumcision as medically unnecessary, economically wasteful and, in a small number of cases, potentially deleterious. In truth, that stance is unexceptionable. After all, Judaism not only fails to demand that non-Jews subject themselves to circumcision but actually discourages the circumcision of non-Jews.[4]

Unfortunately, the measured and nuanced tones of scientific journals become both shrill and discordant when converted to the language of popular publications and the inevitable media reports. The problem currently confronting the Jewish community is discouragement of and opposition—often both strident and vehement in nature—to ritual circumcision of Jews.[5] Far too often, Jews are in the forefront of the movement and occupy leadership positions in organizations whose sole agenda is eradication of circumcision. Their attacks focus both upon the procedure itself and upon the lack of palliation of accompanying pain.

The present undertaking is designed to place the issue of circumcision in perspective. A review of the information that has appeared in the medical literature and the several published statements of the American Academy of Pediatrics reveals a medical consensus that does not oppose ritual circumcision. Although it is superfluous to emphasize that the opinion of the medical profession has no bearing upon the commitment of Jews to fulfillment of divine commandments, it is nevertheless important to separate fact from fiction. Of more significant practical consequence are the halakhic views regarding employment of pain-reducing measures.

I. MEDICAL CONSIDERATIONS

Circumcision is the oldest and most common surgical procedure performed by man.[6] It is estimated that in the United States 1.2 million newborn males are circumcised each year.[7] For a considerable period of time the rate of circumcision among the general population was extremely high. The incidence of circumcision rose to 80% in the years subsequent to World War II,[8] but climaxed in the mid-1980s. Nevertheless, circumcision rates have consistently been higher in the United States than in any other Western country. Circumcision has been particularly prevalent among Caucasians and there has been a uniformly high statistical correspondence between circumcision of infants and the level of parents' formal education.[9]

The attitude of the medical profession toward circumcision has had a somewhat checkered history. Ostensibly, the motivating force behind the high rate of circumcision was its presumed prophylactic value. In the uncircumcised male, disease-causing bacteria adhere to the moist, sticky mucous surface of the foreskin and migrate up the urinary tract as far as the kidneys. Alleged medical benefits included a decrease in the incidence of urinary tract infection and resultant kidney disease, lower susceptibility to sexually transmitted diseases, less likelihood of developing cancer of the penis as well as a lower rate of cervical cancer in sexual partners. Circumcision is also believed to protect against inflammation of the prepuce (posthitis) and of the glans (balinitis).[10] Such inflammation is due to phimosis, i.e., stenosis of the orifice of the foreskin which may be congenital or acquired and results in inability to retract the foreskin behind the corona. Posthitis is more common in warm climates, presumably because the organisms responsible for the inflammation multiply more rapidly in the presence of heat and humidity.[11]

A recent study published in the *New England Journal of Medicine* shows that uncircumcised males are more than three and a half times more likely than circumcised males to contract penile human papillomavirus (HPV) infection and that, probably as a result of the increased incidence of HPV, the spouses of men with a history of multiple sexual partners are more likely to develop cervical cancer than spouses of circumcised men having similar sexual experience. The degree of such risk increases with the number of the husband's previous sexual partners.[12]

A noticeable decline in the incidence of circumcision in the general population followed in the wake of a re-evaluation of the practice in the 1970s by the American Academy of Pediatrics. The 1970 edition of *Standards and Recommendations of Hospital Care of Newborn Infants* published by the Committee on the Fetus and Newborn of the American Academy of

Pediatrics stated that "there are no valid indications for circumcision in the neonatal period."[13] The issue was again reexamined in 1975 by the Ad Hoc Task Force established by that committee. Upon review, the Task Force concluded that "there is no absolute medical indication for routine circumcision of the newborn."[14] In 1983 both the American Academy of Pediatrics and the American College of Obstetrics and Gynecology reiterated that conclusion in a jointly published work.[15]

However, subsequently discovered evidence suggested that circumcision might indeed yield medical benefits. The American Academy of Pediatrics responded to the publication of those findings by establishing a Task Force on Circumcision. In a report issued in 1989, this Task Force concluded that "newborn circumcision prevents phimosis, paraphimosis, and balanoposthitis and has been shown to decrease the incidence of cancer of the penis among U.S. men."[16] The Task Force also found an increased incidence of cancer of the cervix in sexual partners of uncircumcised men infected with human papillomavirus. Evidence of a decreased incidence of urinary tract infection is described as tentative,[17] while evidence regarding the association of sexually transmitted diseases and circumcision is reported as conflicting. In a balanced conclusion the Task Force declared: "Newborn circumcision has potential medical benefits and advantages as well as disadvantages and risks. When circumcision is being considered, the benefits and risks should be explained to the patient and informed consent obtained."[18] The Task Force indicated that the incidence of post-operative complications following circumcision is low but studiously refrained from a recommendation for or against the procedure.

Somewhat later, the pendulum swung back, at least partially, in the direction of the findings of the 1970s. In 1997, the *Journal of the American Medical Association* published a report[19] analyzing data regarding sexual, attitudinal, and health-related experiences of circumcised and uncircumcised Americans. That report analyzed a survey conducted in 1992 that involved a nationally representative probability sample of 1,511 men and 1,921 women between the ages of 18 and 59. The authors of the *JAMA* analysis conclude: ". . . we have discovered that circumcision provides no discernible prophylactic benefit."[20] Contrary to early reports, they found that circumcision "may in fact increase the likelihood of STD (sexually transmitted disease) contraction" but that "circumcised men have a slightly lessened risk of experiencing sexual dysfunction, especially among older men . . . ."[21] The latter phenomenon does not appear to have been considered in any of the earlier studies; on the contrary, earlier discussions focus upon putative diminished sexual gratification on the part of the circumcised male.[22]

Most recently, in March 1999, the Task Force on Circumcision of the American Academy of Pediatrics issued yet another "Circumcision Policy Statement."[23] In all likelihood, that statement was prompted at least in part by the by the 1997 *JAMA* report and is a reaction to its conclusions. In contrast to the *JAMA* report, the latest policy statement of the American Academy of Pediatrics Task Force reiterates the balanced conclusions of the earlier 1989 report and in a nuanced manner is even somewhat more supportive of circumcision.

The 1999 report of the Task Force on Circumcision presents a careful review of numerous studies of urinary tract infection indicating that uncircumcised infants have a 4 to 10 or even 12-fold increased risk of urinary tract infection[24] and also concludes that there is at least a threefold increase in the risk of penile cancer in uncircumcised men. Nevertheless, the Task Force did not feel that either of these considerations is sufficient to warrant a recommendation for routine circumcision since the absolute risk of urinary tract infection is low and penile cancer even in uncircumcised males is rare.

The Task Force also cites studies indicating that circumcised males may have a diminished risk for contracting syphilis[25] and points to a substantial body of evidence linking non-circumcision with HIV infection[26] but declines to recommend circumcision on that account because it regards behavioral factors as far more significant in this regard than circumcision status.

The Task Force readily concedes that "existing scientific evidence demonstrates potential medical benefits of newborn male circumcision" but asserts that "these data are not sufficient to recommend routine neonatal circumcision."[27] The Task Force further unreservedly acknowledges that "it is legitimate for parents to take into account cultural, religious and ethnic traditions" in making a decision with regard to circumcision.[28] The Task Force recommended that, when circumcision is performed, a topical anesthesia be employed.

The ambivalence of the medical profession with regard to the prophylactic benefit of circumcision should not come as a surprise to students of rabbinic literature. One searches in vain among the writings of the classical expositors of the *ta'amei ha-mizvot*, i.e., the meaning and rationale underlying each of the commandments, for an indication that the *telos* of circumcision is avoidance of disease or promotion of health.[29] At the same time, apart from the risk from periopr ative complications which were well known to the Sages of the Talmud and which were far more common and far more serious in days gone by, it would be quite surprising to discover that there are health risks associated with circumcision.

II. ALLEVIATION OF PAIN

In the absence of significant health hazards associated with the procedure, opponents of circumcision have focused upon the pain experienced by the infant.[30] Until recent years, it was generally assumed that the immature and incompletely developed neurological system of neonates left them more or less impervious to pain.[31] Many still-practicing physicians can well remember the days when major surgery was routinely performed upon neonates without benefit of any form of anesthesia other than a dose of ethanol sufficient to induce a mild state of inebriation. Pain is known to vary markedly from individual to individual; different people respond differently to identical pain stimuli. Since pain defies precise quantification it is extremely difficult to compare the pain experiences of different individuals in a scientifically meaningful way. The difficulty of assessing the degree and severity of pain in infants is compounded by their inability to communicate. Hence, despite the fact that it is now generally conceded that newborns are capable of experiencing pain, the nature and intensity of such pain remains largely unknown. Nevertheless, human compassion and decency should dictate that pain-relieving measures be adopted, at least when such measures do not present additional medical risks, even if the presence of, or potential for, pain is a matter of doubt.

The earliest local anesthetic technique for newborn[32] circumcision seems to have been the dorsal penile nerve block developed by Kirya and Werthmann in 1978.[33] The procedure involves the injection of a small quantity of 10% lidocaine (without epinephrine) in the area of the dorsal penile nerves. The work of Kirya and Werthmann received scant attention, perhaps because it was conducted without a control group, and no attempt was made to determine possible genitourinary side effects or long term behavioral effects. However, a series of studies conducted between 1982 and 1985[34] confirmed the original results and served to generate enthusiasm for the procedure.

Those findings were again confirmed in a 1988 study which showed in addition that the procedure also effectively diminished increases in serum cortisol levels.[35] It was shown that infants injected with lidocaine in the appropriate area experienced significantly less stress as evidenced by smaller decreases in transcutaneous oxygen pressure levels, less crying and lower increases in heart rate as compared with infants circumcised in an identical manner without anesthesia.

However, employment of a dorsal nerve block is not entirely problem free. The procedure requires skill in determining the site of the injection and in carrying out the injection itself. In addition, injection of the infant is itself a source of pain. There is also the danger, albeit a low one, of development of a hematoma at the site of the injection and of possible gangrene from accidental puncture of the dorsal artery or vein of the penis in the course of the attempt to infiltrate the underlying dorsal nerves.[36]

Obviously, were a topical anesthetic available, those problems would be avoided entirely. The first attempt to rely upon a topical anesthetic in conjunction with circumcision occurred in 1989 and met with some success.[37] The procedure involved use of a topical 40% lidocaine in acid mantle cream. Two subsequent studies were reported in 1993. In one study reported in *Pediatrics*[38] the concentration was modified and 30% lidocaine in acid mantle cream was employed. In that study the mean heart rate, respiratory rate, oxygen capture and diastolic blood pressure did not vary significantly between the placebo and the lidocaine groups. The mean systolic blood pressure was significantly higher in the placebo created group. The authors of that study reported a rise in the serum b-endorphin level in 11 of 15 infants who did not receive lidocaine while only one third of those receiving lidocaine experienced such an increase. In addition, there was also an increase in various types of crying. Although they noted that no previous studies examined changes in serum b-endorphin concentrations in newborns before and after an invasive procedure such as circumcision, the authors regarded the absence of an increase in serum b-endorphin as a crucial indicator of the absence of pain.

A second study reported in the *Journal of the American*

Medical Association[39] involved use of a eutectic mixture of local anesthetics, *viz.*, lidocaine and prilocaine hydrochloride bases. Heart rate, oxygen saturation, facial action and crying were found to be significantly different in those receiving topical anesthesia as opposed to those receiving a placebo.[40]

There are, however, considerable grounds for skepticism with regard to the need for pain relief in conjunction with neonatal circumcision as traditionally practiced by Jews. Each of the studies that determined the presence of pain as manifested in various physiological phenomena involved examination of infants subjected to surgical circumcision utilizing a Gomco or bell clamp. The procedure described in the 1993 *JAMA* article involved a series of steps, including restraining the child, clamping the dorsal side of the foreskin, longitudinal incision of the foreskin, lysis of adhesions between the foreskin and the glands, application of the Gomco clamp, cutting the foreskin, removing the Gomco clamp and removing the restraints. The time required for completing the cumbersome procedure ranged from six to forty minutes. In contrast, ritual circumcision carried out in the traditional manner involves only separation of the foreskin from the glans, cutting the foreskin and retracting the underlying mucous membrane. Excision of the foreskin is performed rapidly and is accomplished in a matter of seconds. Emblematic of the swiftness of the procedure is the frequently observed phenomenon associated with the *mohel*'s recitation of the blessing for performance of the *mizvah*: The *mohel* begins to pronounce the blessing as he commences to cut. Generally, the cutting of the foreskin is completed well before the *mohel* has managed to finish reciting the twelve-word blessing.

Studies demonstrating pain experienced in conjunction with circumcision utilizing a Gomco clamp are entirely irrelevant to circumcision involving a rapid excision with a sharp knife. Any person who has accidentally cut himself with a very sharp knife knows that the cut itself is virtually painless.[41] It is quite likely that distress evidenced by infants during ritual circumcision is largely discomfort as a result of unwelcome manipulation and positioning rather than a response to pain. It is not uncommon for a baby to cry prior to the circumcision but to serenely and apparently contentedly suck on a bottle of sugar water during the actual severance of the foreskin.

III. PAIN RELIEF AND HALAKHAH

1. *General Anesthesia*

Over the years a number of responsa and other brief remarks discussing the permissibility of performing circumcision under general anesthesia have appeared in rabbinic works. Those discussions deal primarily with adult circumcision in instances of conversion and, occasionally, with circumcision of naturally born Jews who, for whatever reason, were not circumcised in infancy. Utilization of general anesthesia for this purpose presents a number of halakhic issues, both because of the fact that the person circumcised is rendered unconscious during the course of the procedure and because an adult, unlike an infant, is himself personally bound by the commandment regarding circumcision.

Among the earliest authorities to address this topic, R. Yo'av Yehoshu'a Weingarten of Kintzk (Konskie), renowned as the author of *Teshuvot Ḥelkat Yo'av*, writing in the initial issue of a rabbinic journal, *Ohel Mo'ed*, vol. I, no. 1 (Tevet 5686) and R. Yitzchak Elchanan Spektor of Kovno[42] permit the use of general anesthesia, as does R. Shalom Mordecai Schwadron, *Teshuvot Maharsham*, VI, no. 108,[43] while R. Eliyahu Posek, in his classic work, *Koret ha-Brit*, *Naḥal Brit* 261:4, and R. Meir Arak, *Imrei Yosher*, II, no. 140, sec. 3, forbid the practice.[44] Among more recent authorities, circumcision under general anesthesia is permitted by R. Ovadiah Yosef, *Yabi'a Omer*, V, *Yoreh De'ah*, no. 22,[45] but is forbidden by R. Yechiel Ya'akov Weinberg, *Seridei Esh*, III, no. 96; R. Samuel ha-Levi Woszner, *Teshuvot Shevet ha-Levi*, V, *Yoreh De'ah*, no. 147, sec. 2; and R. Moshe Sternbuch, *Teshuvot ve-Hanhagot*, I (Jerusalem, 5752), no. 590 and II (Jerusalem, 5754), no. 510.

Maharsham's brief discussion addresses only one objection raised with regard to the practice. His interlocutor cites a rule governing the principle of agency, *viz.*, "For anything [the principal] cannot do he cannot appoint an agent," i.e., an agent cannot perform an act on behalf of a principal who lacks capacity to perform the act himself. Maharsham suggests that since a person under anesthesia is physically incapable of circumcising himself he lacks the capacity to designate an agent to act on his behalf while he is unconscious. Maharsham dismisses that contention by demonstrating that the power of an agent to act is not suspended while the principal sleeps. Unconsciousness induced by anesthesia, asserts Maharsham, is no different from sleeping.[46] R. Raphael Joseph Hazan, *Ḥikrei Lev*, I, *Even ha-Ezer*, no. 46, reconciles that rule with the validity of an act performed when the principal is asleep by declaring that the rule limits agency only in instances in which the principal lacks legal capacity to act but is not at all applicable in instances in which the principal cannot act because of a physical impediment.[47]

Maharsham adds yet another point that is the subject of considerable analytic discussion among latter-day authorities. Maharsham asserts that since circumcision constitutes a commandment involving one's body (a *miẓvah she-be-gufo*) it cannot be fulfilled through agency. That principle and its applicability to circumcision is elucidated by *Keẓot he-Ḥoshen* 382:2. Indeed, *Shakh*, *Ḥoshen Mishpat* 382:4, as well as *Or Zaru'a*, cited by *Darkei Mosheh*, *Yoreh De'ah* 264:1, rule that if a father is capable of circumcising his son he should not designate an agent to do so on his behalf. However, *Tevu'ot Shor*, *Yoreh De'ah* 28:14, and *Darkei Mosheh* himself maintain that the obligation may be discharged through the act of an agent.[48] Taking note of *Kezot he-Ḥoshen*'s explanation, Maharsham remarks that it must be understood that the authorities who sanction designation of an agent must maintain that the *mizvah* of circumcision is not fulfilled through the act of excising the foreskin but rather that the essence of the *mizvah* is that the person be in a circumcised state, i.e., that his body be sealed with the sign of the covenant. It then follows that, since the *mizvah* is fulfilled as the result of an act rather than by the act *per se*, the *mizvah* is essentially passive in nature, and hence whether or not the person being circumcised is conscious is of no consequence.

Maharsham's latter point, i.e., that the *mizvah* of circumcision is not the performance of the act of circumcision but is fulfilled by being in a circumcised state, is a position first explicitly espoused by the thirteenth-century authority, R. Chaim ben Isaac, *Teshuvot Or Zaru'a*,[49] no. 11.[50] *Teshuvot Or Zaru'a* propounds that thesis in the course of formulating his view that a father need not personally circumcise his son. The father's obligations *vis-à-vis* his son, asserts *Teshuvot Or Zaru'a*, do not require him personally to teach his son Torah, to serve as the son's swimming instructor, to train him in a trade, or to perform the actual act of circumcision; rather, those obligations require the father to assure that those ends are achieved. According to *Teshuvot Or Zaru'a*, the essence of the commandment regarding circumcision of both one's son and oneself is that the sign of the covenant "be sealed in the flesh." In support of that thesis, *Teshuvot Or Zaru'a* cites the statement of the Gemara, *Menaḥot* 43b:

> When David entered the bathhouse and perceived himself standing naked, he said, "Woe unto me that I stand naked without a *mizvah*." But when he remembered the circumcision in his flesh his mind became at ease.

The Gemara cannot be understood as reporting that

David's disquietude was dispelled by the sight of an organ of the body used for fulfillment of a *mizvah* for, were that the case, David might readily have observed that the arm and the head are bodily organs utilized for fulfilling the *mizvah* of donning phylacteries. It is evident that David was not assuaged by the realization that organs of his body had in the past been utilized in fulfillment of a *mizvah*; his concern was that, standing in the bathhouse he was, at that moment, bereft of actual fulfillment of *mizvot*. He found comfort at the sight of his circumcision because, among the organs of the body, only the circumcised membrum represents a continuous and uninterrupted fulfillment of a *mizvah*. If so, it is clear that the essence of the *mizvah* is passive, i.e., the *mizvah* lies in being in a circumcised state, rather than in the performance of the act of circumcision.[51] On the contrary, the act of circumcision is only a means to the end,[52] i.e., it represents a procedure instrumentally necessary in order to achieve the state of being circumcised.[53]

Another issue posed by anesthetization is the inability of the unconscious individual to have *kavannah* or intent to fufill the *mizvah*. If it is assumed that the essence of the *mizvah* is the act of excision of the foreskin and that agency is inoperative in fulfillment of the commandment because it is a *mizvah she-be-gufo*,[54] it then follows that a father who does not personally circumcise his son, or an adult who does not physically circumcise himself, has not performed a *mizvah*; rather the *mizvah* accrues to the *mohel* who performs the act.[55] If that is the case, it follows that no intention whatsoever is required on the part of the person being circumcised, with the result that unconsciousness induced by anesthesia does not present a problem with regard to fulfillment of the *mizvah*. *Seridei Esh* argues that if agency is operative in the circumcision of an adult and hence it is the person being circumcised who fulfills the *mizvah*, circumcision may nevertheless be performed upon an adult while he is asleep because the agent performing the circumcision is alert and has the requisite intent in performing the act that he is empowered to perform by virtue of the principle of agency. *Seridei Esh* suggests, however, that there may be a fundamental difference between the obligation to circumcise one's son and the obligation to circumcise oneself. The obligation to circumcise one's son, since it involves the body of another person, is not a *miẓvah she-be-gufo*, whereas the obligation to circumcise oneself is a *miẓvah she-be-gufo*. Nevertheless, contends *Seridei Esh*, the *miẓvah* to circumcise oneself may be fulfilled in the act of making oneself available and positioning oneself for circumcision rather than by personally performing the act of circumcision.[56] On the basis of that analysis, suggests *Seridei Esh*, the individual must be conscious during the procedure in order to have the requisite intention to fulfill the *miẓvah*.

Seridei Esh further suggests that, even if circumcision is not regarded as a *miẓvah she-be-gufo*, intention to fulfill the *miẓvah* is required and hence the person being circumcised must be conscious. If circumcision is not a *miẓvah she-be-gufo* the act of circumcision may be performed by another person just as another person may blow *shofar* on one's behalf. Nevertheless, the person fulfilling the *miẓvah* of listening to the *shofar* being blown must have the requisite intent. Similarly, the person undergoing circumcision must have the intention of fulfilling the *miẓvah*. Such intent is of course impossible if the person being circumcised is under anesthesia.[57] A similar view is expressed by R. Samuel ha-Levi Woszner, *Teshuvot Shevet ha-Levi*, V, *Yoreh De'ah*, no. 147, sec. 2, who states without elucidation that general anesthesia is unacceptable because of a requirement of intention to fulfill the *miẓvah*. R. Moshe Sternbuch, *Teshuvot ve-Hanhagot*, II, no. 590, also declares that a person must be "awake and in possession of his faculties at the time that he is circumcised" in order to fulfill the *miẓvah*, but adds that "if experts certify that [circumcision] is impossible without general anesthesia" employment of anesthesia is preferable to allowing the person to remain uncircumcised.

It is readily apparent that the foregoing considerations apply only with regard to the circumcision of an adult who is himself subject to the *mizvah* of circumcision. An infant, however, is not under obligation to fulfill *mizvot*. The circumcision of an infant is clearly a *mizvah* incumbent upon the father rather than upon the child. Since the child is under no obligation and performs no *mizvah* there would appear to be no halakhic reason why a child may not be circumcised while he is asleep or when rendered unconscious by anesthesia.[58]

Nevertheless, *Seridei Esh* refuses to sanction general anesthesia even for an infant on the grounds that circumcision represents entry into the covenant of Abraham.[59] *Seridei Esh* asserts that, for that reason alone,[60] the possibility of anesthesia for an adult convert cannot be entertained. Just as a proselyte must accept the yoke of *mizvot*, so must he intend to enter into the covenant of Abraham. Such intent is impossible unless the individual is conscious. *Seridei Esh* further asserts that every circumcision represents entry into the covenant and therefore the individual being circumcised must be conscious. That consideration would serve to preclude anesthesia in the case of an adult. *Seridei Esh* further contends that

> one conducts oneself with a child as with an adult . . . but if [the child] is rendered unconscious he is as an inanimate[61] stone and one does not enter into a covenant with a stone. In the eyes of people, severance of the foreskin of a sleeping child is in the nature of a battery rather than entry into the covenant of our father Abraham.

Quite obviously, the concerns expressed by *Seridei Esh* with regard to general anesthesia do not apply to local anesthesia delivered by injection. From the perspective of Halakhah, a penile nerve block or other injected anesthesia is indistinguishable from topical anesthesia, which is the subject of the following section.

2. *Topical Anesthesia*

Nothing in the foregoing discussion would serve as a barrier to the use of a topical anesthesia in order to prevent pain in either an infant or an adult. Nevertheless, one authority, R. Meir Arak, *Imrei Yosher*, II, no. 140, takes a very strong stand against use of topical anesthesia. In that context, *Imrei Yosher* cites a statement found in *Shemot Rabbah* 47:9:

> "In the self-same day Abraham was circumcised" (Genesis 27:26): R. Abba said, "He felt the smart and suffered pain so that the Lord might double his reward." R. Levi said, "It does not say 'Abraham circumcised himself,' but rather 'Abraham was circumcised;' this intimates that he examined himself and found that he was [already] circumcised." R. Berekiah observed, "It was at that time that R. Abba ben Kahana humiliated R. Levi saying to him, 'It is a lie and a falsehood! He felt the smart and suffered pain so that the Lord might double his reward.' "

In response, *Seridei Esh* correctly points out that the midrashic citation establishes only that Abraham desired heavenly reward for fulfilling the *mizvah* and that such reward is directly commensurate with the pain that is suffered. However, this midrashic statement does not serve to establish an obligation to suffer pain and certainly does not establish a normative principle making it incumbent to inflict such pain upon an unwitting and unwilling infant.

It is, however, a misreading of *Imrei Yosher*'s responsum to infer that the midrashic statement serves as the basis of that scholar's ruling. *Shemot Rabbah* is cited by *Imrei Yosher* only to demonstrate that circumcision is associated with pain; an entirely different halakhic source is cited by *Imrei Yosher* in prohibiting topical anesthesia. The Gemara, *Bava Kamma* 85a, speaks explicitly of amputation of a limb by chemical, rather than surgical, means and describes chemical amputation as being painless.[62] Similarly, the Gemara, *Kiddushin* 21b, declares that a Hebrew slave who refuses to be set free after serving a statutory six-year period and who must therefore undergo a ritual involving the boring of his ear must have his ear pierced by means of a metal implement but not by means of a chemical.[63] The foreskin, asserts *Imrei Yosher*, can also be removed in a like manner by means of application of a chemical. But quite apart from the problem of obviating the pain of circumcision, such a procedure, asserts *Imrei Yosher*, could not be sanctioned for an entirely different reason. *Imrei Yosher* is among the authorities who maintain that the foreskin must be removed by excision rather than by means of some other process.[64] Some commentators find that requirement reflected in the verb "to cut" employed in the biblical idiom that connotes entering into a covenant as in the verse "*ve-kharot imo ha-brit*—and He cut a covenant with him" (Nehemiah 9:8).[65] *Imrei Yosher* comments that the biblical term "*himol*" (Genesis 17:13) indicates excision of the foreskin.[66] That understanding is reflected in Targum Onkelos' translation of the term as "*migzar*."[67] Nevertheless, reasons *Imrei Yosher*, if flesh-eating chemicals were available to the Sages of the Talmud, pain-quelling drugs must have been available to them as well. Yet rabbinic sources make no mention of use of topical anesthesia for purposes of circumcision. This *argumentum ad silencium*, concludes *Imrei Yosher*, demonstrates that such pharmaceutical products may not be used to eliminate pain because experience of pain is one of the elements of circumcision.[68]

R. Israel Veltz, who at the time was a *dayyan* in Budapest, consulted R. Judah Leib Zirelson concerning the circumcision of a five-year-old child. The child had been sickly and was not circumcised in infancy. The child's mother was willing to permit circumcision only on the condition that the pain be assuaged by means of a topical anesthetic. In his response, published in his responsa, *Ma'arkhei Lev*, no. 53, Rabbi Zirelson dismisses the notion that circumcision must be accompanied by pain as being without basis in rabbinic sources. Indeed, *Ma'arkhei Lev* endeavors to show that pain is not at all a required concomitant of circumcision. The Gemara, *Shabbat* 135a, cites conflicting opinions with regard to whether a child born without a foreskin and a prospective proselyte who has been circumcised while yet a gentile require "letting of the blood of the covenant" and explains in detail the considerations of the proponents of the various views. Entirely absent from that discussion is the concept that "letting of blood" is required because pain is a necessary element of circumcision.

Ma'arkhei Lev's argument, however, is readily rebuttable. Pain in itself is certainly not a requirement. The sole issue is whether pain is required as a concomitant or epiphenomenon of circumcision. When no circumcision is possible because the person is already circumcised or because he has no foreskin there can be no requirement of pain for its own sake. In such circumstances, the pain is entirely divorced from the act of circumcision and hence without any significance in fulfillment of the *mizvah*.

Despite his dismissal of the notion that pain is a necessary element of circumcision, *Ma'arkhei Lev* decries the attempt to seek innovative measures to avoid pain but tempers that position with the observation that rigidity with regard to such a policy is inappropriate. Thus, concludes *Ma'arkhei Lev*, if insistence upon following time-hallowed practices would result in failure to carry out the circumcision because of the mother's refusal to grant permission for performance of the procedure if it is to be accompanied by pain, as in the case brought to his attention, a topical anesthesia should be employed.[69]

Despite his disagreement with *Imrei Yosher*'s halakhic reasoning, Rabbi Weinberg declares that he gives greater weight to the stringent view of *Imrei Yosher* than to the balanced position of *Ma'arkhei Lev* because "a custom of Israel is Torah and should not be denigrated." The position of *Imrei Yosher* is also espoused by R. Abraham Jacob Horowitz, *She'erit Ya'akov*, no. 5.[70]

One aspect of this position requires elucidation. Causing unnecessary pain to another human being is certainly not permissible. Causing wanton pain to brute animals is prohibited by virtue of the prohibition against causing *ẓa'ar ba'alei ḥayyim*. There is indeed a controversy with regard to whether humans are included in the ambit of the "*ba'alei ḥayyim*" or "living creatures" protected by that stricture. However, it may well be the case that humans are not included in that prohibition because such a prohibition is superfluous. Ramban, in his *Torat ha-Adam*,[71] declares that the physician's obligation to heal is rooted in the commandment "and you shall love your fellow as yourself" (Leviticus 19:18). That admonition establishes an obligation to manifest love and concern in general for one's fellow and, according to Ramban, in particular, requires one to provide medical attention for the cure of disease and relief of pain.[72] It assuredly serves to prohibit causing grief or pain to one's fellow as is indeed encapsulated in Hillel's aphorism recorded in the Gemara, *Shabbat* 31a, "What is disdainful to you do not do to your friend." Elsewhere,[73] this writer has sought to demonstrate that, when possible, a person is obligated to seek the palliation of pain. Why, then, are these authorities unconcerned by the specter of causing avoidable pain experienced by an infant in the course of circumcision?

The answer lies in the midrashic comment cited by *Imrei Yosher*. The Midrash does more than allude to an act of piety on the part of Abraham. In no other context does one find a rabbinic encomium for seeking out avoidable pain in performing a *miẓvah*. A person who, for example, has an *etrog* conveniently available but seeks to select one from beneath a mass of thorns should not anticipate enhanced heavenly reward because of the pain incurred in the process. Pursuit of pain that is both avoidable and extrinsic to fulfillment of the *miẓvah* is simply masochism. Circumcision is quite different. Although pain is not a necessary condition for fulfillment of the *mizvah*, the *mizvah*, as commanded, does perforce entail a measure of pain. Therefore, although it is not an intrinsic element of the *mizvah*, the pain inherent in the act must be part of the divine *desideratum* and hence, as the Midrash indicates, the pain will be rewarded even when it could have been avoided. It is thus readily understandable that there is no obligation to spare another person from the pain naturally attendant upon circumcision.

This point is also formulated by *Shevet ha-Levi, Yoreh De'ah*, V, no. 147, sec. 2, albeit without raising the issue of an obligation to avoid or diminish pain and without citing either *Imrei Yosher* or *Shemot Rabbah*. Instead, *Shevet ha-Levi* cites the comment of the Gemara, *Gittin* 57b, elucidating the verse "For Your sake are we killed all of the day" (Psalms 44:23). The Gemara interprets the verse as an allusion to circumcision. *Shevet ha-Levi* understands the comment as a reference to the pain entailed in circumcision.[74] Accordingly, contends *Shevet ha-Levi*, the "form" of the *mizvah* involves pain and, moreover, it is certain "that such is the form of the *mizvah* in its source from Sinai."[75] However, the pain to which the Sages allude is only the pain that is ordinarily experienced by an infant.[76] Accordingly, declares *Shevet ha-Levi*, in unusual circumstances in which circumcision would cause inordinate pain,[77] or if the person to be circumcised is not an infant, a topical anesthesia may be used.[78]

There is one additional matter not mentioned by these authorities that must be addressed. Use of a salve or ointment on *Shabbat* or *Yom Tov* involves a biblical transgression and is forbidden other than for reasons of *pikuah nefesh*, i.e., application of a salve is permitted to mitigate danger to life but not to alleviate pain.[79] Accordingly, application of a topical ointment on *Shabbat* or *Yom Tov* by a Jew cannot be condoned even if refusal to employ a topical anesthesia will result in refusal to permit performance of the circumcision.

Although the arguments against use of topical anesthesia

cannot be described as compelling, they are buttressed by the weight of tradition. As noted earlier, the author of *Seridei Esh*, who was hardly an extremist and who was known for his sagacity, regarded topical anesthesia as permissible but nevertheless declined to express approval of its use. *Seridei Esh* well understood that Jewish tradition and practice must not be allowed to bend with changing winds.[80] *Miẓvot* dare not be permitted to be held hostage by the *Zeitgeist* of any particular age. Attacks upon *milah*, whether frontal or peripheral, should be met with proud reaffirmation of the covenant of Abraham together with its time-hallowed traditions.

NOTES

1. The notion that the people of Israel are preserved from extinction in the Diaspora by the *miẓvah* of *milah* is expressed by Ramban, *Commentary on the Bible*, Genesis 15:18, as well as by R. Jacob Emden, *Migdal Oz*, *Breikhah Elyonah* 2:20.
2. See, for example, I Maccabees 1:48.
3. For a survey of methods adopted for this purpose in antiquity, see Robert G. Hall, "Epispasm: Circumcision in Reverse," *Moment*, February, 1992, pp. 34–37. In contemporary times, various forms of foreskin reconstruction are advocated and practiced by members of organizations known as "Recover a Penis" (RECAP), "Brothers United for Future Foreskins" (BUFF) and "UNCircumcising Information and Resources Center" (UNCIRC).
4. See *Bet Yosef*, *Yoreh De'ah* 266; *Levush*, *Yoreh De'ah* 363:5; and *Taz*, *Yoreh De'ah* 363:3. Cf., *Shakh*, *Yoreh De'ah* 363:8. Cf., however, *Shulḥan Arukh*, *Yoreh De'ah* 268:9 and *Teshuvot ha-Rambam*, ed. R. Joshua Blau (Jerusalem, 5718), I, no. 148, reprinted in *Iggerot ha-Rambam*, ed. R. Isaac Shilat (Jerusalem, 5747), pp. 212–214.
5. See, for example, Ronald Goldman, *Circumcision: The Hidden Trauma* (Boston, 1997) and *Questioning Circumcision: A Jewish Perspective* [sic] (Boston, 1998); *idem*, "Circumcision: A Source of Jewish Pain," *Jewish Spectator*, Fall, 1997, pp. 16–20; Jim Bigelow, *The Joy of Uncircumcising* (Aptos, 1998); *JTA Daily News Bulletin*, March 3, 1999; and "Is Brit *Milah* Cruel and

Unnecessary?" *The Jerusalem Report*, November 22, 1999, p. 104. See also Gershon Gorenberg, "I. and A. com: Weird World Web," *Jerusalem Report*, Aug. 6, 2002, p. 53. An attack on circumcision based upon the "blatant sexist implications" of the ritual is presented by Lawrence A. Hoffman, *Covenant of Blood: Circumcision and Gender in Rabbinic Judaism* (Chicago, 1996). A brief critique of much of this literature is the subject of an article by Jon D. Levenson, "The New Enemies of Circumcision," *Commentary*, March, 2000, pp. 29–36.

6. T. E. Wiswell and W. E. Hachey, "Urinary Tract Infection and the Uncircumcised State: An Update," *Clinical Pediatrics*, vol. 32, no. 3 (March, 1993), p. 130.
7. American Academy of Pediatrics, Task Force on Circumcision, "Circumcision Policy Statement," *Pediatrics*, vol. 103, no. 3 (March, 1999), p. 686.
8. It has been suggested that circumcision became popular in the United States during the post-World War II period because of the practice in the U.S. training camps of circumcising army recruits with tight foreskins. This practice was apparently instituted because of two considerations: 1) Poor hygiene and desert sand resulted in many cases of severe foreskin infections among soldiers, particularly in the North African campaign. 2) The experience of military surgeons convinced them that circumcision protected against certain venereal diseases. See Edgar J. Schoen, "The Circumcision Decision," *Moment*, October, 1977, p. 46.
9. See Edward O. Laumann, Christopher M. Masi *et al.*, "Circumcision in the United States: Prevalence, Prophylactic Effects, and Sexual Practices" *Journal of the American Medical Association*, vol. 277, no. 13 (April 2, 1997), pp. 1053–1057. See also "Circumcision Policy Statement," supra, note 7, pp. 686–693.
10. It should be noted that testing urine for the presence of bacteria is simpler and less traumatic in the circumcised infant. Since bacteria in the foreskin of an uncircumcised child may contaminate the urine, it is necessary to bypass the foreskin by inserting a needle into the bladder. Such traumatic intervention is unnecessary in a circumcised child since his voided urine is uncontaminated. See Schoen, p. 46.
11. See Joseph Katz, "The Question of Circumcision," *International Surgery*, vol. 62, no. 9 (September, 1977), p. 490.

12. Xavier Castellsague, F. Xavier Bosch, Nubia Muñoz *et al.*, "Male Circumcision, Penile Human Papillomavirus Infection, and Cervical Cancer in Female Partners," *New England Journal of Medicine*, vol. 346, no. 15 (April 11, 2002), pp. 1105–1112.
13. American Academy of Pediatrics, Committee on the Fetus and Newborn, "Report of the Ad Hoc Task Force on Circumcision," *Pediatrics*, vol. 5, no. 4 (October, 1975), p. 611.
14. American Academy of Pediatrics, Committee on the Fetus and Newborn, *Guidelines for Perinatal Care*, 1st edition (Evanston, 1983), p. 87.
15. American Academy of Pediatrics, "Report of the Task Force on Circumcision," *Pediatrics*, vol. 84, no. 4 (August, 1989), pp. 388–390.
16. *Ibid.*, p. 390.
17. Curiously, an Israeli study involving only circumcised male infants found an overall higher incidence of urinary tract infections in infancy but found that males were affected more commonly than females during the first four weeks of life. The authors of that study indicate that this phenomenon may be attributed at least in part to pain-induced urine retention occurring immediately following circumcision but suggest that such an infection may be the product of non-sterile techniques used during the procedure and accordingly urge that stricter sterile techniques be employed. See Michael Goldman, Joseph Barr, Tsvy Bistritzer and Mordechay Aladjem, "Urinary Tract Infection Following Ritual Jewish Circumcision," *Israel Journal of Medical Sciences*, vol. 32, no. 11 (November, 1996), pp. 1098–1102.
18. "Report of the Task Force on Circumcision," *supra*, note 15, p. 390.
19. "Circumcision in the United States," *supra*, note 9, pp. 1052–1057.
20. *Ibid.*, p. 1057.
21. *Loc. cit.*
22. Masters and Johnson report no difference in exteroceptive and light tactile discrimination on either the ventral or dorsal surfaces of the glans as a result of circumcision. See Warren H. Masters and Virginia E. Johnson, *Human Sexual Response* (Boston, 1966), pp. 189–191.

It should however be noted that Rambam, in his *Guide for the Perplexed*, Book III, chap. 49, states that circumcision is designed to mitigate sexual desire and counteract excessive lust by weakening the power of sexual excitement and, at times, by lessening natural enjoyment. It is of interest to note that the authors of a recent article have argued: 1) Keratinization of the glans lowers the sensitivity and hence the sexual excitability of a circumcised male's genitals; the result is lowering of excitability and raising the threshold for sexual arousal. 2) In antiquity, societies instituted the practice of circumcision in order to make young males less sexually excitable and distractable and hence more amenable to acceptance of the group's authority. See Ronald S. Immerman and Wade C. Mackey, "A Bicultural Analysis of Circumcision," *Social Biology*, vol. 44, no. 3–4 (Fall–Winter, 1997), pp. 265–275. The authors present the same material in a somewhat modified form in a second article, "A Proposed Relationship between Circumcision and Neural Reorganization," *Journal of Genetic Psychology*, vol. 159, no. 3 (September, 1998), pp. 367–378. In the latter article they further suggest that abated male sexual drive as a result of circumcision more closely parallels that of the female and serves to reduce extramarital liaisons. Accordingly, they argue, those societies instituted circumcision in order to benefit from strengthened and more durable marriages.

Also of interest are Philo's comments in *The Special Laws*, trans. F. H. Colson (Cambridge, 1937), I, 9, p. 105. Philo writes that, apart from "the explanations handed down to us from the old-time studies of divinely gifted men," he considers circumcision to be a "symbol" designed to "dock the organ which ministers to intercourse, thus making circumcision the figure of the excision of excessive and superfluous pleasure, not only of one pleasure but of all the other pleasures signified by one, and that the most imperious." Philo differs from Rambam in regarding removal of the foreskin as merely symbolic of curtailment of sensual pleasure.

23. *Supra*, note 7.
24. The report suggests that this phenomenon may be due to the fact that there are increased numbers of uropathogenic organisms in the area of the urethral meatus of uncircumcised

infants. Such periurethral colonization decreases in all infants after the first six months of life. See T. E. Wiswell, G. M. Miller, H. M. Gelston *et al.*, "Effect of Circumcision Status on Periurethral Bacterial Flora During the First Year of Life," *Journal of Pediatrics*, vol. 113, no. 3 (September, 1988), pp. 442–446. It has also been demonstrated that these bacteria adhere to, and readily colonize, the mucosal surface of the foreskin that is removed in circumcision but do not adhere to the keratinized skin surface. See E. N. Fussell, M. B. Kaack, R. Cherry and J. A. Roberts, "Adherence of Bacteria to Human Foreskins," *Journal of Urology*, vol. 140, no. 5 (November, 1988), pp. 997–1001.

25. See L. S. Cook, L. A. Koutsky and K. K. Holmes, "Circumcision and Sexually Transmitted Diseases," *American Journal of Public Health*, vol. 84, no. 2 (February, 1994), pp. 197–201 and J. Newell, K. Senkoro, F. Mosha *et al.*, "A Population-Based Study of Syphilis and Sexually Transmitted Disease Syndromes in Northwestern Tanzania." II. "Risk Factors and Health Seeking Behaviour," *Genitourinary Medicine*, vol. 69, no. 6 (December, 1993), pp. 421–426.

26. See S. Moses, F. A. Plummer, J. E. Bradley *et al.*, "The Association Between the Lack of Male Circumcision and the Risk for HIV Infection: A Review of the Epidemiological Data," *Sexually Transmitted Diseases*, vol. 21, no. 4 (July-August, 1994), pp. 201-210; J. Seed, S. Allen, T. Mertens, *et al.*, "Male Circumcision, Sexually Transmitted Disease, and Risk of HIV," *Journal of Acquired Immune Deficiency Syndrome and Human Retrovirology*, vol. 8, no. 1 (January 1, 1995), pp. 83–90; J. K. Kreiss and S. G. Hopkins, "The Association Between Circumcision Status and Human Immunodeficiency Virus Infection among Homosexual Men," *Journal of Infectious Diseases*, vol. 168, no. 6 (December, 1993), pp. 1404–1408; M.W. Tyndall, R. Ronald, E. Agoki *et al.*, "Increased Risk of Infection with Human Immunodeficiency Virus Type 1 among Uncircumcised Men Presenting with Genital Ulcer Disease in Kenya," *Clinical Infectious Diseases*, vol. 23, no. 3 (September, 1996), pp. 449–453; J. Bwayo, F. Plummer, M. Omau, *et al.*, "Human Immunodeficiency Virus Infection in Long-Distance Truck Drivers in East Africa," *Archives of Internal Medicine*, vol. 154, no. 12 (June 27, 1994), pp. 1391–1396; J. Pepin, M. Quigley, J. Todd *et al.*, "Association between HIV-2 Infection and Genital Ulcer Diseases among Male Sexually Transmitted

Disease Patients in Gambia," *AIDS* vol. 6, no. 5 (May, 1992), pp. 489–493; and J. N. Simonsen, D.W. Cameron, N. M. Gakinya *et al.*, "Human Immuno-deficiency Virus Infection among Men with Sexually Transmitted Diseases: Experience from a Center in Africa," *New England Journal of Medicine*, vol. 319, no. 5 (August 4, 1988), pp. 274–278. This phenomenon is explained on the basis of the fact that the mucous surface of the uncircumcised penis allows for viral attachment to lymphoid cells at or near the surface of the mucous membrane. There is also increased likelihood of minor abrasions in the uncircumcised foreskin that may provide an avenue for HIV infection.

A number of later studies confirm that circumcised men have a reduced risk of HIV-1 infection compared with uncircumcised men. See L. Lavreys, J. P. Rakwar, M. L. Thompson *et al.*, "Effect of Circumcision on Incidence of Human Immunodeficiency Virus Type 1 and Other Sexually Transmitted Diseases: A Prospective Cohort Study of Trucking Company Employees in Kenya," *Journal of Infectious Diseases*, vol. 180, no. 2 (August, 1999), pp. 330–336; H. A. Weiss, M. A. Quigley and R. J. Hayes, "Male Circumcision and Risk of HIV Infection in Sub-Saharan Africa: A Systematic Review and Meta-Analysis," *AIDS*, vol. 14, no. 15 (October 20, 2000), pp. 2361–2370; and S. J. Reynolds, M. E. Shepherd, A. R. Risbud *et al.*, "Male Circumcision and Risk of HIV-1 and Other Sexually Transmitted Infections in India," *Lancet*, vol. 363, no. 9414 (March 27, 2004), pp. 1039–1040. The study reported in *Lancet* was undertaken, in part, in response to suggestions that circumcision is simply an epidemiological marker of reduced behavior involving HIV-1 infection, including religious or cultural factors. The researchers report a 6.7-fold reduction in risk of HIV-1 infection of circumcised men but far lower protective effect upon other sexually transmitted diseases, *viz.*, HIV-2, syphilis and gonoccoccal urethritis. The disparity in the relative incidence of HIV in the two groups compared with the incidence of other sexually transmitted diseases indicates a biological rather than behavioral explanation for the protective effect of circumcision.

27. "Circumcision Policy Statement," *supra*, note 7, p. 691.
28. *Loc. cit.*

29. Philo, who was not a rabbinic scholar, regards circumcision as designed to increase fertility as well as to promote cleanliness and health. See *De Circumcisione*, ed. T. Mangey (1785), II, 210, and *The Special Laws*, I, 4–9, pp. 103–105. It has been suggested that Philo made the association between circumcision and fecundity, which he describes as "the most vital reason" for the practice of circumcision, because the birth of Isaac came closely upon the circumcision of Abraham. See J. D. Eisenstein, *Oẓar Yisra'el* (New York, 5712), V, 170.
30. See, for example, the letters to the editor published in *Lancet*, vol. 345 (April 8, 1995), p. 927, as well as Thomas J. Ritter and George C. Denniston, *Say No to Circumcision*, 2nd ed. (Aptos, 1966), secs. 3–4.
31. See, for example, "The Question of Circumcision," *supra*, note 11, p. 491.
32. It should be noted that, as will be discussed in the following section, a significant number of responsa dating from the beginning of the century refer to use of topical anesthesia in the circumcision of adults and older children. The novelty of this and subsequent medical studies lies in the fact that the subjects were newborns.
33. See C. Kirya and Milton Werthmann, "Neonatal Circumcision and Penile Dorsal Nerve Block: A Painless Procedure," *Journal of Pediatrics*, vol. 92, no. 6 (June, 1978), pp. 998–1000.
34. See C. A. Sara and C. J. Lowry, "A Complication of Circumcision and Dorsal Nerve Block of the Penis," *Anesthesia and Intensive Care*, vol. 13, no. 1 (February, 1985), pp. 79–82.
35. Howard J. Stang, Megan R. Gunnar, Leonard Snellman *et al.*, "Local Anesthesia for Neonatal Circumcision: Effects on Distress and Cortical Response," *Journal of the American Medical Association*, vol. 259, no. 10 (March 11, 1988), pp. 1507–1511. An earlier study found no such distinction. See Paul S. Williamson and Nolan Donavan Evans, "Neonatal Cortisol Response to Circumcision with Anesthesia," *Clinical Pediatrics*, vol. 25, no. 8 (August, 1986), pp. 412–415.
36. See "A Complication of Circumcision and Dorsal Nerve Block of the Penis," *supra*, note 34.
37. See Diane Mudge and Janet B. Younger, "The Effects of Topical Lidocaine on Infant Response to Circumcision," *Journal of Nurse Midwifery*, vol. 34, no. 6 (November-December, 1989), pp. 335–340.

38. Kathleen B. Weatherstone, Lynn B. Rasmussen, Allen Erenberg *et al.*, "Safety and Efficacy of a Topical Anesthesia for Neonatal Circumcision," *Pediatrics*, vol. 93, no. 5 (November, 1993), pp. 710–714.
39. Franca Benini, C. Celeste Johnston, Daniel Faucher and J. Aranda, "Topical Anesthesia During Circumcision in Newborn Infants," *Journal of the American Medical Association*, vol. 270, no. 7 (August 18, 1993), pp. 850–853.
40. A subsequent Australian clinical trial of EMLA cream, a eutetic mixture of lignocaine and prilocaine, showed a marked decrease in the crying of infants during circumcision. See C. T. Russell and J. Chase Ling, "Topical Anaesthesia in Neonatal Circumcision: A Study of 208 Consecutive Cases," *Australian Family Physician*, suppl. 1: 30–34 (January, 1996). More recently, in a presentation at the 2002 World Congress on Regional Anaesthesia and Pain Medicine, a Croatian research group recommended use of EMLA cream plus diclofenac suppository rather than penile block. In addition to avoiding the complications associated with penile block, they reported that the infants voided sooner. See Michael Vlessides, "Pain Medicine News: EMLA Cream Plus Diclofenac Offers Circumcision Analgesia," *Anesthesiology News* (September, 2002), p. 27.
41. For sources substantiating the absence of pain attendant upon incision with a sharp knife, see this writer's *Contemporary Halakhic Problems*, III (New York, 1989), 209, note 18.
42. See the brief responsum of R. Yitzchak Elchanan Spektor published in *Sefer Zikkaron le-Maran Ba'al "Paḥad Yiẓhak" Zaẓal*, cd. R. Joseph Buchsbaum (Jerusalem, 5744), p. 554.
43. R. Aryeh Leib Grossnass, *Lev Aryeh*, I, no. 2, permits general anesthesia for the circumcision of a convert but, by implication, not for the circumcision of a naturally-born Jew. *Lev Aryeh* bases himself upon R. Abraham Kahana-Shapiro, *Teshuvot Dvar Avraham*, II, no. 25, who terms the circumcision of a proselyte a mere preparation (*hekhsher*) for a *miẓvah*.

    Cf., R. Abraham Isaac ha-Kohen Kook, *Da'at Kohen*, no. 194 who, *en passant*, refers to the use of both general and topical anesthesia in conjunction with circumcision and offers no criticism of the practice. Use of general anesthesia is also permitted by R. Moshe Dov Welner, *She'ilat Ḥemdat Ẓevi*, no. 4. R. Aaron Epstein, *Kappei Aharon*, no. 19, similarly assumes as a matter of course that use of general anesthesia is permissible.

Kappei Aharon expresses doubt with regard to whether the person being circumcised should recite the blessing "to enter the covenant of Avraham" before the anesthetic is administered or whether, since a significant period of time will elapse before the incision is made, the blessing should be recited by the *mohel. Koret ha-Brit, Naḥal Brit* 261:4, considers the problem of recitation of the blessing as an additional reason not to employ general anesthesia.

44. This responsum originally appeared in *No'am*, XII (5729), 1–10.
45. See also R. Shalom Yosef ha-Levi Feigenbaum, *Ohel Mo'ed*, vol. I, no. 2 (Shevat 5686), p. 36 and *idem*, *Teshuvot Meshiv Shalom*, no. 318.
46. *Koret ha-Brit, Naḥal Brit* 261:4, cryptically comments, "Perhaps one should distinguish between natural sleep and sleep such as this," but offers no rationale to support that distinction.
47. Cf., however, *Maḥaneh Efrayim, Hilkhot Gerushin* 3:15, who cites a discussion recorded in *Bava Kamma* 110a from which it may be inferred that the exclusion must be understood quite literally and hence is applicable in instances of physical impediment as well. This also seems to be the understanding of *Tosafot Yeshanim, Eiruvin* 13a.
48. This is also the position of *Teshuvot Maharil*, no. 7, as cited in *Binat Adam, Sha'ar Issur ve-Hetter*, sec. 7. R. Joseph Dov ha-Levi Soloveitchik, *Bet ha-Levi*, I, no. 10, asserts that the *miẓvah* of circumcision can be fulfilled through an agent but that the additional *miẓvah* devolving upon a father to circumcise his son can be fulfilled only by the father himself.
49. The author of this responsa collection is the son of R. Isaac of Vienna who was the author of the frequently cited compendium *Or Zaru'a*. For a discussion of the view of R. Isaac of Vienna with regard to this matter, see R. Abraham Dov Ber Kahane, *Dvar Avraham*, II, no. 1, sec. 7.
50. See also *Maharit, Kiddushin* 29a, s.v. *oto ve-lo otah*.
51. Further support for the position of *Teshuvot Or Zaru'a* may be found in the statement of the Gemara, *Shevu'ot* 38b. Genesis 24:3 records that Abraham demanded that Eliezer swear a solemn oath not to select a bride for Isaac from among the daughters of Canaan. Genesis 24:2 states that Abraham also demanded that Eliezer place his hand "under my thigh" while

swearing the oath, i.e., that Eliezer hold the site of Abraham's circumcision in his hand while swearing the oath. The Gemara comments: "From here it is derived that a person being administered an oath must seize an object [of a *mizvah*] in his hand." See also Rashi's comment on Genesis 24:2. The problem reflected in this talmudic text is similar to the problem addressed by *Or Zaru'a*: Why does the circumcised glans serve as an "object of a *mizvah*" more so than, for example, a hand or scalp used for donning *tefillin*? The answer must lie in the fact that a hand is merely functionally related to fulfillment of the *mizvah* but is not itself intrinsic to the *mizvah*. The role of the membrum with regard to the act of excising of the foreskin is entirely similar. The *mizvah* of circumcision, however, also includes a commandment to bear the sign of the covenant at all times. As the organ in which the sign of the covenant is continuously borne the circumcised membrum constitutes an actual object of a *mizvah* in a manner entirely similar to the sense in which phylacteries or a Torah scroll constitute an object of a *mizvah*. See R. Shimon Moshe Diskin, *Ohel Yehoshu'a: Mas'et ha-Melekh*, 3rd edition (Jerusalem, 5758), *Parashat Ḥayyei Sarah*. See also the discussion of R. Yitzchak Bezalel Morgenstern, *Ha-Me'asef*, vol. XVIII, no. 6 (I Adar 5673), and R. Jacob Denison, *Ha-Me'asef*, vol. XIX, no. 1 (Tishri, 5674).

52. *Bet ha-Levi*, I, no. 10 maintains that the *mizvah* is twofold in nature, i.e., the act of excising the foreskin constitutes fulfillment of the *mizvah,* in addition to which there is an ongoing *mizvah* to be in a circumcised state. See also *Bet ha-Levi*, II, no. 47 and *Bet ha-Levi*, *Parashat Lekh Lekha*. For further elaboration see R. Ya'akov Kanievsky, *Kehillot Ya'akov*, *Kiddushin*, no. 32, sec. 3.

53. R. Ovadiah Yosef, *Yabi'a Omer*, V, *Yoreh De'ah*, no. 22, suggests that *Teshuvot Or Zaru'a*'s analysis of the nature of the *mizvah* of circumcision is the focal point of a controversy between *Tosafot* and Rambam. *Tosafot*, *Yevamot* 72a, maintain that a person who elongates the remaining foreskin in order to appear uncircumcised is categorized as uncircumcised and is forbidden to partake of *terumah* only by virtue of rabbinic decree, whereas Rambam, *Hilkhot Milah* 3:8, rules that a person performing such an act incurs the biblical punishment of excision (*karet*). [Cf., however, Rambam, *Hilkhot Teshuvah* 3:6; see also *Mishneh le-Melekh*, *Hilkhot Melakhim* 10:7; *Ma'aseh Rokeaḥ*,

Hilkhot Teshuvah 3:6; R. Abraham Litsh Rosenbaum, *Teshuvot Ben Yehudah*, no. 90; and R. Naphtali Zevi Judah Berlin, *Ha'amek Davar*, Genesis 17:13.] Rabbi Yosef suggests that the controversy flows from conflicting analyses of the *mizvah*: If the *mizvah* lies in the severance of the foreskin, once the act is completed the person has irreversibly discharged his obligation; if the *mizvah* is fulfilled by being in a circumcised state, the *mizvah* is ongoing and may be frustrated because this state is reversible. R. Yosef Engel, *Ben Porat*, no. 2, sec. 4, points to Rambam's ruling, *Hilkhot Milah* 1:2, that failure to perform circumcision does not entail *karet* so long as the person is yet alive and Ra'avad's conflicting view that the person is liable to the penalty of *karet* every moment. Mahari Engel asserts that, for Ra'avad, the *mizvah* is to be circumcised and hence every moment that a person remains in an uncircumcised state occasions punishment anew, whereas for Rambam the *mizvah* is a single act that can be performed at any moment so long as the person is alive. Neither the analysis of *Yab'ia Omer* nor that of Mahari Engel is compelling.

54. The ruling recorded in *Shulḥan Arukh, Yoreh De'ah* 264:8, to the effect that a minor may perform circumcision would seemingly indicate either that the commandment is passive in nature or that no intent is required. Cf., *Minḥat Ḥinnukh*, no. 2. *Seridei Esh*, III, no. 96, asserts that circumcision by a minor is efficacious only in the sense that the person upon whom the minor performs the procedure is not regarded as uncircumcised for purposes of partaking of *terumah* or of the paschal sacrifice and is not subject to the punishment of *karet* but that the *mizvah* remains unfulfilled. See *Teshuvot Ḥatam Sofer, Yoreh De'ah*, nos. 132 and 200, who makes the same point in explaining the position of those authorities who regard circumcision performed by a gentile as valid.

55. This is the view of *Shakh, Ḥoshen Mishpat* 382:4, as understood by *Kezot he-Ḥoshen*. R. Abraham Kahana-Shapiro, *Dvar Avraham*, II, no.1, explains that agency is inoperative, not because circumcision is a *mizvah she-be-gufo*, but because, upon failure of the father to circumcise his son, every Jew is obligated to perform the *mizvah*; hence, the person performing the circumcision is perforce acting on his own behalf rather than as an agent. See also *Bet ha-Levi*, I, no. 10. Ramban, *Shabbat* 137b, adopts a position of this nature in declaring that circumcision of a convert does not involve agency because any

person who performs the circumcision is fulfilling his own *mizvah*. Rashba, *ad locum*, makes the same point with regard to the members of the *Bet Din* who are charged with circumcising an infant when the father fails to do so.

56. *Seridei Esh* bases this argument upon the comments of *Taz, Oraḥ Ḥayyim* 328:1.
57. See also *Koret ha-Brit, Naḥal Brit* 261:4.
58. See *Koret ha-Brit, Naḥal Brit* 262:3, who cites a report to the effect that *mohalim* routinely refuse to perform circumcision while a child is asleep lest the child become a "*nikhpeh*," i.e., lest the circumcision cause an epileptic seizure. There is, however, no known medical basis for that concern.
59. A similar argument is advanced by R. Moshe Sternbuch, *Teshuvot ve-Hanhagot*, I, no. 590, II, no. 510 and III, no. 308. In *Teshuvot ve-Hanhagot*, III, no. 308, Rabbi Sternbuch reports that an unnamed rabbi, apparently in South Africa, had advised a candidate for conversion to undergo surgical circumcision under anesthesia and later to perform the relatively painless "letting of the blood of the covenant" (*hatafat dam brit*) for purposes of conversion as would be the procedure for any previously circumcised person seeking to become a proselyte. Rabbi Sternbuch objects to that solution because of Rabbenu Ḥananel's view that a previously circumcised non-Jew who converts to Judaism is not permitted to marry a Jewish woman. The opinion of Rabbenu Ḥananel (or, according to some versions, Rabbenu Tam) is cited by *Tur Shulḥan Arukh* 268. Although Rabbenu Ḥananel's view is not normative, Rabbi Sternbuch is of the opinion that it should not be ignored in situations in which other options are available.
60. R. Moshe Sternbuch, *Teshuvot ve-Hanhagot*, I, no. 767, sec. 3, in a questionable proposal, suggests that a male proselyte not be permitted even a topical anesthesia in order to encourage him to withdraw his candidacy for conversion because of aversion to pain.
61. The Hebrew term used in this context, *viz*., "*domem*" can also be translated as "mute." *Seridei Esh* may well have intended a *double entendre*.
62. Cf., Aretaeus, *De Curatione Morborum Diuturnorum*, Book I, chap. xiii, and Caelius Aurelianus, *On Acute Diseases and on Chronic Diseases*, trans. I. E. Drabkin (Chicago, 1950), Book III, chap. iv, p. 753.

63. See also *Avodah Zarah* 28a: "Jacob the sectarian prepared a medicine for [R. Abbahu's] leg and were it not for R. Ammi and R. Asi who licked his leg he would have cut his leg off."
64. See R. Alter Saul Pfeffer, *Avnei Zikaron*, III, no. 3. Cf., *Ḥamudei Dani'el* cited by *Pitḥei Teshuvah*, *Yoreh De'ah* 264:13.
65. The issue is whether the foreskin must be severed by cutting or whether it may also be destroyed either by chemical means or by cutting off the blood supply and thereby causing necrosis of the tissue. Both the Gomco clamp and the Magen are designed to cause necrosis with the result that the dead tissue may be simply sloughed off rather than severed by cutting. Use of the Gomco clamp was banned by the Union of Orthodox Rabbis of the United States and Canada for this and for other reasons. The full text of that ban was published in *Ha-Pardes*, Shevat 5711, p. 31. Objections to use of the Gomco clamp and the Magen are detailed by R. Moshe Sternbuch, *Dat ve-Halakhah* (Jerusalem, 5730), no. 2. See also R. Yosef Eliyahu Henkin, *Edut le-Yisra'el* (New York, n.d.), p. 144; R. Yitzchak Ya'akov Weisz, *Teshuvot Minḥat Yiẓhak*, V, no. 24, sec. 2 and VIII, no. 89; R. Eliezer Waldenberg, *Ẓiẓ Eli'ezer*, VIII, no. 29 and X, no. 38; and R. Moshe Feinstein, *Iggerot Mosheh*, *Yoreh De'ah*, II, no. 119 and *Yoreh De'ah*, III, nos. 98- 99. Cf., R. Moshe Bunim Pirutinsky, *Sefer ha-Brit*, *Likkutei Halakhot* 264:68 and 268:75.
66. See, however, *Tosafot Ri ha-Lavan*, *Ketubot* 5b, who explicitly permits use of a chemical for this purpose. R. Israel Isserlein, renowned as the author of *Terumot ha-Deshen*, apparently espouses a similar view as reflected in a work by his student R. Joseph ben Moshe, *Leket Yosher*, ed. Jacob Freimann (Berlin, 5663), p. 51.
67. Cf., however, *Teshuvot Ḥatam Sofer*, *Yoreh De'ah*, no. 249, who understands the term as connoting only "removal." That is also the position of *Teshuvot Divrei Ḥayyim*, II, *Yoreh De'ah*, no. 114.
68. Of interest, albeit lacking halakhic import, are the comments of the nineteenth century authority R. Eliyahu Guttmacher in his only recently published commentary on *Shabbat* 130a. R. Eliyahu Guttmacher remarks that prayers for the sick etc. are particularly propitious at the time of circumcision because on such occasions the prayers ascend to heaven together with the cries of the newly circumcised child.

69. A similar view was expressed by R. Aryeh Zevi Frommer, *Teshuvot Ereẓ Ẓevi, I,* no. 56, in a situation involving somewhat different but extraordinary circumstances.
70. *She'erit Ya'akov* is published as an appendix to that author's *Teshuvot Ẓur Ya'akov*.
71. *Torat ha-Adam, Kitvei Ramban*, ed. Bernard Chavel (Jerusalem, 5724), II, 48.
72. The Gemara, *Sanhedrin* 73a, declares that the verse, "and you shall restore it to him" (Deuteronomy 22:2) mandates not only the return of lost property but, *a fortiori*, preservation of life as well. Thus, the verse does not refer solely to the return of objects of material value. R. Judah Leib Zirelson, *Teshuvot Aẓei ha-Levanon*, no. 61, argues cogently that restoration of health to a person suffering from an illness is included in the commandment "and you shall restore it to him." Accordingly, it may be argued that the commandment "and you shall restore it to him" also includes an obligation to restore a person to a pain-free state.
73. *Infra*, chap. 6, "Palliation of Pain," pp. 166–168.
74. Cf., however, Rashi, *ad locum*, who understands the application to circumcision quite literally, i.e., circumcision may, at times, result in loss of life.
75. See Abraham S. Abraham, *Nishmat Avraham*, V, *Yoreh De'ah* 260:1, note 1, who reports that R. Ya'akov Hillel, head of Yeshivat ha-Mekubbalim in Jerusalem, noted that kabbalistic sources assert that the pain of childbirth is designed to expiate the sin of Eve but that, despite that consideration, no one has voiced an objection to easing the pain of labor. Nor, it should be added, does the fact that pain associated with illness is designed to atone for transgression in any way mitigate the obligation to palliate pain. Rabbi Woszner's point, regardless of the weight assigned to it, is entirely different. His argument is that, unlike pain designed to expiate sin, the pain of circumcision is, in some sense, intrinsic to the *mizvah*.
76. Although a statement by R. Joseph Shalom Eliashiv himself is not available, in a letter dated 5 Shevat 5758, a copy of which is in the possession of this writer, Rabbi Nachum Eisenstein reports that Rabbi Eliashiv accepts the position of *Imrei Yosher*, but permits use of a topical anesthesia in situations in which there is a particular medical need.
77. Even more fundamentally, only pain that is a natural accom-

paniment of simple excision may be tolerated. Accordingly, any extrinsic procedure causing additional pain is prohibited, including the pain of crushing the foreskin inherent in use of the Gomco clamp or the Magen as described in "Topical Anesthesia During Circumcision in Newborn Infants," *supra*, note 39, p. 852 and in *Lancet*, April 8, 1995, p. 927. See Rabbi Henkin, *Edut le-Yisra'el*, p. 144, who declares that, even absent other considerations, that concern is in itself sufficient to prohibit use of such devices.

78. Cf., R. Moshe Sternbuch, *Teshuvot ve-Hanhagot*, I, no. 590, and II, no. 510, who prefers that the topical anesthesia be administered in a manner that will yet allow for "some pain."

79. Application of a salve or ointment constitutes an act of *memaḥek*, one of the thirty-nine prohibited categories of labor. However, were the pharmaceutical agent to be formulated as a liquid there would be no objection to its use on *Shabbat* provided that the liquid not be applied by expressing it from gauze, cotton or cloth.

80. See also the comments of *Teshuvot Meshiv Shalom*, no. 318, s.v. *ve-hineh*.

3

Circumcision of a Child Born *Sine Concubito*

In vitro fertilization was successfully accomplished for the first time less than thirty years ago. Artificial insemination was performed for the first time in London in 1790. Both procedures were unknown during the talmudic period. Nevertheless, the Gemara, *Ḥaggigah* 14b, queries whether a high priest is permitted to marry a pregnant virgin. The Gemara considers it possible that the woman may have become pregnant as a result of bathing in water into which a man had previously discharged semen. There is also a midrashic source that relates that Ben Sira was conceived *sine concubito* by the daughter of Jeremiah and that the child's father was Jeremiah himself. Jeremiah, it is reported, was forced by a band of wicked men to ejaculate in a bath and his daughter became pregnant when she subsequently bathed in the same bathhouse.[1]

Rabbenu Ḥananel, *Ḥaggigah* 16a, explains the Gemara's remarks concerning a woman who conceives from semen emitted in a bath in a manner that has practical halakhic ramifications with regard to a child born of in vitro fertilization and perhaps for a child born of artificial insemination as well. Rabbenu Ḥananel, who apparently had a different manuscript version of the talmudic passage, understands the Gemara's question to be focused upon whether or not a woman who gives birth to a child conceived *sine concubito* is subject to the ritual defilement associated with childbirth. According to Rabbenu Ḥananel, the term "*ishah ki tazri'a*" (Leviticus 12:2) connotes pregnancy resulting from natural fertilization of the ovum but excludes a woman who conceives as a result of unnatural "miraculous" fertilization in the manner described by the Gemara.

Rabbi Leib Baron, in his most recent volume, *Neẓaḥ Ya'akov* (Jerusalem, 5757), no. 35, notes that, according to Rabbenu Ḥananel, a child conceived from semen emitted into bath water may not be circumcised on *Shabbat*. The Gemara, *Shabbat* 135a, notes the juxtaposition of the regulation concerning ritual impurity occasioned by childbirth recorded in Leviticus 12:2 and the immediately following statement "And on the eighth day the flesh of his foreskin should be circumcised" (Leviticus 12:3) and declares that a child may be circumcised on the eighth day when it occurs on *Shabbat* only if the baby's birth occasioned ritual impurity of the mother. As stated by the Gemara, *Niddah* 40a, a woman who gives birth by Cesarean section does not become ritually impure because talmudic exegesis understands Leviticus 12:2 as declaring that only a woman who "gives birth from the place in which she conceives" becomes ritually impure. Rabbenu Ḥananel interprets that statement in a novel manner and regards it as disassociating all forms of unnatural procreation from ritual impurity. The Gemara declares that, since a woman who delivers by Cesarean section does not become ritually impure, the baby born in that manner may not be circumcised on *Shabbat*.

Rabbi Baron observes that it therefore follows that, according to Rabbenu Ḥananel, a child born as a result of emission of semen in bath water should similarly not be circumcised on *Shabbat*. Rabbi Baron further notes that, according to Rabbenu Ḥananel, the status of a child conceived in a petri dish is identical to that of a child conceived from semen emitted into bath water, i.e., the mother is not subject to ritual impurity occasioned by childbirth[2] and hence the child should not be circumcised on *Shabbat.*[3] Indeed, in vitro fertilization is even more unnatural than bathhouse pregnancy. In the latter case, conception takes place within the mother's body; in the case of in vitro fertilization conception takes place externally and, according to Rabbenu Ḥananel, is certainly not encompassed within the meaning of "*ishah ki tazri'a.*"

R. Shlomoh Zalman Auerbach, *Minḥat Shlomoh*, III, no. 98, sec. 4, makes the same point, albeit somewhat tentatively with regard to pregnancy resulting from artificial insemination and questions whether a boy conceived in that manner should be circumcised on *Shabbat.* Artificial insemination, he maintains, is entirely analogous to bathhouse insemination. In both cases conception occurs internally; in both cases pregnancy occurs sine concubito. Since it is the absence of a sexual act that places the conception outside the ambit of "*ishah ki tazri'a,*" it should follow that, according to Rabbenu Ḥananel, neither a child born of in vitro fertilization nor a child born of artificial insemination should be circumcised on *Shabbat.*

R. Samuel ha-Levi Woszner, *Teshuvot Shevet ha-Levi*, IX, no. 210, does not discuss the issue posed in the case of a child born of in vitro fertilization but does address the case of a child conceived by means of artificial insemination. *Shevet ha-Levi* maintains both that the mother of a child born as a result of artificial insemination is subject to ritual impurity and that the child should be circumcised on *Shabbat* even according to Rabbenu Ḥananel. *Shevet ha-Levi* asserts that Rabbenu Ḥananel's ruling is limited to bathhouse insemination which is both "unusual" (*eino shekhiaḥ*) and unnatural and proceeds to distinguish artificial insemination from bathhouse insemination on the grounds that in the case of artificial insemination "placement of the semen in the proper place causes conception of the fetus and natural childbirth." However, it may well be contended, contrary to the position of *Shevet ha-Levi,* that artificial insemination is certainly not "usual" and is, arguably, unnatural as well.

Be that as it may, the fact that, unlike a Caesarean section, artificial insemination results in natural childbirth is, according to Rabbenu Ḥananel, in itself entirely irrelevant, since bathhouse insemination also results in natural childbirth. Accordingly, it would appear that *Shevet ha-Levi* would concede that in vitro fertilization is unnatural by virtue of the fact that it occurs outside the mother's body and hence a child born of in vitro fertilization should not be circumcised on *Shabbat*.

According to the manuscript versions accepted by Rashi, *Tosafot* and other early-day commentators, there seems to be no basis for the halakhic ramifications that flow from Rabbenu Ḥananel's interpretation of his version of the talmudic text. Nevertheless, since the classical codifiers of Halakhah omitted any reference to the matter, Rabbi Baron is certainly correct in adopting the position that the opinion of an early-day authority of the stature of Rabbenu Ḥananel should not be ignored, particularly when a possible biblical transgression of *Shabbat* laws is involved. Parents who do not wish it to be known that the child was conceived other than in the usual manner may offer other reasons, e.g., the residual presence of physiologic jaundice, in explanation of why the circumcision is delayed until Sunday.

NOTES

1. See *Alfa Beta de-Ben Sira* in *Oẓar ha-Midrashim*, ed. J. D. Eisenstein (New York, 1928), p. 43. The veracity of this account is challenged by R. David Gans, *Ẓemaḥ David* (Warsaw, 5619), I, 13a.
2. The mother would nevertheless require immersion in a *mikveh* both because of the contradictory opinion of other authorities and because of the consideration that all bleeding is now treated as a menstrual flow.
3. Both Rabbi Baron and R. Shlomoh Zalman Auerbach, *Minḥat*

Shlomoh, III, no. 98, sec. 4, maintain that despite Rabbenu Ḥananel's employment of the term "miraculous" the distinction between bathhouse pregnancy and usual pregnancy lies in its "unnatural" rather than its "miraculous" nature. Since there is nothing "miraculous" in a Caesarean section that understanding of Rabbenu Ḥananel is probably correct.

4

Genetic Screening

I. THE PURSUIT OF SCIENCE

Commenting upon the verse "In the six hundredth year of Noah's life . . . all the fountains of the great deep opened up and the windows of heaven were opened" (Genesis 7:11), the *Zohar* declares that in the latter part of the sixth millennium the gates of wisdom will open on high and fountains of wisdom will open below. This phenomenon is depicted as preparation for the seventh millennium. When the sun begins its declension on the latter part of the sixth day a person begins to ready himself to welcome the approaching Sabbath. So also during the latter part of the sixth millennium does the world begin to prepare itself for the approaching seventh millennium that marks the advent of the eschatological era.

The genome project involving the identification of every one of the approximately 100,000 genes in the human body represents a major scientific accomplishment and is to be heralded as a providential milestone in the ongoing revelation of the mysteries of the universe. Unlocking the secrets of the natural order serves as a harbinger of the messianic era. Precisely how mapping human chromosomes and identifying the function of individual genes will affect health and life ex-

---

This paper was originally delivered in a different form at a symposium on "Modern Medicine and Jewish Law" sponsored by Maimonides Medical Center and the Associations of Orthodox Jewish Scientists in New York, February 1999.

pectancy is not yet known. For that matter, the eschatological import of those discoveries is not at all contingent upon any resultant therapeutic benefit. The *Zohar* makes no mention of the pragmatic effects of the scientific revelations of the sixth millennium. Perfection of the universe lies in the opening of the "gates of Heaven" and in showering pure scientific wisdom upon mankind.

It is instructive to read the statement of the *Zohar* side by side with Rambam's elucidation of the *mizvah* of "And you shall love the Lord your God" (Deuteronomy 6:5) as formulated in *Hilkhot Yesodei ha-Torah* 2:2. For Rambam, "love" and "knowledge" are synonymous terms. The commandment "And you shall love the Lord your God" as well as the commandment "the Lord your God you shall fear" (Deuteronomy 6:13) are fulfilled by acquiring knowledge of God in the only way that man can know God, *viz.*, through His wondrous works. Thus, mastery of the theoretical postulates of the pure sciences is not merely salutary; it is a *mizvah*. As the secrets of physics, chemistry and the life sciences are unraveled, the mystery of creation is better understood; correspondingly, the knowledge—and hence love—of God becomes more intense. The *Zohar* must be understood as teaching that the eschatological era cannot commence until man discovers all that is discoverable in the realm of science, until man comprehends as many of the secrets of nature as are comprehensible to the human intellect and until he grasps as much of the divine blueprint for creation as he is capable of apprehending.

II. PARTICIPATION IN GENETIC RESEARCH

The identification of BRCA1 and BRCA2 is but one small, but hardly insignificant, piece of the cosmic jigsaw puzzle. Their discovery is undoubtedly part of the divine providential plan and hence of the divine mandate.

During the course of the past several years a question has been raised in some circles: Should Jews allow themselves to become subjects of genetic studies designed to further understanding of hereditary or genetic traits prevalent in the Jewish population?[1] In light of the foregoing, the answer must be a clear and resounding yes. Such studies are to be enthusiastically welcomed even if they yield no therapeutic benefit whatsoever for the simple reason that their contribution to understanding *ḥokhmat ha-Shem* is incontrovertible. Of course there is every reason to hope—and to pray—that the theoretical knowledge gleaned in such studies will eventually lead to practical therapeutic benefits.

By virtue of scientifically valid considerations, Jews constitute an excellent population group for studies of this nature. Jews, much more so than most ethnic groups, have been endogamous and as a result, have preserved a homogeneous genotype over a period of millennia. To be sure, Jews are not unique in this respect. Geneticists have recently come to realize that virtually the entire indigenous population of Iceland is descended from a small band of ninth- and tenth-century Norse settlers and a few early Irish slaves and hence the inhabitants of that relatively isolated island share a unique genotype.[2] That Icelanders have preserved a unique genotype is an accident of geography; in the Jewish community this phenomenon has occurred by design and should be a badge of pride.

Thus it is not surprising that there do exist so-called Jewish genetic diseases, including Tay-Sachs, Gaucher disease and Niemann-Pick disease, to name the most widely known maladies affecting Ashkenazic Jews. Those diseases are by no means limited to Jews, although their rate of incidence is markedly higher among Jews than among others. For that matter, genetic mutations responsible for breast cancer are found among other ethnic groups as well.[3] Many ethnic groups manifest a higher incidence of other diseases, the best known of which is probably sickle-cell anemia in the Afro-American population. Undoubtedly, medical science will discover a multitude of genetic traits associated with a host of other diseases much in the same way that it has discovered genetic traits associated with breast and colon cancer.

Such phenomena should not give rise to ethnic self-consciousness. Every human being is a carrier of many genes that can result in defects in offspring. Given the totality of genetic defects, it is unlikely that any particular ethnic group of significant size carries a greater genetic burden than any other group. The sole difference is that in groups, such as Jews, whose gene pool is isogeneic the risk for a particular disease can be assessed more accurately.

Even if much more information regarding genetic propensity becomes available than at present, it would be a gross error to conclude that Jews are somehow less healthy than others. Concern regarding participation in such studies born of a fear that detractors of Jews will point an accusatory finger and make such a claim should certainly not be a deterrent. As far as anti-Semites are concerned, such phenomena are not the cause of ill-will and disdain; they serve as excuses rather than as reasons. If such persons do not have one excuse they will find another. Moreover, what are the consequences of labeling Jews, whether correctly or falsely, as carriers of an inordinate number of negative genetic traits? The primary consequence would be that members of other ethnic groups will consider Jews to be undesirable as marriage partners. Such a result should not at all be regarded as a calamity, but as an undisguised and unmitigated blessing![4]

Mapping the genome, determining the function of specific genes and the linkage between a malady and a particular gene are in the realm of pure science. But when tests are available to determine whether or not a person carries a gene that predisposes him or her to a particular disease, should that person avail himself or herself of the test? At that point the test is not necessary to advance the cause of science. Satisfaction of idle curiosity is certainly not a compelling reason to seek such information. The information may, however, be useful in a number of ways. If both parents possess the same defective gene it will be passed on to their offspring in accordance with Mendelian ratios. Assuming that the gene is not inexorably linked with a disease but is associated only with a higher propensity for a given disease, if both parents are carriers the probability of their progeny being affected rises dramatically. Depending upon the severity of the potential affliction, a person armed with this information might be well advised to exercise genetic prudence in selecting a spouse. More significantly, when such information is received, the carrier may be in a position to take prophylactic measures to avert the disease, to modify dietary or environmental factors that combine with genetic susceptibility to cause the disease or to seek early diagnosis in order to enhance the likelihood of effective therapy. Should a God-fearing Jew seek genetic information for any or all of those reasons or should he or she simply rely upon divine providence?

That issue is forthrightly addressed in a letter written by R. Moshe Feinstein in the early days of Tay-Sachs testing and now published in *Iggerot Mosheh, Even ha-Ezer*, IV, no. 10. Rabbi Feinstein takes cognizance of the argument that a person ought to place his trust in God as reflected in Rashi's comment on Deuteronomy 18:13, ". . . and do not attempt to discern the future; rather, accept wholeheartedly whatever befalls you," only to dismiss it out of hand with the remark that, with the availability of a simple test to determine the carrier state, failure to undergo the test is tantamount "to closing [one's] eyes [in order not] to see that which it is possible to see." Rabbi Feinstein adds the caveat that, since "many people will not believe" the testimony of physicians declaring that the carrier state, in and of itself, is entirely innocuous and hence the carrier may be regarded as undesirable as a marriage partner, precautions should be taken to assure confidentiality. He also voices concern that, since "particularly in this country" many people suffer from "nerves" with the result that they erroneously perceive minor inconveniences as major problems and insignificant risks as inordinate hazards, genetic testing should not be conducted upon immature adolescents who are not yet of marriageable age.

Rabbi Feinstein's observation regarding limitations that must be placed upon simple trust in divine providence is unassailable. A person is certainly not entitled to cross a busy intersection without looking to see if there is oncoming traffic. The Sages taught unequivocally that a person dare not rashly expose himself to danger.[5] In hazardous circumstances, turning a blind eye to danger is not an act of unquestioning faith but an act of rash conceit. Both knowledge of the genetic nature of disease as well as development of the technology to determine the genetic propensity for possible affliction are themselves the products of providential guardianship of man. Refusal to seek out available information is tantamount to the rejection of providential beneficence.

There is a well-known tale of a certain Jew who considered himself to be a great *ba'al bitaḥon*, a person who placed his trust solely in God and relied upon Him implicitly and unquestioningly. Once there were reports of anticipated torrential rains and resulting flooding. The *ba'al bitaḥon* was not at all concerned and went about his business as usual, confident that God would preserve him from any misfortune. The rain came, the streets flooded and the water reached floor level. The authorities ordered an evacuation and dispatched flat-bed trucks to transport the inhabitants of the town to safety. A truck arrived at the home of the *ba'al bitaḥon* but he demurred, declaring that since he had placed his trust in God no harm would befall him. The rain continued unabated and the water reached the second storey. The authorities sent a boat to search for any individuals who might have been overlooked in the earlier evacuation. They pleaded with the *ba'al bitaḥon* to come aboard the boat, but he refused to do so, declaring that in light of his tremendous faith it would be unthinkable that God might forsake him. The rain continued and the water rose higher and higher. The *ba'al bitaḥon* was forced to seek refuge on the roof. The authorities sent a helicopter to circle the city to determine if anyone had been left behind. The pilot spotted our *ba'al bitaḥon* and threw him a rope so that he might be hoisted into the helicopter. But the *ba'al bitaḥon* refused to be rescued, insisting all the while that his faith rendered him impervious to danger. The water continued to rise and the *ba'al bitaḥon* soon drowned. Coming before the divine throne he waxed indignant: "How could You do this to me! After all, I was such a staunch *ba'al bitaḥon*. Why didn't You save me?" To which God replied: "Save you? I sent a truck; I sent a boat; and I sent a helicopter. What more did you want?"

The moral of the story is quite simple. Providence manifests itself through the natural order. God provides the wherewithal to satisfy human needs. Man retains freedom of the will and the autonomy either to accept or to reject that which God provides. *Bitaḥon* does not render genetic testing redundant.

III. TAY-SACHS

To the extent that it is based on fact, Rabbi Feinstein's caveat is also unexceptionable. Jewish law regards as inviolate the privacy of personal information that a person does not wish to disclose to others. Jewish law demands that confidences be respected not only by professionals with whom one has entered into a fiduciary relationship but also by friends and acquaintances and even strangers to whom such information has been imparted.[6] *A fortiori*, information of a personal nature that may be used unjustly and irrationally to a person's detriment dare not be divulged. Nor should information that is likely to cause a person physical harm or emotional distress be imparted to that individual.

However, when the concern is with regard to the carrier state for Tay-Sachs disease one cannot fail to be taken aback by the discovery that such concern exists. As Rabbi Feinstein himself forthrightly acknowledges, a Tay-Sachs carrier is at absolutely no increased risk for any physical or mental disease or handicap. Nor, unless he marries another Tay-Sachs carrier, are his children exposed to the risk of anything worse than themselves being Tay-Sachs carriers. There are no scientific or rational grounds for a non-carrier to shun a Tay-Sachs carrier as a marriage partner or for any other form of social or economic discrimination. No scientist worthy of that appellation would lend credence to any such assertion. Since there is absolutely no physical or mental burden, either actual or potential, associated with the carrier state, discovery that one is a carrier should not bring psychological trauma in its wake. Any resultant trauma is entirely the product of misinformation.[7]

Why, then, is misinformation regarding the Tay-Sachs carrier state so widespread in our community? To our regret and harm, many persons who lack basic education in the sciences are lacking in even elementary knowledge with regard to genetics. They do not grasp the difference between dominant and recessive traits, cannot properly distinguish between incipient disease and propensity for disease, cannot distinguish between necessary causation and statistical probability and sometimes they do not even understand that the demonstrated absence of a defective gene in a child assures that the genetic disease or propensity has not been inherited.

What is the solution? The proper solution, the simplest solution, the solution with the most salutary cost-benefit ratio and certainly the most enlightened solution, is education. The requisite information can readily be reduced to clear and concise language and disseminated both widely and repeatedly. Information saturation effectively dispels ignorance.

To their eternal credit, a number of sincere and self-sacrificing individuals have dedicated themselves to the eradication of Tay-Sachs disease as well as of a number of other genetic diseases prevalent in the Jewish community. They have indeed been markedly successful in achieving their objective. The system that has been instituted involves testing young men and women for the carrier state, but not revealing the results to the parties tested. Instead, the information is retained by the testing organization which, when called upon to do so, matches the results with those of a prospective marriage partner. If both are carriers, they are advised not to go forward with their marriage plans. If only one is a carrier, they are simply informed that there is no impediment to their marriage, but the results of the test are not divulged, because of a perception that there is a stigma and/or a psychological burden attached to knowing that one is a carrier. However, in refusing to divulge the results of genetic tests to either the young men and women affected or to their parents, a negative stereotype is dramatically reinforced. The hocus-pocus of assigning numbers and later announcing that the prospective marriage of the bearers of matched numbers will either be propitious or will not be propitious imbues the process with a Byzantine-like quality. Assuredly, refusal to test for the carrier state until announcement of an engagement is imminent takes a toll in psychological trauma during the waiting period, not to speak of heartache caused those forced to abandon wedding plans already formulated and to go their separate ways. The entire process confirms and reinforces a certain primitiveness and know-nothingism prevalent in certain sectors of our community.

Nor is the procedure cost effective. On the contrary, it is quite wasteful. The additional record keeping and the bureaucratic intermediaries represent an unnecessary expense. It is certainly simpler, less traumatic, less time-consuming and less costly to draw blood for a Tay-Sachs test in conjunction with a routine blood test performed by a pediatrician during childhood. Moreover, if neither parent is a Tay-Sachs carrier there is no way that any of their children can possibly be a carrier. It is certainly cheaper and more efficient to screen two adults, even if they are beyond child-bearing age, than to test each child of a union blessed with multiple offspring.

Paradoxically, it is precisely in the community that utilizes this service that the underlying problem could be dealt with most expeditiously. Although arranged marriages are not the norm, arranged meetings between prospective marriage partners are very much the norm in those sectors of our community. Before the parties and their respective families agree to even an initial encounter much information is exchanged, some of it significant, much of it frivolous. Were genetic information destigmatized, such details could be exchanged with the same complete lack of reticence that accompanies, for example, disclosure of educational background, height or pulchritude.

IV. BRCA

The advantages of Tay-Sachs testing are obvious; the advantages of screening for BRCA1 and BRCA2 are much less obvious. An individual who becomes aware that he or she is a Tay-Sachs carrier is on notice to ascertain that a prospective marriage partner is not a carrier as well. It has, however, been argued that there is no point in screening for the BRCA gene because, if a woman is found to carry a defective gene, either she will develop cancer or she will not, but there is nothing she can do to prevent the disease.

That, however, is simply not the case. There are indeed measures available that may either prevent the disease entirely or maximize the chance for cure. The most extreme option is a prophylactic bilateral mastectomy and/or removal of the ovaries.[8] To state that the option is available is not to state that it is either medically or halakhically advisable. The information in the medical literature with regard to the statistical probability that such a procedure actually serves to increase longevity anticipation is somewhat equivocal. Strange as it may appear to the layman, there are respected medical authors who, at least in the past, suspected that the benefits are nil or, at best, marginal.[9] Presumably, this is so, at least in part, because no mastectomy removes all mammary tissue.[10] One recent retrospective study of both moderate and high-risk women with a family history of breast cancer who underwent prophylactic mastectomy found a statistically significant reduction in the incidence of breast cancer and death from breast cancer as compared with the expected incidence in women with a family history who did not undergo the procedure. The reduction in the risk of breast cancer was found to be in the neighborhood of 90 percent.[11] It would be prudent for a woman who knows that she is a carrier to seek the advice of recognized experts[12] and to inform herself of the results of further studies that surely will be undertaken.

Halakhically, even if medically recommended, the procedure is certainly not mandatory, particularly since the surgery itself is not devoid of risk. Indeed, the surgery may be impermissible for that very reason. A number of rabbinic authorities have advanced the view that therapeutic measures carrying with them a hazard to life cannot be accepted by a person who, absent such treatment, enjoys a longevity anticipation of at least twelve months.[13] Such a person, those authorities argue, has no right to gamble the virtual certainty of twelve month survival for the doubtful prospect of an even longer life-span. Women who test positive for the BRCA gene but who are symptom-free certainly enjoy a longevity anticipation of years and even decades. On the other hand, the surgical risk might conceivably be regarded by some as within the parameters of "The Lord preserves the simple" (Psalms 116:6), i.e., a risk not commonly deemed onerous and hence halakhically acceptable. Those are issues that a woman prompted to consider such a radical measure should discuss first with her physician and then with a competent rabbinic decisor.[14]

Another form of treatment now under discussion is chemoprevention therapy involving use of tamoxifen and raloxifene in high-risk women as a prophylactic measure before the onset of disease. The crucial issue is the potential danger associated with the treatment. In one study tamoxifen was found to reduce the risk of invasive cancer by 49 percent during median follow-up of fifty-five months.[15] However, tamoxifen is believed to increase the risk of uterine cancer significantly over a period of time.[16] Although they are rare, tamoxifen has side effects, including venous thromboembolism, cataracts and, as already indicated, endrometrial cancer. The higher a woman's risk of breast cancer, the more likely it is that the reduction in the incidence of breast cancer will outweigh other risks.[17]

Short of such draconian measures, there are other modalities of care that are available. Women who carry a BRCA1 or BRCA2 mutation will be advised to begin cancer monitoring practices at an earlier age than others and to engage in such monitoring practices at more frequent intervals than women in the general population. Gynecologists, following the recommendations of the National Cancer Institute[18] and the American Cancer Society,[19] now advise all women above the age of forty to have a mammogram annually. But carriers of the BRCA gene are advised to have annual mammograms at a much earlier age. While there is some question with regard to whether the annual procedure should commence at age twenty-five or at age thirty-five, all agree that early testing is imperative.[20] The argument that, since every woman can begin her annual mammogram at the age indicated for a woman at risk, no woman need be burdened by the knowledge that she is a carrier in order to protect herself in this manner is medically unsound. The effects of radiation are cumulative. Hence each exposure to radiation carries with it some degree of risk. A responsible physician recommends exposure to X-rays only when the risk is medically warranted and always employs precautionary measures in order to minimize the risk to the extent that it is possible to do so. Although some physicians dismiss the risk as negligible, early mammography for non-carriers is simply not medically prudent. Physicians discourage mammography at an earlier age in the absence of known risk factors because, due to their higher breast density, screening mammography in younger women yields a higher rate of false positive results which cause anxiety and unnecessary biopsies[21] and because they do not regard the benefit to be commensurate with the cost.[22]

Moreover, the data indicate that shorter screening intervals may be valuable in mutation carriers. For unexplained reasons tumors in mutation carriers grow rapidly and many appear in the interval between annual mammograms. The median size of such interval cancers is 1.7 cm. and half of those tumors have spread to axillary lymph nodes by the time they are detected.[23] More frequent mammograms would detect such tumors at an earlier stage.

Perhaps more significant is the fact that it has now been established that magnetic resonance imagery (MRI) appears to be more sensitive than mammography in detecting tumors in women with inherited susceptibility to breast cancer.[24] Mammography often fails to detect breast cancers in mutation carriers, particularly in younger women who have denser breasts. In contrast, MRI is virtually uninfluenced by breast density. On the other hand, some tumors that are not detected by MRI are visible on mammography. At present there are no data that support the use of MRI in screening women at normal risk.[25] However, BRCA carriers may well be advised to undergo both mammographic and MRI screening on a regular basis.

Determination of the carrier state for the BRCA gene also may have significant implications for decisions regarding postmenopausal hormone-replacement therapy. Some studies suggest that postmenopausal hormone-replacement therapy decreases the risk of coronary heart disease and osteoporosis by as much as fifty percent, but increases the risk of breast cancer by thirty to forty percent.[26] Since, for most women, the risks associated with coronary heart disease are much greater than those of breast cancer, most experts argue that the benefits of the treatment outweigh the risks.[27] However, the balance between the risks and benefits of hormone-replacement therapy may shift for women who are at increased risk for breast cancer. According to one study, hormone-replacement therapy may be contraindicated for women with a lifetime breast cancer risk above thirty percent.[28]

Early detection by means of an annual mammogram beginning in young adulthood is one response to identification as a carrier. Annual transvaginal ultrasounds and CA-125 tests for early diagnosis of ovarian cancer is another. Equally important are regular breast examinations carried out at six-month intervals or even more frequently.[29] To be sure, breast examinations are non-invasive and risk-free. If so, why burden women with BRCA testing in order to encourage breast examination? Let every woman simply undergo regular, routine breast examinations as frequently as is advisable for a known carrier. The answer is probably not recorded in the annals of medical literature but is to be found in halakhic sources. In point of fact, it is well known that people are often lax with regard to routine examinations. But more significantly, in a matter requiring the care, concentration and diligence of a breast examination, the likelihood of missing something significant in the course of a routine examination or of erroneous dismissal of an anomaly as insignificant is quite real. A physician who knows his patient to be a BRCA carrier is likely to be much more vigilant in his examination and more cautious in his judgment.

That phenomenon is reflected in the remarks of R. Akiva

Eger in a gloss commenting upon *Shakh*, *Yoreh De'ah* 1:5. *Shulḥan Arukh*, *Yoreh De'ah* 1:3, rules that, although a ritual slaughterer must be proficient in the laws of ritual slaughter, one who has not mastered those laws may perform the act of slaughter provided that a person who is proficient in such matters observes the act of slaughter in its entirety from beginning to end and ascertains that it has been performed properly. Rema disagrees in part in ruling that, although an act of slaughter carried out under such circumstances is valid *post factum*, nevertheless, a person who is not proficient in the laws of slaughter should not be entrusted with performance of the act. *Shakh* modifies the impact of Rema's divergent ruling. *Shakh* fully agrees that unless there is a positive indication of the fact that a ritual slaughterer is proficient in the pertinent regulations the animal must be regarded as forbidden. Nevertheless, *Shakh* asserts that if it is not known whether or not the slaughterer is qualified in that manner, it is permissible even *ab initio* to entrust him with the act of slaughter provided that the act is supervised by a person known to be proficient. In effect, *Shakh* rules that, since the slaughterer may well be qualified and it is also likely that any error will be detected by the observer, those two factors combine to render the likelihood of irregularity sufficiently remote as to be below the threshold of halakhic concern.

R. Akiva Eger takes sharp issue with *Shakh*'s determination. R. Akiva Eger points to an apparent discrepancy between two different rules: An act of slaughter performed by a minor or mentally deficient person under the supervision of a competent individual renders the animal permissible at least *post factum*. However, the act of a ritual slaughterer who is later found to be ignorant of information he was presumed to possess is invalid even if the act of slaughter was observed by a qualified person and nothing amiss was noted. The distinction, observes R. Akiva Eger, lies in a simple psychological phenomenon. A minor or mentally defective person is known to be incompetent and quite likely to err in performing the act of slaughter. Hence, the observer understands that he bears full responsibility for assuring the *kashrut* of the animal. Accordingly, he recognizes that he must be extremely vigilant and must scrutinize the act of slaughter with total concentration. In contradistinction to that situation, a person observing a slaughterer whom he has no reason to assume to be ignorant or incompetent is likely to perform his task *pro forma* and not exercise the vigilance necessary to catch every possible error. For that reason, asserts R. Akiva Eger, when there is doubt with regard to a person's competence as a slaughterer one should not initially rely upon an observer to assure that the act has been performed properly. Although it may appear paradoxical, there is more reason to rely upon the observer when the slaughterer is known to be incompetent than when his competence is merely a matter of uncertainty.

The nature of the human psyche is such that constant vigilance is well nigh impossible. A physician who performs breast examinations routinely and repeatedly and who is well aware of the high statistical probability that any particular examination will result in innocuous findings is, on occasion, likely to be less that totally vigilant. Knowledge that the patient is at risk by virtue of a known carrier state will certainly prompt the physician both to be more attentive in his examination and more concerned in exercise of judgment. Although the BRCA carrier may have been known to be a member of a high-risk group even before testing for the carrier state was undertaken, the physician's vigilance is likely to be even greater when the patient is actually known to carry the BRCA gene.

But is there a halakhic obligation to undergo procedures designed to disclose evidence of a malignant disease—mammograms, breast examinations by a physician, self-examination and the like? And, if yes, is there an obligation to determine one's carrier status in order to make such diagnostic procedures more effective? Is every woman obliged to seek BRCA screening or are only members of high risk groups obliged to do so?[30]

I suspect that the intuitive answer is that such obligations do exist. Citation of the verse "*Ve-nishmartem me'od le-nafshoteikhem*—And you shall be exceedingly watchful of your lives" (Deuteronomy 4:15) is virtually an automatic response. Somewhat curiously, in codifying the prohibition against engaging in hazardous conduct, Rambam, *Hilkhot Roẓeaḥ* 11:4, quotes an entirely different verse, "*Rak hishamer lekha u-shemor nafshekha me'od*—Only take heed to yourself and be exceedingly watchful of your life" (Deuteronomy 4:9).

The Gemara, *Berakhot* 32b, relates that a gentile government official came upon a pious Jew praying by the side of the road. The official took umbrage because the Jew did not interrupt his prayers in order to greet him. Emphasizing that he could readily have punished the Jew's lack of courtesy with immediate death, the gentile addressed the Jew and chastised him for transgressing an admonition "written in your Torah" and proceeded to quote both Deuteronomy 4:9 and Deuteronomy 4:15. The official was quite obviously taking the Jew to task for disregarding his own safety and well-being. Maharsha, in his commentary *ad locum*, points out that the gentile misapplied the verses he cited. Read literally, Deuteronomy 4:9 is a general admonition not to transgress the commandments handed down at Sinai. Maharsha, however, observes that, as stated in Avot 3:8, the verse constitutes a prohibition against forgetting any aspect of Torah and that Deuteronomy 4:15 is a prohibition against "believing in" or deifying any image.

Nevertheless, Rambam, apparently without the support of any other talmudic source, accepted the interpretation of Deuteronomy 4:9 ascribed by the Gemara to the gentile as being entirely valid and as establishing a normative obligation. Rambam may well have accepted the similar interpretation of Deuteronomy 4:15 to which the gentile gave voice as equally valid but omits reference to the second verse much in the same manner that in other instances he does not cite multiple verses reiterating a single commandment. Rambam may have cited Deuteronomy 4:9 rather than Deuteronomy 4:15 simply because it occurs earlier in Scripture. More likely, he recognized Deuteronomy 4:15 as an admonition limited to fashioning graven images. To be sure, Deuteronomy 4:9 also has a different meaning and commands the listener to take heed "lest you forget the things that you eyes saw and lest they depart from your heart all the days of your life." Understood literally, the term "*nefesh*" in each of those verses connotes "soul" rather than "life." Consistent with that meaning, the phrase "be exceedingly watchful of your soul" in Deuteronomy 4:9 is a general exhortation not to disregard the commandments received at Sinai. In talmudic exegesis that verse serves as an admonition not to forget the Torah one has studied. Thus neither verse appears to command preservation of life or health. Nevertheless, perhaps because the term "*nefesh*" is a homonym connoting both "soul" and "body," Rambam understands Deuteronomy 4:9, since it is couched in general terms, as a commandment establishing an obligation to preserve health whereas Deuteronomy 4:15 clearly has a different and very particular meaning.

The difficulty inherent in Rambam's position is compounded by a seeming inconsistency: Rambam does not cite Deuteronomy 4:9 in his enumeration of the 613 precepts in the *Sefer ha-Miẓvot*; nor, despite the title, *Hilkhot Roẓeaḥ u-Shemirat ha-Nefesh*—Laws of Murder and Preservation of Life—does Rambam list health among the *miẓvot* in the headnote indicating the commandments to be discussed in the ensuing section of the *Mishneh Torah*.

Failure to categorize a halakhic prescription as a fulfillment of one of the 613 biblical commandments in no way compromises its normative status. There are indeed innumerable biblical obligations that, for one reason or another, are not categorized among the 613 *mizvot*. The obligation to protect one's health does, however, appear to be recognized by Rambam as flowing from one of the 613 enumerated biblical commandments. In introducing his regimen for healthful living, Rambam, *Hilkhot De'ot* 4:1, declares:

> Since having a healthy and complete body is among the ways of God because it is impossible to understand or to know [any] matter pertaining to knowledge of the Creator if one is ill, therefore a person must distance himself from matters that destroy the body and conduct himself in accordance with matters that promote health and cure.

Rambam regards a healthy body as a necessary condition for achieving "knowledge of the Creator." In *Hilkhot Yesodei ha-Torah* 2:2 he declares knowledge to be a necessary condition for fulfillment of the commandment "And you shall love the Lord your God. . . ." According to Rambam, love of God can be achieved only by means of contemplation and reflection upon the wondrous nature of that which God created. In *Hilkhot Yesodei ha-Torah* 4:12 Rambam adds that love of God increases in a manner commensurate with enhanced understanding of the nature of God's handiwork. The human mind is incapable of engaging in meaningful intellectual pursuits while the body is racked by pain and thus, for Rambam, avoidance of disease and promotion of physical well-being are commanded as necessary measures to fulfill the *mizvah* of "And you shall love the Lord your God."

Rambam follows his opening statement in *Hilkhot De'ot* 4:1 with a detailed enumeration of rules for healthful living. It is clear that the prescriptions he offers are not intended to be exhaustive. Rambam's employment of the phrase "*ve-elu hem*" does not constitute a limitation; it is simply an indication of broad rules of general applicability. Other matters, particularly at other times and for some individuals, may be no less obligatory. Any medically indicated prophylactic or diagnostic procedure must certainly be regarded as integral to the obligation posited by Rambam. Delineation of what is medically prudent is certainly dependent upon scientific knowledge at any particular time and is to be determined by members of the medical profession. Genetic testing, including testing for BRCA1 and BRCA2, should be regarded as halakhically mandated in circumstances in which medical science believes that the results are likely to affect treatment in a manner that will enhance longevity anticipation or well-being. Certainly, a person identified as being at risk for a specific disease is obligated to pursue all available measures in order to ward off the disease or to diagnose its presence while the disease is yet in an incipient stage and still amenable to cure.

V. DISCRIMINATION AGAINST CARRIERS

Prospective resistance to as yet unavailable genetic testing and already expressed opposition to BRCA testing which is more immediate is born of fear of discrimination, not in the sense of social stigma, but in employment and in the writing of insurance polices. Those concerns are economic and real. There is reason to fear that an employer who is aware that a prospective employee is at risk for a disease that will cause the employee to be absent from work or to become impeded in performing his duties will hire another applicant in his stead. Insurance companies will certainly wish to take into account the statistical probability of an applicant actually developing a malady for which he has a genetic propensity, both in determining eligibility for health and life insurance and for establishing premium rates for such policies.[31] However, those fears are probably greatly exaggerated. As of 1998, laws have been enacted in over half the states to prohibit health insurance companies from requiring genetic testing as a condition of coverage or from denying coverage or charging higher rates based upon the results of a genetic test.[32] New York's Insurance Law §4224, as well as the applicable law in eight other states,[33] requires that underwriting of both health and life insurance policies be based upon sound actuarial principles. In New York, Insurance Law §3234 places the same restriction upon discrimination in the underwriting of disability insurance. Similar statutes were enacted in eight other states.[34] New York Civil Rights Law §296 and the laws of seventeen other states[35] prohibit discrimination in employment on the basis of a genetic predisposition.

It would be necessary to research the applicable law in each of the other states in order to determine what protection against discrimination in employment, if any, is available to genetic carriers in each of those jurisdictions.[36] Fortunately, such a determination may not be necessary. The federal Americans with Disabilities Act of 1990[37] prohibits discrimination against any person on the basis of a physical handicap. Fortunately, §706 of that act contains a definition of a physical handicap sufficiently broad in nature to encompass a genetic predisposition. Indeed, in 1995, the Office of Economic Opportunity issued a ruling confirming that interpretation of the statute and declared that the definition of disability includes individuals at risk for future health problems based on genetic abnormalities.[38] The federal statute is national in application and supersedes state law. However, the interpretation of the statute by the Equal Employment Opportunity Commission has not been tested in any court. Hence, at least at present, the Americans with Disabilities Act cannot be relied upon with certainty for protection against discrimination in employment.[39]

Despite what clearly appears to be the state of the law many people are either uninformed or skeptical. Concerns with regard to the impact of the results of genetic testing upon employability have been expressed repeatedly and quite forcefully not only in the popular press but also in scientific and medical journals. Those concerns are expressed even in jurisdictions in which state law unequivocally prohibits discrimination in employment. If people are concerned that there is a problem, there is a problem. Ofttimes the perception of a problem is itself the problem—and this is one of those times. What, then, is the solution? The medical community, the legal community and the rabbinic community, separately and in concert, must do whatever is necessary to remove any ambiguity in the law and/or in the mind of the public.[40] They must also act to assure that health care coverage is available at affordable rates in all jurisdictions.

We now stand at the cusp of major breakthroughs in the field of genetics. The specter of discrimination, real or imagined, either in insurability or in employment will have a drastically chilling effect both upon availability of subjects for genetic research and for implementation of testing programs designed to preserve lives and to eliminate disease. Public policy dictates that impediments to achieving those benefits be eliminated. That can be accomplished only by establishing a level playing field in which, by operation of law, discovery of a genetic predisposition must be ignored insofar as negative economic consequences to carriers of defective genes are concerned.

Legislation can solve the substantive problems with regard to economic discrimination. Social discrimination, particularly discrimination in eligibility for selection as a marriage partner, cannot be addressed by legislation. There is no question that identification of a person as a carrier of, for example, the BRCA gene will cause serious *shiddukhim* problems not only for the woman so identified but for her children as well.

The first of those problems is whether the carrier state, when ascertained, must be disclosed to a prospective marriage partner. An extreme case—and one in which the answer is obvious—is identification of an individual as a carrier of the gene responsible for Huntington's disease. The gene is dominant and lethal; the disease manifests itself at a comparatively young age and is both debilitating and terminal. It seems quite evident that disclosure of the fact that a prospective marriage partner harbors the gene is mandatory. In fact, it is even arguable that failure to disclose the carrier state for Huntington's disease constitutes a halakhic basis for annulment of the marriage. The certainty of premature interruption of normal marital life may constitute a serious physical defect of the magnitude of a *mum gadol*, i.e., a major defect, with the result that the marriage may be void *ab initio* on grounds of *kiddushei ta'ut*, i.e., error in its inception.[41]

However, disclosure of the carrier state for a recessive gene that is deleterious or of a defective gene that may or may not lead to some type of physical disability is an entirely different matter.

The primary source for delineation of what information a third party must reveal to a person considering the eligibility of a marriage partner and what he dare not disclose is *Ḥafeẓ Ḥayyim, Hilkhot Issurei Rekhilut, klal* 9. *Ḥafeẓ Ḥayyim* distinguishes between two types of physical problems. One he calls a "*ḥoli*"; the other, he terms a "*meiḥush*." A "*ḥoli*" is defined by *Ḥafeẓ Ḥayyim* as a malady or impediment that is likely to interfere with normal marital life. *Ḥafeẓ Ḥayyim* declares that if the malady or impediment is of a gravity such that, if informed, the person in question is unlikely to agree to enter into the marriage, and provided that disclosure of such information is not accompanied by personal animus, disclosure of the condition or defect is mandatory. If, however, the physical problem is not of a degree of severity such that it is likely to impede marital life materially, it may not be disclosed by a third party. The term "*meiḥush*" may or may not be related etymologically to the term "*ḥeshash*" which connotes suspicion or concern. Physical weakness, infirmity, vague aches and pains are matters of concern and may portend future illness that is serious in nature but such forms of malaise fail to constitute clinical evidence of an imminent physical impediment to marital life.

The precise degree of statistical probability of developing a serious illness that triggers an obligation of disclosure has not been pinpointed by rabbinic scholars. At an earlier period in the investigation of the BRCA genes it was reported that the correlation between the presence of the defective gene and development of breast cancer was approximately 85%.[42] More recent reports suggest that carriers of the defective gene have a 55% risk of developing breast cancer over the course of a lifetime. It must be noted that it is the risk of developing breast cancer, not the mortality risk, that is estimated to be 55%.[43] The mortality risk, particularly if available diagnostic procedures are utilized to ensure early detection, is much lower.

In light of that information it is doubtful that any rabbinic authority would require, or even permit, a third party to disclose the BRCA carrier state. That, however, does not imply that a young lady should not disclose such information to a prospective fiancé at an appropriate time in their developing relationship. A successful marital relationship must be based upon a bedrock of mutual trust and openness. Concealing such information, even if halakhically justifiable, is unwise, to say the least.

Such advice might well lead to an unintended and unwarranted conclusion. If disclosure of a genetic defect is deemed necessary for any halakhic, ethical or pragmatic reason, then would it not be prudent to forego testing in the first place? After all, one cannot disclose what one does not know. If testing is not performed, the dilemma of whether to disclose or not to disclose will not arise. Ignorance may indeed be bliss.

Such a posture is unacceptable for two reasons. First, burying one's head in the sand does not cause the danger to disappear. The person who rejects testing procedures remains at risk. Secondly, at least insofar as members of high risk groups are concerned, the selfsame considerations that would compel disclosure of unwelcome information obtained as a result of genetic testing should require disclosure of membership in the high-risk group. The situation is analogous to that of a person who, while in the process of selling his automobile, hears strange noises under the hood. If he takes the car to a mechanic and the mechanic finds a defect in the motor he will have an absolute obligation to disclose that information to the purchaser. Would he be justified in avoiding a visit to his mechanic on the plea that the noise may well be but an innocuous rattle? Failure to disclose a defect that is serious enough to void the sale is forbidden.[44] It is far from certain that failure to disclose a defect of a lesser magnitude is halakhically defensible.[45] But, apart from the possibility of actual transgression, a person who keeps the knowledge of the noise to himself and proceeds with the sale is assuredly not a "*dover emet be-levavo*," i.e., he is not a person who "speaks the truth that is in his heart" (Psalms 15:2).[46] Full disclosure of all salient information, even when not absolutely mandated, represents the ethical norm Judaism seeks to promote. A member of a high-risk group who purposely eschews testing procedures in order to avoid becoming privy to information that must be disclosed is certainly not a *dover emet be-levavo*.

The ultimate question, of course, is whether discovery of a genetic problem such as a defective BRCA gene should be permitted to influence marital decisions. When R. Iser Zalman Meltzer, of blessed memory, was about to become engaged to his future wife the bride's family became aware of the fact that he was rather sickly. And so they went to the *Ḥafeẓ Ḥayyim*, not for a halakhic opinion, but for sage counsel. Should they go forward with the marriage or should they terminate the relationship? The *Ḥafeẓ Ḥayyim* responded by saying, "The *Ribbono shel Olam* bestows many blessings. It is He who bestows the blessing of health and it is He who bestows the blessing of long years. But the two do not always go hand in hand!" R. Iser Zalman may have been sickly, but he was blessed with a long and productive life.

A 55% chance of developing breast cancer over the course of a lifetime is a 55% chance of developing a serious malady. But sickness and longevity are not mutually exclusive phenomena. Longevity is not determined solely by BRCA1, BRCA2 or by any one of the vast majority of other defective genes. Every human being carries quite a number of "bad" genes. Every person has a genetic predisposition to one malady or another; indeed, we are probably all genetically predisposed to multiple diseases. Rejecting a prospective marriage partner because of the presence of a defective BRCA gene in no way assures that another prospective marriage partner is not endowed with an equally problematic genotype. Doubtless, by the time that all genetic implications are fully unraveled, no one will receive a clean bill of genetic health. If every prospective mate is rejected because of one genetic reason or another, marriage—and with it the human race—will become obsolete!

VI. DESTIGMATIZATION: AN IMPERATIVE

The genome project looms so ominously and *genetic testing* is feared so greatly because our community has come to accept a certain type of "know-nothingness." We have accepted that posture, the medical community has cooperated in our acceptance, and the rabbinic community has not only cooperated but has encouraged such acceptance. The end result is that we have allowed myths to grow and stigmatization of carriers to permeate the community. Until the present, when the science of genetics was still in its infancy or adolescence, the economic, emotional and social costs of this posture, although they have been significant, have nevertheless been contained. The real cost is the paradigm it has created for the future. As the science of genetics continues to develop, genetic links will be discovered for an ever-increasing panoply of diseases and more and more people will be identified as carriers of a rapidly expanding list of negative genetic traits. As a community, it is imperative that we embark upon a process of destigmatization.

The Gemara, *Niddah* 13b, teaches that God created a certain finite number of souls, each of which awaits the opportunity to descend to earth. The Gemara further teaches that Israel will not be redeemed until the last of those souls is incarnated in the body of a newly conceived baby. Prevention of the birth of a child serves to delay the moment of redemption. A decision not to proceed with a *shiddukh* is a decision to postpone the *ge'ulah*.

We carry an awesome responsibility. As the earlier-cited statement of the *Zohar* tells us, we are living in an age that is the precursor of the eschatological era. Divine providence showers us with harbingers of that era; we dare not, heaven forfend, impede, rather than hasten, the advent of redemption.

"*Tamim tiheyeh im ha-Shem Elokekha*—You shall be wholehearted with the Lord your God" (Deuteronomy 18:13), is unquestionably a divine command. There is a point beyond which one should not attempt to discern what lies in the future, a point beyond which one should not endeavor to prevent the unpreventable, a point at which we must recognize that we dare not be overly concerned and overly protective of ourselves and our progeny. Only by acting prudently and rationally, while yet being "*tamim im ha-Shem Elokekha*," can we create the conditions in which redemption can become a reality.

NOTES

1. See "Concern Among Jews is Heightened as Scientists Deepen Gene Studies," *New York Times*, April 22, 1998, p. A24.
2. See Michael Specter, "Decoding Iceland," *The New Yorker*,

January 18, 1999, pp. 41–51 and Simon Mawer, "Iceland, the Nation of Clones," *New York Times*, January 23, 1999, p. A19.

3. For a report of specific mutations found in other ethnic groups, including Japanese, Swedes, and Italians, see B. Keoun, "Ashkenazim not Alone: Other Ethnic Groups Have Breast Cancer Gene Mutations, Too," *Journal of the National Cancer Institute*, vol. 89, no. 1 (January 1, 1989), pp. 8–9.
4. Cf., however, "Should Ashkenazi Jews Volunteer for Gene Studies?" *Moment*, April, 1999, pp. 32–33.
5. See *Shabbat* 32a and *Ta'anit* 20b. For a discussion of circumstances in which assumption of risk is permissible see *infra*, chapter 8.
6. For a discussion of confidentiality in Jewish law, see this writer's "Rabbinic Confidentiality," *Contemporary Halakhic Problems*, vol. V, chap. 2.
7. Indeed, the overwhelming majority of patients who learn that they are carriers of the much more serious BRCA mutation do not suffer untoward psychological consequences. See C. Lerman, S. Narod, K. Schulman *et al.*, "BRCA1 Testing in Families with Hereditary Breast-Ovarian Cancer: A Prospective Study of Patient Decision Making Outcomes," *Journal of the American Medical Association*, vol. 275, no. 24 (June 26, 1996), pp. 1885–1892 and R. Croyle, K. Smith, J. Botkin *et al.*, "Psychological Responses to BRCA1 Mutation Testing: Preliminary Findings," *Health Psychology*, vol. 16, no. 1 (January, 1997), pp. 63–72. Even more remarkably, in a Huntington's disease testing program levels of depression returned to baseline levels by one year after disclosure despite the fact that the patients realized that early demise was a certainty. See M. Bloch, S. Adams, S. Wiggins *et al.*, "Predictive Testing for Huntington's disease: The Experience of Those Receiving an Increased Risk," *American Journal of Medical Genetics*, vol. 42, no. 4 (February 15, 1992), pp. 499–507.
8. BRCA carriers are also at risk for developing ovarian cancer, although the risk is not as great as for breast cancer. See *infra*, note 39. Oophorectomy, i.e., surgical removal of the ovaries, is performed more frequently than preemptive mastectomy both because the surgery is less radical and because current screening techniques for early-stage ovarian cancer are not especially effective.
9. See Katherine A. Schneider, "Genetic Counseling for BRCA1/

BRCA2 Testing," *Genetic Testing*, vol. 1, no. 2 (November 2, 1997), p. 94. See also W. Burke, M. Daly, J. Garber, *et al.*, "Recommendations for Follow-Up Care of Individuals with an Inherited Predisposition to Cancer. II. BRCA 1 and BRCA 2," *Journal of the American Medical Association*, vol. 277, no. 12 (March 26, 1997), pp. 997–1003. One group of researchers has developed a decision analysis model that shows a three- to five-year gain in life expectancy of BRCA1/BRCA2 mutation carriers if they undergo prophylactic mastectomy at age thirty and a three-month to two-year gain if prophylactic oophorectomy is performed, but found only marginal benefit as a result of prophylactic surgery after age sixty or in oophorectomy before age forty. See Deborah Schrag, Karen M. Kuntz, Judy E. Garber and Jane C. Weeks, "Decision Analysis—Effects of Prophylactic Mastectomy and Oophorectomy on Life Expectancy among Women with BRCA1 or BRCA2 Mutations," *New England Journal of Medicine*, vol. 336, no. 20 (May 15, 1997), pp. 1465–1471. Another study estimated that, dependent upon her cancer risks, prophylactic mastectomy improved survival for a thirty-year-old woman by 2.8 to 3.4 years, prophylactic oophorectomy improved survival by 0.4 to 2.6 years and both procedures in combination improved survival by 3.3 to 6.0 years. See also V. R. Grann, K. S. Panageas, W. Whang *et al.*, "Decision Analysis of Prophylactic Mastectomy and Oophorectomy in BRCA1 Positive or BRCA2 Positive Patients," *Journal of Clinical Oncology*, vol. 16, no. 3 (March, 1998), pp. 979–985.

10. See N. F. Hicken, "Mastectomy: Clinical Pathologic Study Demonstrating Why Most Mastectomies Result in Incomplete Removal of Mammary Glands," *Archives of Surgery*, vol. 40, no. 1 (January, 1940), pp. 6–14.
11. Lynn C. Hartmann, Daniel J. Schaid, John F. Woods *et al.*, "Efficiency of Bilateral Prophylactic Mastectomy in Women with a Family History of Breast Cancer," *New England Journal of Medicine*, vol. 340, no. 2 (January 14, 1999), pp. 77–84.
12. In addition to statistical probability, clinical features such as the consistency of breast tissue and the resultant ease of examination as well as breast density are factors to be considered. See Hartmann, p. 83.
13. See R. Shlomoh Kluger, *Ḥokhmat Shlomoh, Yoreh De'ah* 155:1; R. Abraham I. Kook, *Teshuvot Mishpat Kohen*, no. 144, sec. 3; and R. Moshe Feinstein, *Iggerot Mosheh, Ḥoshen Mishpat*, II,

no. 75, sec. 2. Cf., however, R. Moshe Zev Zorger, *Teshuvot Va-Yashev Mosheh* (Jerusalem, 5746), I, no. 75, sec. 1.

14. A poignant report of decisions reached by a number of women on the basis of various considerations, both objective and subjective, is presented by Craig Horowitz, "Time Bomb Genes," *New York Magazine*, February 8, 1999, pp. 29–33 and 89.
15. See B. Fisher, J. P. Constantino, D. L. Wickerham *et al.*, "Tamoxifen for Prevention of Breast Cancer: Report of the National Surgical Adjuvant Breast-Bowel Project P-1 Study," *Journal of the National Cancer Institute*, vol. 90, no. 18 (Sept. 16, 1998), pp. 1371–1388. However, two European studies showed that tamoxifen prophylaxis had no significant impact on the incidence of breast cancer. The latter studies are not entirely comparable both because they involved fewer participants and because the patients were of different age and risk levels. Those studies also reflect differences in lengths of follow-up and other treatment. See T. Powles, R. Ecles, S. Ashley *et al.*, "Interim Analysis of the Incidence of Breast Cancer in the Royal Marsden Hospital Tamoxifen Randomized Chemoprevention Trial," *Lancet*, vol. 352 (July 11, 1998), pp. 93–97 and U. Veronesi, P. Maisonneuve, A. Costa *et al.*, "Prevention of Breast Cancer with Tamoxifen: Preliminary Findings from the Italian Randomized Trial Among Hysterectomized Women," *Lancet*, vol. 352 (July 11, 1998), pp. 93–97.
16. See Fischer *et al.*
17. See K. Armstrong, A. Eisen and B. Weber, "Assessing the Risk of Breast Cancer," *New England Journal of Medicine*, vol. 342, no. 8 (Feb. 24, 2000), p. 565.
18. See National Cancer Institute: *National Institutes of Health, Understanding Breast Changes* (September, 1977), p. 5; *idem*, "Cancer Facts," October 23, 1999, p. 1. The National Cancer Institute recommends a screening mammogram "every one to two years."
19. See American Cancer Society, *Breast Cancer Facts and Figures 1999–2000*, p. 11. The American Cancer Society's guidelines recommend an "annual mammogram." See also Armstrong *et al.*, p. 565.
20. See Burke, *et al.*
21. See Koria Kerlikowske, Deborah Grady, John Barclay *et al.*, "Positive Predictive Value of Screening Mammography by Age

and Family History of Breast Cancer," *Journal of the American Medical Association*, vol. 270, no. 20 (November 24, 1993), pp. 2444–50.

22. See Armstrong *et al.*, p. 565.
23. See Laura Liberman, "Breast Cancer Screening with MRI—What Are the Data for Patients at High Risk?" *New England Journal of Medicine*, vol. 351, no. 5 (July 29, 2004), p. 497.
24. See Micke Kriege, Cecile T. M. Brekelmans, Carla Boetes *et al.*, "Efficacy of MRI and Mammography for Breast-Cancer Screening in Women with a Familiar or Genetic Predisposition," *New England Journal of Medicine*, vol. 351, no. 5 (July 29, 2004), pp. 427–437. See also the accompanying editorial by Laura Liberman, *ibid.*, pp. 497–500.
25. See Liberman, *ibid.*, p. 500.
26. See Francine Grodstein, Meir J. Stampfer, Graham A. Colditz *et al.*, "Postmenopausal Hormone Therapy and Mortality," *New England Journal of Medicine*, vol. 336, no. 25 (June 19, 1997), pp. 1769–1775; A. R. Folsom, P. J. Mink, T. A. Sellers *et al.*, "Hormonal Replacement Therapy and Morbidity and Mortality in a Prospective Study of Postmenopausal Women," *American Journal of Public Health*, vol. 85, no. 8 (August, 1995), pp. 1128–1132; and Graham A. Colditz, Susan E. Hankinson, David J. Hunter *et al.*, "The Use of Estrogens and Progestins and the Risk of Breast Cancer in Postmenopausal Women," *New England Journal of Medicine*, vol. 332, no. 24 (June 15, 1995), pp. 1589–1593.
27. D. Grady, S.M. Rubin, D.B. Petitti *et al.*, "Hormone Therapy to Prevent Disease and Prolong Life in Postmenopausal Women," *Annals of Internal Medicine*, vol. 117, no. 12 (December 15, 1992), pp. 1016–1037; and Nanada F. Col, Mark H. Eckman, Richard H. Karas *et al.*, "Patient-Specific Decisions About Hormone Replacement Therapy in Postmenopausal Women," *Journal of the American Medical Association*, vol. 277, no. 14 (April 9, 1997), pp. 1140–1147.
28. See Armstrong *et al.*, p. 564.
29. Since BRCA is associated with a somewhat higher risk of prostate and colon cancer, carriers should be urged to adhere to the recommendations of the American Cancer Society regarding screening for prostate and colon cancer. Males, who may also be carriers of the BRCA gene, should undergo annual digital rectal examination and PSA tests beginning at age

fifty. Both male and female carriers should undergo sigmoidoscopy every three to five years and fecal occult tests beginning at age fifty. See Burke *et al.*

30. It should be stressed that negative results do not mean that the woman is devoid of risk; it means only that her risk is the same as that of the general population. Moreover, a negative result is meaningful only if a family member afflicted by breast cancer has already been identified as a BRCA carrier. If the person has not been so identified, the negative result for BRCA is meaningless since, in that family, some other unidentified genetic cause may be responsible for the disease.
31. For a cursory survey of the legal protection against disclosure and use of genetic information, see Philip R. Reilly, "Laws to Regulate the Use of Genetic Information," *Genetic Secrets*, ed. Mark A. Rothstein (New Haven, 1997), pp. 369–391.
32. For a listing of the state laws, see B. A. Trolino, ed., *Mapping Public Policy for Genetic Technologies: A Legislator's Guide* (Denver, 1998). Colorado prohibits use of genetic information in conjunction with issuance of long-term care insurance. See Colo. Rev. Stat. Ann. §10-3-1104.7 (3) (b) (West 1998).
33. See Ariz. Rev. Stat. Ann. §20-448 (West 1998); Cal. Ins. Code §10148; Me. Rev. Stat. Ann. tit. 24-A, §2159-c (West 2000); Md. Code. Ann., Ins. §27-208(a)(2)(i) (2000); Mont. Code Ann. §33-18-206(4) (1998); N.J. Stat. Ann. §17B:30-12(f) (West 2000); N.M. Stat. Ann. §§24-21-3 to -4; Michie. 2000; and Wis. Stat. Ann. §631.89(3)(b)(2) (West 2000).
34. See Ariz. Rev. Stat. Ann. §20-448 (West 2000); Cal. Ins. Code §10148; Me. Rev. Stat. Ann. Tit. 24-A §2159-C (West 2000); Md. Code Ann. Ins. §27-208(a)(2)(i), and §27-909 (2000); Mont. Code. Ann. §33-18-206(4) (2000); NJ Stat. Ann. §17B:30-12 (f) (West 2000); N.M. Stat. Ann. §24-21-3 to -4, (Michie 2000); and Wis. Stat. Ann. §631.748 (West 2000).
35. See Ariz. Rev. Stat. 41-1463(B)(3) (West 1992 & Supp. 1997) (enacted 1997); Act of July 3, 1998, ch. 99, 1998 Cal. Legis. Serv. 468 (West) (enacted 1998); 1998 Conn. Legis. Serv. 98-180 (West) (enacted 1998); Del. Code Ann. tit. 18, §2317 (1998) (enacted 1998); Iowa Code Ann. §729.6 (1993) (enacted 1992); N.H. Rev. Stat. Ann. §141-H:3.I(b) (1997) (enacted 1995); 1998 N.M Adv. Legis. Serv. ch. 77 (enacted 1998); N.Y. Exec. Law §296(1)(a) (Consol. 1998) (enacted 1996); N.C. Gen. Stat. §95-28.1A (1997) (enacted 1997); Okla. Stat.

tit. 36, §3614.1 (1998) (enacted 1998); R.I. Gen. Laws §28-6.7-1 (1995) (enacted 1992); Tex. Lab. Code Ann. §§21.410-.402 (West Supp. 1998) (enacted 1997); Vt. Stat. Ann. tit. 18, §9333(a) (1998) (enacted 1998); and Wis. Stat. Ann. §111.372 (West 2000) (enacted 1992).

36. For a brief discussion of the provisions of applicable statutes in some of those states, see Mark A. Rothstein, "The Law of Medical and Genetic Privacy in the Workplace," *Genetic Secrets*, pp. 291–293.

37. Americans with Disabilities Act of 1990, Pub. L. No. 101–336, 104 Stat. 328, 42 U.S.C. §§12101-12213 (1994).

38. See Equal Employment Opportunity Commission, *Compliance Manual*, vol. 1 (March 14, 1995), §§902-45, reprinted in *Daily Labor Report* (March 16, 1995), E-1, E-23.

39. One commentator has summarized the effect of the statute by stating that, "Discrimination in health benefits is permissible under the ADA so long as it is based on valid actuarial principles and is not a subterfuge for disability dicrimination." See Mark A. Rothstein, *Genetic Secrets*, p. 295. Elsewhere, the same author has pointed out that the statute does not serve to bar discrimination against unaffected carriers of recessive or X-linked disorders whose prospective employers might be concerned about the health care costs of future dependents. Examples of such situations include individuals whose carrier state creates a risk of having a child afflicted with Duchenne muscular dystrophy or cystic fibrosis. See Mark A. Rothstein, "Genetic Privacy and Confidentiality: Why They Are So Hard to Protect," *Journal of Law, Medicine & Ethics*, vol. 26, no. 3 (Summer, 1998), p. 202.

40. See the valuable suggestions offered by Rothstein, "Genetic Privacy;" Richard A. Bornstein, "Genetic Discrimination, Insurability and Legislation: A Closing of the Legal Loopholes," *Journal of Law and Policy*, vol. 4, no. 2 (1996), pp. 551–610; and Eric M. Holmes, "Solving the Insurance/Genetic Fair/Unfair Discrimination Dilemma in Light of the Human Genome Project," *Kentucky Law Journal,* vol. 85, no. 3 (1996–1997), pp. 503–664.

41. See *Iggerot Mosheh, Even ha-Ezer,* IV, no. 73, sec. 2, who advises that a person must disclose that he suffers from Marfan's syndrome, a condition that may cause sudden and premature death, lest the marriage be *kiddushei ta'ut.*

42. See D. Ford, D. F. Easton, D.T. Bishop *et al.* and The Breast Cancer Linkage Consortium, "Risks of BRCA1-Mutation Carriers," *Lancet*, vol. 343 (March 19, 1994), pp. 692–695 and R. Wooster, S.L. Neuhausen, J. Mangion *et al.*, "Localization of a Breast-Cancer Susceptibility Gene, BRCA2 to Chromosome 13q12-13," *Science*, vol. 265 (Sept. 30, 1994), pp. 2088–2090. Associated risk estimates of ovarian cancer were reported as being between 30%–65% for BRCA1 mutation carriers and between 10%–20% for BRCA2 mutation carriers.
43. Jeffery P. Struewing, Patricia Hartge, Sholom Wacholder *et al.*, "The Risk of Cancer Associated with Specific Mutations of BRCA1 and BRCA2 among Ashkenazi Jews," *New England Journal of Medicine*, vol. 336, no. 20 (May 15, 1997), pp. 1401–1408.
44. See *Shulḥan Arukh, Ḥoshen Mishpat* 228:6. *Iggerot Mosheh, Even ha-Ezer*, IV, no. 73, sec. 2, declares that the prohibition against fraud certainly applies in marital matters and "perhaps it is even more stringent in such matters than in commercial transactions."
45. See the discussion of this matter by R. Ya'akov Blau, *Pitḥei Ḥoshen*, IV, 12:1, note 2.
46. Cf. the citation of this verse by the Gemara, *Makkot* 24a, in connection with commercial dealings as elucidated by Rashi, s.v. *Rav Safra*.

5

Genetic Engineering

I. PERMISSIBILITY OF GENETIC MANIPULATION

Genetic engineering has made it possible to manipulate the DNA of microorganisms, animals and plants in order to satisfy human needs. Science has developed bacteria that ingest petroleum in order to alleviate the environmentally devastating effects of oil spills, bacteria to produce insulin, sheep whose milk contains a drug used in treatment of cystic fibrosis and a host of genetically modified foods. One third of the harvest of corn, soybeans and canola in the United States is genetically modified to make the crops resistant to insects. At least in the laboratory, it is possible to remove from a salmon DNA that keeps the fish from freezing and to introduce it into strawberries in order to produce a freeze-proof strawberry. It is also possible to introduce animal genes into plants. A small company in Syracuse has contracted with a scientist at the University of Connecticut to develop a genetically engineered cat that will not cause allergies, an effort that may prove to be highly profitable, since it would allow countless numbers of people who cannot now do so to keep cats as pets. Scientists at the University of Florida have patented a method of implanting a silkworm gene into grapevines to make the vines resistant to Pierce's disease, a blight currently menacing vineyards in California. The silkworm gene kills the bacterium responsible for the blight.

There is, of course, reason to be concerned with regard to possible deleterious effects of genetically modified foods upon humans. There is evidence that corn that has been genetically modified to produce a toxin that kills a caterpillar called the European corn borer may also kill monarch butterflies. Genetically modified crops may produce unfamiliar proteins that might prove to be allergenic, toxic or carcinogenic. These concerns are appropriately addressed both by the scientific community and by government regulatory agencies.

The theological and religious question is whether man has the right to intervene in the natural order by mixing and mingling the genetic material of diverse species. As has already been demonstrated in an earlier chapter,[1] there is no reflection in Jewish tradition of a doctrine that establishes a global prohibition forbidding man to tamper with known or presumed *teloi* of creation. There are, however, indeed individual thinkers who have explained the rationale underlying particular *mizvot* in a manner echoing such a concept. Biblical commandments prohibiting interbreeding of species and the mingling of diverse agricultural species certainly lend themselves to such an interpretation. Although Rashi, in his commentary to Leviticus 19:19, regards those restrictions as *ḥukkim*, i.e., arational statutes not subject to human inquiry, Ramban, in his commentary on the same verse, takes sharp issue with Rashi and opines that interbreeding and prohibited mingling of species are forbidden as constituting illicit tampering with creation. Ramban states that every creature and every plant is endowed by God with cosmically arranged distinctive features and qualities and is designed to reproduce itself as long as the universe endures. Interbreeding and cross-fertilization produce a reconfiguration of those distinctive qualities and also compromise reproductive potential. By engaging in such activities man usurps the divine prerogative in producing a new species or entity with its own novel set of attributes and, presumably, a species less than optimally suited to fulfill the divinely ordained *telos* associated with the original species.

Ibn Ezra has been understood as presenting the matter in a somewhat different light in declaring that the Torah prohibits crossbreeding of species because the act thwarts propagation of the species and hence represents an injustice to the animals who are prevented from fulfilling the divine purpose of propagating their respective species.[2] Ibn Ezra has similarly been understood as explaining the prohibitions against the mixture of agricultural species as well as the combination of linen and wool in the cloth of a garment as violative of the natural order decreed by the Creator.[3] R. Samson Raphael Hirsch had no difficulty in explaining the prohibition regarding *sha'atnez* (the mixing of linen and wool) in similar terms. Indeed, R. Hirsch understood all *ḥukkim* as being reflective of the principle that man should not interfere with the order and harmony—and hence the *telos*—of creation.[4] According to R. Hirsch, such laws are distinguished from *mishpatim*, or so-called rational commandments, only because our duties toward our fellow men are more intelligible to us by virtue of our recognition of our own needs and aspirations. That particular purposes are similarly assigned to animals and even to inanimate objects is not immediately grasped by the human intellect and hence *ḥukkim* are depicted as arational. It is noteworthy that, although R. Hirsch regards these commandments as designed to prevent interference with divinely ordained *teloi*, unlike natural law theologians, he regards the *teloi* themselves as not being readily apparent to human reason. That understanding of the nature of *ḥukkim* is certainly confirmed by the fact that no natural law philosopher has ever asserted that the manufacture of linsey-woolsey or even agricultural hybridization is intuitively perceived as interfering with the divine plan for creation.

Were it to be assumed that tampering with the ostensive or presumed nature of animal species is always forbidden, most forms of genetic engineering would be illicit. No bacterium is designed by nature to clean up oil spills by metabolizing petroleum or to excrete human insulin for use by diabetics. In the absence of evidence in rabbinic sources to the contrary, it must be assumed that, even accepting Ramban's explanation of the prohibition against interbreeding or R. Hirsch's broader analysis of the rationale underlying *ḥukkim* in general, biblical strictures must be understood as limited to those matters explicitly prohibited.[5]

There is, to be sure, a perceptible tension between the concepts enunciated by Ramban and R. Samson Raphael Hirsch and the many midrashic sources indicating that man is an active partner in the process of creation and, as such, is charged with bringing creative processes to completion. Indeed, the biblical charge to Adam exhorting him to "fill the earth and conquer it" (Genesis 1:28) seems to give Adam *carte blanche* to engage in any form of conduct that is not specifically proscribed. The problem is readily resolved if it is understood that, in general, the functions and *teloi* of the products of creation are not immutable; that the Creator did not intend to bar man from applying his ingenuity in finding new uses and purposes for the objects of creation;[6] and that there is no injustice to animal species or inanimate objects in doing so. Immutability of function and *telos* is the exception, not the rule. Thus, for example, it has never been suggested that manufacture and use of synthetic fibers in the making of clothes is in any way a contravention of either the letter or the spirit of the law.[7] The exceptions were announced by the Creator as formal prohibitions. It is precisely because human reason cannot intuit, or even comprehend, when and under what circumstances contravention of the natural order is inappropriate that these commandments are in the nature of *ḥukkim*.

More generally, man's creative power, at least to the extent that it does not involve creation of novel species, is extolled in rabbinic sources. The divine appellation "*Shaddai*" is understood in rabbinic exegesis as an acronym "*she-amarti le-olami 'dai'*—"Who said to My universe, 'Enough!' " Thus the verse, "I, the Lord *Shaddai*" (Genesis 17:1) is rendered by *Midrash Rabbah* 46:2, "I am the Lord who said to the universe 'Enough!' " R. Jonathan Eibeschutz, *Tiferet Yonatan*, *ad locum*, followed by R. Joseph Dov Soloveichik, *Bet ha-Levi*, *ad locum*, explains that, in His creation of various artifacts, God arrested their development before completion. Man plants a seed, the seed germinates, a stalk grows and kernels of wheat develop. The Creator could well have made it possible for the kernels to crumble into flour, for the flour to absorb rain or moisture from the atmosphere, for the wind to churn the water-drenched flour so that dough be formed and for the heat of the sun to bake the mixture in order to yield a product that might literally be termed a "breadfruit." Instead, the Creator arrested the process long before its completion and ordained that grinding the wheat, mixing the flour with water, kneading the dough and baking the bread be performed by man. Similarly, the flax plant could have been endowed with properties causing strands of flax to separate and intertwine themselves in a cloth which might grow in the shape of a cloak. Instead, the process is arrested and brought to completion by man. Indeed, the Gemara, *Shabbat* 30b, declares that in the eschatological era the Land of Israel will yield "cakes" and "linen garments." *Bet ha-Levi* explains that the import of that statement is simply that, in the end of days, God will allow the processes of creation to reach their destined end by modifying the natural order in a manner that will permit the creative process to become complete and thus spare man any travail. In the interim, however, He has declared, "Enough!" i.e., He has precipitously interrupted the process of creation and co-opted man, who must complete the process, as a collaborator in fashioning the universe.

It is abundantly clear that human intervention in the natural order is normatively interdicted only to the extent that there are explicit prohibitions limiting such intervention. Moreover, there is no evidence either from Scripture or from rabbinic writings that forms of intervention or manipulation not expressly banned are antithetical to the spirit of the law. Quite to the contrary, Jewish tradition, although it certainly recognizes divine proprietorship of the universe, nevertheless, gratefully acknowledges that while "The heavens are the heavens of God" yet "the earth has He given to the sons of man" (Psalms 115:16). In bestowing that gift upon mankind, the Creator has granted man dominion over the world in which he lives and over the living species that are co-inhabitants of that world. Man has been given license to apply his intellect, ingenuity and physical prowess in developing the world in which he has been placed subject only to limitations imposed by the laws of the Torah, including the general admonition not to do harm to others, as well as by the constraints imposed by good sense and considerations of prudence.

The tension between the role of man as the agent of completing the work of creation and biblical prohibitions against certain forms of interference in the natural order is elucidated by R. Judah Loew, popularly known as Maharal of Prague, in his *Be'er ha-Golah*, chap. 2:3, s.v. *Masekhet Pesaḥim*. The Gemara, *Pesaḥim* 54a, states that the creation of a number of entities was planned by God before the first Sabbath but they were not actually created until the conclusion of the Sabbath. Upon the conclusion of the Sabbath "the Holy One, blessed by He, bestowed understanding upon Adam and he took two stones, rubbed them one upon the other and fire emerged; [Adam] brought two animals, mated one with the other and from them emerged a mule." Clearly, this statement reflects the notion that the potential for both fire and interspecies is the product of divine creation and that the potential became actualized through the intermediacy of human intelligence which is itself a divine gift.

Maharal notes that, although interbreeding of diverse animal species was clearly interdicted by the Torah, the Sages certainly regarded the breeding of mules by Adam as a fulfillment of the divine plan. Maharal boldly declares that the fact that God has prohibited a certain act does not necessarily mean that God has renounced the effect of that act. Thus crossbreeding of animal species was prohibited to Israel at Sinai but was not forbidden to Adam because the breeding of mules was incorporated in the divine blueprint for creation. Thus a distinction must be drawn between act and effect. And, if disdain for the effect is not the rationale underlying the prohibition of the act, there exists no basis for expanding the prohibition to encompass any act that is not formally within its ambit.

Man's role is "completion" (*hashlamah*) of the process of Creation. Insofar as "completion" of creation is concerned, it is the divine plan that such development take place. Maharal asserts that it is the divine will that even interspecies such as the mule come into being, although not in circumstances that involve violation of Torah law. Thus crossbreeding was permitted to Adam because emergence of interspecies is integral to "completion" of the universe. According to Maharal, crossbreeding by a person who is not commanded otherwise (or in situations in which the prohibition does not apply) does not constitute a violation of the divine will or of the divinely ordained *telos* because "the way of Torah is one thing and the way of completion is another matter entirely."

Genetic manipulation involving even the introduction of a gene of one species into the genotype of an alien species does not constitute a violation of the prohibition against crossbreeding. *Ḥazon Ish*, *Kila'im* 2:6, notes that violation of the commandment occurs only in directly causing copulation between two living animals. *Ḥazon Ish* declares that artificial insemination designed to produce an interspecies is not forbidden just as an *inter vivos* organ transferred from one species to another is not forbidden. It is thus quite obvious that genetic manipulation, since it does not entail a sexual act involving partners who are members of different species, cannot be regarded as forbidden.

A similar principle applies to genetic manipulation of agricultural species. R. Shlomoh Zalman Auerbach, *Minḥat Shlomoh*, II, no. 97, sec. 27, declares that pollination of one species with pollen of another species does not result in a fruit that would be halakhically classified as a hybrid. Thus, although Rabbi Auerbach affirms that the fruit of an *etrog* tree produced as the result of grafting of a lemon branch may not be used on *Sukkot* for purposes of fulfilling the *miẓvah* of the four species, he nevertheless regards pollination as an entirely different matter. Accordingly, rules Rabbi Auerbach, if an *etrog* is pollinated with the pollen of a lemon tree the resultant fruit is an *etrog* and may be used for fulfilling the *miẓvah*. Rabbi Auerbach declares that the prohibition against hybridization of species applies only to the planting or grafting of vegetative material that might independently yield fruit or a seed capable of germinating independently. Pollen can never grow into fruit; hence, for purposes of Halakhah, introduction of foreign pollen[8] does not affect species identity. Again, it is quite obvious that such pollination conducted artificially by humans is not prohibited. Similarly, it follows that introduction of a gene of a foreign species is not forbidden as a form of hybridization since an isolated gene can never develop into a tree or into a plant.

II. *KASHRUT* IMPLICATIONS

The major halakhic issue with regard to non-human genetic engineering is the identity of the resultant genetically engineered entity. It seems entirely obvious that a tomato modified to prevent freezing by insertion of a salmon gene is a plant and not an animal. Accordingly, the blessing to be recited before eating the genetically modified tomato remains identical to the blessing pronounced over unmodified tomatoes. But what is the status of a cow whose genotype has been modified by splicing in genes derived from a pig? Does the *kashrut* status of an animal depend upon the status of the gestational mother or upon its own genetic make-up? If the latter, is species identity determined by the source of the majority of the animal's genes or, if its genes are derived from animals of two or more species, is the genetically engineered animal regarded as a hybrid to be treated as a member of each of those species? Another ramification of that issue lies in the area of interbreeding: If genes of a sheep are introduced into a cow does the genetically modified animal remain a cow that may legitimately be bred with a bull or does it acquire at least the partial identity of a sheep that may not be crossbred with a bull? For that matter, may two such animals genetically engineered in an identical manner, but one a male and the other female, be bred with one another?

These issues began to receive scholarly attention due to rumors that circulated in B'nei Brak several years ago concerning genetically engineered poultry. The reports were quite vague in nature and told only of genes of non-kosher birds being introduced into poultry which, according to one rabbinic writer,[9] "led to offspring with odd changes in the shape of their necks and the manner in which they stand on their feet." Another writer[10] describes those chickens as sporting feathers on their legs and further asserts that, when perched on a pole, rope or wire, those chickens separate their toes by placing two digits on either side of the object on which they are perched. The latter phenomenon is recorded in *Shulḥan Arukh, Yoreh De'ah* 82:2, as one of the defining criteria of a non-kosher species. One observer claims that he has observed one such chicken seizing its food with its feet,[11] a phenomenon that, in the opinion formulated by Rashi, *Niddah* 50b,[12] is denoted by the term "*dores*" employed by the Mishnah as descriptive of the primary criterion of a non-kosher bird.

The fear expressed by these rabbinic scholars is that similar genetic manipulation may have occurred with regard to other commercially available poultry but that those genetic changes may have yielded no recognizable anomalies. There are also reports[13] of commercially slaughtered chickens of unknown provenance that lack feathers on their necks and whose skin in the area of their necks turns red when the chickens are frightened. A series of responsa dealing with this issue were collected by R. Hizkiyahu Yosef Cohen for inclusion in his as yet unpublished *Teshuvot Avnei Ḥen.*[14] Among those items are responsa authored by R. Yisra'el Ya'akov Fisher and R. Moshe Sternbuch, both of the *Bet Din* of Jerusalem's *Edah ha-Ḥaredit*, R. Nathan Gestetner, author of the multi-volume work, *Le-Horot Natan*, R. Samuel ha-Levi Woszner, author of *Teshuvot Shevet ha-Levi*, as well as Rabbi Cohen's own comments. Rabbi Fisher's responsum has been published in his own responsa collection, *Teshuvot Even Yisra'el*, VIII, no. 55.

In a communication to a colleague, a copy of which is in the possession of this writer, Dr. Lawrence Shore, a member of the Department of Human Research of the Kimron Veterinary Institute in Bet Dagan, advises that transgenic poultry were never offered for sale but that such reports gained currency as a result of extremely interesting research that he had conducted. Dr. Shore reports that he successfully crossed a chicken with a jellyfish by inserting a gene from a jellyfish into a chicken. The gene thus transferred is responsible for the green pigmentation of jellyfish. The result was a green chicken. Dr. Shore further reports that the transfer procedure he employed is patented, that all research specimens were destroyed and that such chickens are not commercially available.[15] Accordingly, the rumors represent little more than a halakhic tempest in a scientific teapot. The aforesaid does not at all imply that halakhic discussions of the issues involved are irrelevant. We live in a world in which yesterday's science fiction is today's laboratory experiment and tomorrow's commonplace reality.

A discussion of the halakhic ramifications of the issues involved must begin with one well-established point. As noted by R. Moshe Sternbuch in his responsum, the halakhic issue is quite similar to one posed by grafting a branch of a newly-grown sapling onto a mature tree. The fruit of the mature tree, i.e., a tree more than three years old, is no longer subject to the prohibition of *orlah*; the fruit of the young sapling is subject to that prohibition. Nevertheless, for purposes of *orlah*, the branch of the younger tree acquires the identity of the older tree and, accordingly, its fruit is permitted. In effect, the identity of the sapling becomes submerged in the identity of the tree onto which it has been grafted. Presumably, the same provision would apply to an individual gene that is "grafted" or spliced into the germ cell of another species.

However, in his responsum, Rabbi Nathan Gestetner ignores this consideration with regard to rules governing *orlah* and hence fails to discuss its applicability or non-applicability to products of genetic manipulation. Instead, Rabbi Gestetner simply assumes that the transferred gene does not lose its halakhic identity as a particle of a forbidden entity. Nevertheless, he finds grounds to permit at least the progeny of the genetically altered bird on the basis of a principle of Halakhah applicable to the product of multiple causes. That principle is formulated, *inter alia*, in association with the prohibition against deriving benefit from any deified object. This prohibition notwithstanding, *Shulḥan Arukh, Yoreh De'ah* 142:11, rules that, during the summer, even in climes in which vegetables need shade in order to grow, it is permitted to plant vegetables under a tree that has been made the object of pagan adoration. The halakhic principle reflected in that ruling is "*zeh va-zeh gorem muttar*," i.e., the product of two causes, one permissible and one forbidden, is permissible. Germination and growth of the vegetables in question are attributable to two causes, *viz.*, 1) nutrients provided by the soil which are entirely permissible and 2) the shade provided by the prohibited tree.

Similarly, the Gemara, *Ḥullin* 58a, declares that eggs laid by a bird suffering from a congenital anomaly or which has sustained a trauma such that it has the status of a *treifah* may nevertheless be eaten. As Rashi explains, that is so because, according to the talmudic principle, eggs are the joint product of both the father bird and the mother bird.[16] Although, in the case of a *treifah*, the meat of the mother may not be consumed, nevertheless, since the father is not a *treifah*, the resultant egg is permissible on the basis of the principle of *zeh va-zeh gorem*, i.e., it is the product of two separate causes. Accordingly, argues Rabbi Gestetner, a genetic complement containing genes from both a permitted species and a non-permitted species should have the status of *zeh va-zeh gorem* and hence all progeny should be permissible. Even more significantly, if only one of the progenitors of the chicken was the product of genetic engineering, but the other was not, the offspring are certainly the product of two separate "causes" and hence permissible.

However, as Rabbi Gestetner observes, that conclusion is not compatible with the position of Ramban, *Avodah Zarah* 49a, cited by *Bet Yosef, Yoreh De'ah* 142, who asserts that the principle of *zeh va-zeh gorem* is applicable only in situations in which two elements, one permitted and one forbidden, combine to generate a single cause, e.g., foliage which acts as fertilizer that combines with permissible nutrients found in the soil, but is not applicable to situations involving two distinct causes such as shade and soil. The Gemara, *Niddah* 31a, declares that each parent is the source of different parts of the body: the father produces the "white" portion that forms bones, sinews, etc., while the mother contributes the "red" portion that becomes skin, flesh, etc. If so, in the case of poultry, since each parent is a separate cause producing a unique effect, the causes are distinct and separate. Hence, according to Ramban, the principle of *zeh va-zeh gorem* would not apply.

Rabbi Gestetner takes note of the fact that, in apparent contradiction to Ramban's thesis, the Gemara, in two separate instances, *Temurah* 30b and 31a, applies the principle of *zeh va-zeh gorem* to an animal born of a prohibited mother and a permitted father. It is quite possible that Ramban assumes that the talmudic statement indicating that the father contributes the "white" while the mother contributes the "red" establishes a principle with regard to humans but not with regard to animals. In any event, *Shulḥan Arukh, Yoreh De'ah* 142:11, rejects Ramban's position in ruling that *zeh va-zeh gorem* is permissible even in the case of two independent causes.[17]

Nevertheless, the principle of *zeh va-zeh gorem* may not be applicable to genetic manipulation that yields recognizable physical characteristics of the forbidden cause because of an entirely different reason. Rabbenu Nissim, *Avodah Zarah* 48b, asserts that *zeh va-zeh gorem* is not an independent halakhic principle; rather, he argues, it is an application of the general concept of nullification (*bittul*), i.e., just as a forbidden substance loses its identity when it becomes submerged in a quantity sixty times as great, so also does a causal agent fail to preserve its identity in the effect it has produced in instances in which another identifiable cause is also present. Yet, as recorded in *Shulḥan Arukh, Yoreh De'ah* 98:4, a forbidden substance that has become mixed with a quantity of a permitted substance sixty times as great but which nevertheless remains recognizable is not nullified. The applicable principle is that a recognizable substance never loses its identity. Genes that are responsible for particular physical characteristics do not lose their identity by reason of nullification, argues Rabbi Gestetner, because they remain recognizable in the physical characteristics for which they are responsible. Thus, since *zeh va-zeh gorem*, according to Rabbenu Nissim, is naught but a form of nullification, the principle cannot be invoked in situations in which the effect of a gene derived from a nonkosher source is perceivable.[18]

R. Yisra'el Ya'akov Fisher points out that, if *zeh va-zeh gorem* is indeed predicated upon the principle of nullification, any foodstuff produced by dual causes, one kosher and one non-kosher, is permissible only *post factum*. It would therefore follow that it is forbidden purposely to employ that principle in engaging in transgenic procedures in order to breed animals or poultry for consumption by Jews just as purposeful adulteration of a forbidden food is forbidden.

There is yet one other factor to be considered that is relevant only to the *kashrut* of genetically engineered fowl but not to mammalian species. The *kashrut* of any particular animal species is determined on the basis of whether or not the species is endowed with split hoofs and whether or not the animal chews its cud.[19] Once the *kashrut* status of an animal species is determined, individual animals born to members of the species are kosher or non-kosher depending upon the status of the parent animals. Accordingly, insofar as offspring are concerned, the presence or absence of the physical criteria of kosher species is irrelevant in determining their *kashrut*. Thus, hypothetically, a piglet born to a cow as the result of genetic mutation would be kosher; conversely, a calf born to a mare would not be kosher. The applicable principle as formulated by the Mishnah, *Bekhorot* 5b, is: "A pure animal that gives birth to [what appears to be an animal of] an impure species, [the offspring] is permitted for eating; an impure [animal] that gives birth to [what appears to be an animal of] a pure species, [the offspring] is prohibited for eating, for that which emerges from the impure is impure and that which emerges from the pure is pure."

The situation with regard to avian mutations is more complex. Scripture does not distinguish between kosher and non-kosher birds on the basis of anatomical or physiological criteria. Instead, Leviticus 11:13–19 and Deuteronomy 14:12–18 enumerate twenty-four species of non-kosher birds; all others are declared to be kosher.[20] Nevertheless, the Mishnah,

Ḥullin 59a, does present a number of physical criteria that serve empirically to assist in distinguishing between kosher and non-kosher birds. The principle that that which emerges from the impure is impure and that which emerges from the pure is pure is to be understood simply as meaning that any creature that "emerges from," or is born of, another creature has the halakhic status of the creature from which it is born. An animal that gestates in the womb of the mother certainly emerges from the mother and hence has the selfsame halakhic status as the mother. However, unlike mammals, birds do not gestate their young; instead, they lay eggs. Eggs do indeed "emerge" from the female and hence have the same *kashrut* status as the mother. Eggs and milk are kosher or non-kosher depending upon the status of the animal that gives the milk or lays the eggs.[21] Thus, without question, eggs laid by a non-kosher bird are not kosher. And since hatchlings emerge from the eggs, it might readily be assumed that the baby bird is also endowed with the same species identity and halakhic status as the egg from which it emerged. That is indeed the view of *Tosafot*, *Ḥullin* 62b, and of Rambam, *Hilkhot Ma'akhalot Assurot* 3:11, as understood by *Maggid Mishneh*, *ad locum*.[22] Thus, in line with the earlier discussed consideration of the fact that the gene contributed by the non-kosher animal is recognizable in physical anomalies it produces, it should be concluded that such a genetically engineered chicken should be regarded as non-kosher since the bird, at least in part, is the *yoẓei*, i.e., the derivative, of a non-kosher entity that has not been nullified.

However, Rashi and *Tosafot*, *Niddah* 50b, adopt an opposing view.[23] Noting that a hatchling does not gestate within its mother but emerges from an egg, *Tosafot* point to the fact that the Gemara, *Temurah* 31a, declares that, in the course of gestation, the egg putrefies and becomes "dust" unfit for consumption by man or beast. In the process the egg loses its status as either a kosher or non-kosher food. Since the egg is destroyed or rendered into "dust" in the course of gestation, the emerging bird, declare *Tosafot*, is not the *yoẓei* of any entity or, to put the matter somewhat differently, the bird is halakhically deemed to be *sui generis*.[24] As such, each bird that emerges from an egg is tantamount to the primordial bird that served as the progenitor of a species whose halakhic status is determined entirely on the basis of the physical criteria that distinguish one species from another.[25] According to that opinion[26]—and that opinion alone[27]—genetically engineered poultry would always be kosher provided that they exhibit the physical criteria of an identifiable species of kosher fowl.[28] Citing this statement of *Tosafot*, but without citing the conflicting statement of *Tosafot*, *Ḥullin* 62b, or of other authorities who concur in the latter view, Rabbi Sternbuch dismisses the halakhic problem out of hand and rules that transgenic poultry are kosher provided that they do not manifest the criteria of non-kosher birds.

Rabbi Sternbuch asserts that, even if some individual transgenic chickens are in the category of animals that are "*dores*," the species is nevertheless kosher. Presumably, that is also the case if some individual chickens separate their digits when placed upon a pole, rope or wire which is an indication that the bird is "*dores*." He asserts that those criteria serve only to establish the status of a heretofore unidentified species but are irrelevant in determining the status of individual members of a species whose status has already been established. In response, Rabbi Cohen points to the statement of *Shakh*, *Yoreh De'ah* 82:6, declaring that, if a single bird is found to manifest criteria of a non-kosher species, any previously existing tradition establishing the *kashrut* of the species is thereby abrogated.

However, it seems to this writer that *Shakh*'s ruling is not applicable to the case at hand. Evidence that a member of a species is *dores*, for example, is presumptive evidence that the entire species is not kosher. That characteristic, however, is not the factor that renders the bird non-kosher; it is only evidence establishing that the species is one of the twenty-four biblically enumerated non-kosher species. When the presence of that characteristic can be cogently explained in some other manner, e.g., by virtue of genetic manipulation that lacks halakhic significance, it ceases to be evidence that the species to which the bird belongs is non-kosher.

Rabbi Sternbuch does, however, express reservations with regard to use of such poultry for an entirely different reason. Rabbi Sternbuch cites Rema, *Yoreh De'ah* 60:1, who forbids consumption of the meat of an animal that has been fattened primarily by being fed forbidden foods and tentatively suggests that if an animal has been subjected to growth-stimulating genes of non-kosher origin it may have the status of an animal fattened by forbidden foods. However, Rabbi Sternbuch candidly concedes that the latter case can be distinguished from the subject of Rema's ruling.

The comparison of genetically modified animals to animals fattened on forbidden foods is tenuous to say the least. The Gemara, *Menaḥot* 69a, discusses the status of objects such as wheat, barley or utensils consumed by animals and subsequently excreted. One example is the suitability of kernels of wheat that have been eaten by an animal for subsequent use in a meal-offering. The Gemara concludes that if the swallowed wheat remains whole it retains its status as wheat. However, once the kernel of wheat begins to be digested it loses its status as wheat and becomes an integral part of the animal that has consumed it.

Tosafot, *Temurah* 31a, understand the Gemara's conclusion as pertaining only to the issue of ritual impurity. Living animals are not susceptible to impurity. Accordingly, once an animal has begun to digest an object and it becomes part of the animal itself, it can no longer be subject to impurity. Nevertheless, at least at that point, the object has not lost its own identity and hence, if it is a non-kosher foodstuff, it may not be eaten. However, *Tosafot*, *Menaḥot* 69a,[29] Rash and Rosh, *Oholot* 11:7, as well as an earlier authority cited by Rosh, *Bekhorot* 1:8, maintain that in the course of the process of digestion any food product loses its previous identity with regard to all matters of Halakhah.

Rema, *Yoreh De'ah* 60:1, follows the view of *Tosafot*, *Temurah* 31a, in ruling that the meat of an animal raised exclusively on forbidden food may not be eaten because it is a *yoẓei* of a forbidden entity. If the animal has been fed both kosher and non-kosher food it does not acquire non-kosher status by virtue of the earlier discussed principle of *zeh va-zeh gorem*. As discussed earlier, an animal whose progenitor had received genes from a non-kosher animal is, at worst, the product of *zeh va-zeh gorem* and hence is permitted for food, at least when there is no manifestation of the physical characteristics of the non-kosher donor of the transformed gene.

Moreover, *Shakh*, *Yoreh De'ah* 60:5, as well as numerous other authorities disagree with Rema's ruling and permit consumption of the meat of an animal that has been fed forbidden food exclusively. *Shakh* maintains that the early-day authorities who serve as the sources for Rema's ruling maintained only that forbidden foods do not lose their identity or status simply because the digestive process has commenced and therefore remain prohibited. However, argues *Shakh*, once digestion is complete and those forbidden foods are assimilated by the host animal's body, the meat of an animal raised in such a manner is permissible because the forbidden food is completely destroyed in the process of digestion before its nutrients are absorbed by the animal's body. Hence, an animal raised in such manner is not to be regarded as the *yoẓei* or derivative of a forbidden food. Therefore, according to *Shakh*, since even an animal fattened on exclusively forbidden foods is permissible, there can be no analogy to transgenic animals or poultry.[30]

Rabbi Sternbuch raises yet another concern. He reports

that he has been informed that rodent genes may be implanted in poultry to stimulate growth but that such genetic manipulation would give rise to no other recognizable physical characteristics. Rabbi Sternbuch takes note of the statement of the Sages, *Yoma* 39a, declaring that forbidden foods are *metamtem*, or "stop up," the heart, i.e., forbidden foods dull the heart and cause the development of undesirable character traits and of the comment of Rema, *Yoreh De'ah* 81:7, who discourages use of the services of a gentile wet-nurse for the same reason as well as of a statement of Rambam[31] who asserts that partaking of forbidden foods causes intellectual deficiencies in those who consume them and may cause those persons to espouse heretical views. Indeed, the Palestinian Talmud, *Ḥaggigah* 2:1, cites one opinion to the effect that the heresy of Elisha ben Abuyah was a consequence of his mother's conduct during her pregnancy. Elisha ben Abuyah's mother had been wont to inhale the odors of idolatrous sacrifices. Rabbi Sternbuch expresses the fear that transgenic manipulation involving the genes of a non-kosher species may yield food that engenders similarly deleterious consequences.[32]

The permissibility of transgenic poultry is but the first halakhic question involving genetic manipulation to be addressed by rabbinic scholars. It may certainly be anticipated that there will be further discussions of this problem as well as of similar matters. This emerging area of halakhic inquiry represents yet another challenge to the intellectual prowess of halakhic decisors who must apply age-old principles to issues that could not have been fathomed, much less formulated, in earlier ages.

NOTES

1. See *supra*, pp. 9–14. This material is repeated because of its crucial relevance to the issue under discussion in this chapter.
2. See R. Abraham ibn Ezra, *Commentary on the Bible*, Leviticus 19:19 and R. Judah Leib Krinsky, *Karnei Or*, *loc. cit.* See also

R. Abraham Chill, *The Mitzvot: The Commandments and Their Rationale* (Jerusalem, 1974), p. 236.

3. See the supercommentary to Ibn Ezra of R. Shlomoh Zalman Netter, Leviticus 19:19, published in the *Horeb* edition of the Pentateuch (Jerusalem, London, New York, 5711). A similar interpretation was earlier advanced by *Ohel Yosef* and *Mekor Ḥayyim* in their respective works on Ibn Ezra published in *Margaliyot Torah* (Stanislaw, 5687). *Mekor Ḥayyim* also understands Ibn Ezra's comments regarding interbreeding of animal species in a like manner. However, these scholars' understanding of the passage in question is less than compelling. Cf., R. Abraham Chill, *The Mitzvot*, p. 236.
4. See R. Samson Raphael Hirsch, *The Nineteen Letters of Ben Uziel*, Eleventh Letter; *idem*, *Horeb*, sec. 327.
5. Rambam, *Guide for the Perplexed*, Book III, chap. 37, regards the *ḥukkim* as prohibitions designed to deter idolatrous conduct. The actions in question, he asserts, were cultic practices associated with pagan worship and sacrifice. According to Rambam's understanding of these commandments, there is no hint of a negative attitude with regard to intervention by man in the natural order.
6. Cf., R. Joseph B. Soloveitchik, "Confrontation," *Tradition*, vol. VI, no. 2 (Spring-Summer, 1964), p. 20.
7. It is indeed the case that one finds occasional comments in rabbinic writings representing those prohibitions in phraseology that is general and unqualified. See, for example, the sources cited *supra*, note 2. Nevertheless, it seems to this writer that those comments must be understood in the manner herein indicated.
8. An apparently contradictory statement by R. Shlomoh Zalman Auerbach appears in a different volume, *Minḥat Shlomoh, Tinyana* (Jerusalem, 5760), no. 100, sec. 7. In that work Rabbi Auerbach writes that hybridization of trees is forbidden "even if the hybridization is [performed] only by means of injection of sap that, if planted in the ground, would not at all sprout." In context, Rabbi Auerbach's statement in *Minḥat Shlomoh, Tinyana* seems to be offered in order to establish a negative view regarding genetic manipulation of agricultural species. Nevertheless, in the same discussion, Rabbi Auerbach emphasizes that, with regard to animals, genetic manipulation since it does not involve a sexual act does not constitute a violation

of the prohibition against crossbreeding.

9. R. Nathan Gestetner, in an unpublished work, *Teshuvot Avnei Ḥen*, ed. by R. Hizkiyahu Yosef Cohen.
10. R. Yisra'el Ya'akov Fisher, *Teshuvot Avnei Ḥen*. R. Moshe Sternbuch, in a responsum included in the same unpublished work, similarly cites reports of separation of the toes in this manner.
11. Rabbi Fisher, *loc. cit.*
12. Cf., Rashi, *Ḥullin* 59a, where he defines "*dores*" as a bird that seizes its food with its claws and lifts it from the ground. Rashi, in his commentary on *Niddah* 50b, adds the comment "But I say that [the bird] stomps on its food with its feet to hold [it] so that [the food] does not come to [the bird's] mouth in its entirety." *Tosafot*, *Ḥullin* 61a, define "*dores*" as a bird that stomps upon its prey and eats it when it is yet alive. Many early-day authorities understand the term as a reference to a bird that kills its prey by piercing it with its claws and emitting a poison. See *Shakh, Yoreh De'ah* 82:3 and *Arukh ha-Shulḥan, Yoreh De'ah* 82:5.
13. Cited by Rabbi Fisher, *Teshuvot Avnei Ḥen*.
14. This author is indebted to Dayan Y. Y. Lichtenstein of London's Federation of Synagogues for having made those responsa available to him. See Dayan Lichtenstein's article, "Halachic Aspects of Cloning Chickens," *Hamaor*, vol. 34, no. 2 (Pesach 5761), pp. 6–7.
15. The gene of sea coral has been successfully transferred to zebrafish causing the latter to appear red in normal light and to glow under ultraviolet light. The transgenic GloFish is readily available in pet stores. See *New York Times*, January 25, 2004, section 3, p. 5.
16. The operative principle is that the hen produces eggs as a result of stimulation experienced in intercourse. Alternatively, the egg may be produced without benefit of a rooster by means of "friction from the dust." In the absence of a contributory cause attributable to a rooster, the Gemara, *Ḥullin* 58a, expressly categorizes the egg laid by a hen that is a *treifah* as prohibited because it is the product of a single non-kosher cause.
17. See *Bi'ur ha-Gra, Yoreh De'ah* 142:29 and *Teshuvot Avnei Milu'im*, no. 7.
18. Rabbi Fisher asserts that, even if *zeh va-zeh gorem* is regarded as

forbidden, if the gene of the forbidden animal is taken from a non-kosher father rather than from a non-kosher mother the offspring must be regarded as permissible on the basis of the talmudic opinion, *Ḥullin* 79a, that "No cognizance is taken of the seed of the father." *Avnei Nezer, Yoreh De'ah*, no. 75, sec. 8, similarly declares that, even if "No cognizance is taken of the seed of the father," a bird born of a non-kosher mother and a father of a kosher species is permissible on the basis of *zeh va-zeh gorem muttar.* That conclusion is at variance with the thesis developed by R. Chaim ha-Levi Soloveitchik, *Ḥiddushei R. Ḥayyim ha-Levi al ha-Rambam, Hilkhot Ma'akhalot Assurot* 3:11. According to R. Chaim, the latter principle is dispositive only with regard to determination of membership in a species in instances of crossbreeding or in establishing a paternal-filial relationship in animal species but is not applicable to determination of the kosher or non-kosher status of particular offspring. Thus, even if "No cognizance is taken of the seed of the father" who is a *treifah*, the offspring is permissible only on the basis of *zeh va-zeh gorem.* Or, as expressed by *Tosafot, Ḥullin* 58a, "No cognizance is taken of the seed of the father" is applicable only if both father and mother are kosher animals. Similarly, if the father is a member of a non-kosher species, even though "No cognizance is taken of the seed of the father," the *kashrut* of the progeny can be established only by incorporating the principle *zeh va-zeh gorem.* See also R. Menachem Ziemba, *Zera Avraham*, no. 11, sec. 16 and *Avnei Nezer, Yoreh De'ah*, no. 75, secs. 5–8.

Rabbi Fisher, however, further asserts that, if the female is genetically altered in this manner, poultry produced by her eggs are certainly prohibited since, on the basis of the principle "No cognizance is taken of the seed of the father," the rooster's role is of no consequence. Rabbi Fisher does not seem to grasp the fact that the hen does not represent a single non-kosher cause but is itself an amalgam both of kosher and non-kosher causes.

19. *Teshuvot ha-Rivash*, no. 492, asserts that determination of the *kashrut* of animals is made solely on the basis of physical criteria to the exclusion of other otherwise relevant considerations. Thus, he rules that the principle of *rov* does not apply to determination of the identity of a particular animal as a member of a kosher versus a non-kosher species. Rivash explains that the Torah commands Jews "to distinguish between the clean

and the unclean" (Leviticus 11:16), i.e., that determination of the *kashrut* status of an animal be made on the basis of examination for the presence of the biblically described physical characteristics. That admonition, asserts Rivash, requires that discrimination between kosher and non-kosher animals be predicated solely upon the basis of those physical criteria and not on the basis of other halakhic principles such as *rov*. See R. Yitzchak Ya'akov Rabinowitz' elucidation of that position in his *Zekher Yiẓḥak*, I, no. 80 as well as this writer's *Be-Netivot ha-Halakhah*, I (New York, 5756), 129–131. That ruling is, however, limited to reliance upon the principle of *rov* for the purpose of identification of an animal as a member of a species (*kol de-parish*) but not to *rov* in the sense of nullification in instances of adulteration (*bittul be-rov*). In discussing a related point, Rabbi Fisher seems to have missed that important distinction.

20. Cf., however, *Tosafot, Niddah* 50b, who suggest that any species manifesting the four criteria of an eagle (*nesher*) enumerated by the Gemara, *Ḥullin* 61a (*viz*., members of the species lack an "extra" or separated digit; lack a craw; the lining of the stomach does not peel away; are "*dores*" their food), is forbidden even if not included in the biblical list of forbidden birds. For the identity of the "*nesher*" see *Tosafot, Ḥullin* 63a; for an elucidation of various opinions regarding the denotation of the term "extra digit" see the comments of Rashi and Ran, *Ḥullin* 63a. See also *Arukh ha-Shulḥan, Yoreh De'ah* 82:3.

21. There is, however, a difference between the offspring of a non-kosher animal and the eggs or milk produced by that creature: the prohibition attendant upon the offspring of a non-kosher species is identical to that of its forebears, *viz*., a negative commandment punishable by forty stripes; whereas the prohibition against partaking of the milk or eggs derived from non-kosher species represents a lesser infraction. In effect, the identity of the mother is transferred to the young while the prohibition against consumption of a foodstuff produced by a member of a non-kosher species reflects only the derivative nature of that foodstuff. See *Tosafot, Ḥullin* 58a and *Ḥiddushei R. Ḥayyim al ha-Ramban, Hilkhot Ma'ahkalot Assurot* 3:11.

22. See also *Bet Me'ir, Yoreh De'ah* 86, who attributes such a view to *Pri Ḥadash, Yoreh De'ah* 86:8 as well as to *Imrei Binah, Hilkhot Treifot*, no. 11. Cf., however, R. Nathan Gestetner, *Teshuvot le-Horot Natan*, VI, no. 58, sec. 8.

23. The Gemara, *Ḥullin* 62b and *Niddah* 50b, records a dictum attributed to Rav Pappa to the effect that a certain *tarnegol de-agma* is forbidden but that a certain *tarnegalta de-agma* is permissible. Rashi, noting that *tarnegol* is a male noun and *tarnegalta* is a female noun, explains that the birds are members of the same avian species known as *tarnegol de-agma* (the chicken of the swamp) but that within that species the female is kosher while the male is not kosher. The problem is that, logically, the species is either kosher or non-kosher and, accordingly, all young of the species, whether male or female, should have the halakhic status of their progenitors. Accordingly, *Tosafot*, *Ḥullin* 62b, identify the *tarnegol de-agma* and the *tarnegalta de-agma* as entirely different species rather than the male and the female of the same species. For an analysis of that controversy, see *infra*, note 27.
24. In his talmudic novellae, *Ḥullin* 63b, reprinted in his *Teshuvot Ḥatam Sofer*, *Yoreh De'ah*, no. 74, *Ḥatam Sofer* explains an otherwise difficult biblical verse: Deuteronomy 14:11 declares, "Of all clean birds you may eat." The immediately following verse reads: "And this is what you shall not eat of them." Scripture then continues with an enumeration of the twenty-four non-kosher avian species. The term "of them" appears to be incongruous. Grammatically, the governing noun is "birds" and is modified by the adjective "clean." But the enumerated prohibited species are certainly not "clean birds!" *Ḥatam Sofer* explains that the term "of them" (*mehem*) should not be understood as "of them" but in the equally correct linguistic sense of "from them," i.e., produced by them. In context, then, the verse tells us that the enumerated forbidden species are prohibited (even) when they are produced by parent birds that are "clean birds," i.e., the progeny of kosher birds are prohibited if they are recognizable members of any one of the enumerated non-kosher species because the principle of *yoẓei* is not applicable.
25. *Ḥatam Sofer*, *Ḥullin* 66a, observes that, since fish also develop from eggs deposited by the female outside her body, this principle applies to fish as well. Thus the rule that "the impure which emerges from the pure is pure" does not apply to fish. Accordingly, he asserts, since the egg putrefies before the young are produced, a fish that emerges from the egg of a mother that is a member of a kosher species but which, as a result of genetic mutation or of some other cause, is born with-

out fins and scales is to be regarded as non-kosher. That conclusion reflects the position of *Tosafot, Niddah* 50b, as cited by *Ḥatam Sofer*. However, according to the contradictory opinion of Rashi and *Tosafot, Ḥullin* 62b, who maintain that species identity is transmitted by the mother to her young even in the case of birds, a fish lacking fins and scales that is born of the egg of a kosher fish would be kosher. [Cf., however, *Teshuvot Ḥatam Sofer, Yoreh De'ah*, no. 75, in which he declares that a fish born of a non-kosher species is kosher even if it lacks fins and scales. In that responsum *Ḥatam Sofer* presumably maintained that, unlike the eggs of birds, the eggs of fish do not putrefy in the course of gestation.]

The converse, however, would not be the case. Even according to the position expressed by *Ḥatam Sofer, Ḥullin* 66a, a fish possessing fins and scales born of a non-kosher fish would not be kosher because, according to the controlling opinion expressed by the Gemara, *Avodah Zarah* 40a, non-kosher fish do not deposit their eggs in water. See *Be-Netivot ha-Halakhah*, I, 131–133.

Accordingly, some years ago, the late R. Shlomoh Zalman Auerbuch, *Minḥat Shlomoh*, II (Jerusalem, 5759), no. 97, sec. 29, cautioned that non-kosher fish might one day be genetically modified to develop fins and scales. Since such fish and their progeny would remain non-kosher, the presence of fins and scales, he cautioned, would no longer in itself demonstrate the *kashrut* of a particular fish.

26. This is also the opinion of Ramban, *Bekhorot* 6b; *Ba'al Halakhot Gedolot*, as cited by Ramban, *loc. cit.*, and Rabbenu Nissim, *Ḥullin* 64b. See *Bet Me'ir, supra*, note 22.

27. See, however, *Avnei Nezer, Yoreh De'ah*, no. 75, sec. 8, who accepts the position of *Tosafot, Ḥullin* 62b, but asserts that the mother remains a "cause." Nevertheless, he rules that the hatchling is permitted because even if "No cognizance is taken of the seed of the father" the father is nevertheless also a "cause" and *zeh va-zeh gorem* is permissible.

28. It seems to this writer that the controversy between the Tosafists should be understood in light of the recognition that there are in fact two distinct aspects to the doctrine of *yoẓei*. As recorded by the Gemara, *Bekhorot* 6a, the offspring of a kosher animal is kosher regardless of its physical characteristics. The principle reflected in that ruling is that the identity

of the mother as a member of a particular species transfers to her progeny, making the offspring a member of that species as well. However, the milk of a non-kosher animal is forbidden for consumption, not because the identity of the non-kosher mother is in some manner transposed to its milk, but because it is produced by, or derived from, a non-kosher entity. Since the identity of the mother is not transposed to the milk, that form of *yoẓei* is prohibited solely on the basis of a pleonasm as formulated by the Gemara, *Ḥullin* 112b, *Ḥullin* 120a and *Bekhorot* 6b, and punishment for violation of the stricture against partaking of such *yoẓei* is less severe than the punishment for consuming the flesh of the mother. Nevertheless, the punishment for eating the meat of the progeny of members of non-kosher species, even if the offspring lacks the identifying criteria of a non-kosher species, is identical to the punishment for eating the meat of its mother for the simple reason that the species identity of the young of the species is identical to that of its progenitor. To put the matter somewhat differently, the offspring of a species are descriptively *yoẓei* but are halakhically indistinguishable from the progenitor. However, the product of a forbidden animal, e.g., milk or eggs, has the halakhic status of *yoẓei*, i.e., of a derivative, but not the intrinsic status of the forbidden entity from which it is derived.

It is because of precisely that distinction that, as a forbidden animal grows and matures, the weight that it gains is not regarded as having the halakhically less severe status of *yoẓei* but as having the same status as the newly-born offspring. Thus, the status of all parts of a mature cow is the same as that of the calf at the time that it emerges from its mother's womb. Cf., Rashi, *Ḥullin* 90a, s.v. *alma*. The halakhic identity of the newly-born calf is transposed to the mature cow and, indeed, common sense readily agrees that they are the same animal. Insofar as identification as a member of a species is concerned, Halakhah similarly attributes the species identity of the mother cow to the calf to which it gives birth in the sense of "Your sons shall be in the stead of your father" (Psalms 45:17).

As has been explained, the Gemara, *Temurah* 31a, establishes that a hatchling of a bird born of an egg laid by a *treifah* is kosher despite the fact that it is the *yoẓei*, i.e., it is derived from, and produced by, a non-kosher bird. The rationale is that the egg turns to "dust" before the hatchling is formed and hence is not at all the *yoẓei* or product of a non-kosher bird. *Tosafot, Ḥullin* 62b, maintain that the same is true with regard to species identity. The egg of every bird is destroyed in the process of gestation. Hence Halakhah regards the young as born *sui generis* and prohibited, not because it acquires the identity of its progenitor, but because of its own intrinsic identity as a non-kosher bird. However, Rashi and *Tosafot, Niddah* 50b, disagree and maintain that the species identity is transmitted even to a bird hatched from an egg. It may be posited that Rashi and the author of *Tosafot, Niddah* 50b, maintain that species identity is a function of spatio-temporal contiguity rather than of causal factors. The causal agent of a bird hatched from an egg is indeed "dust" which, since it itself is not non-kosher, cannot yield a non-kosher derivative. Nevertheless, with regard to species identity, *Tosafot, Niddah* 50b, apparently maintain that status as a member of a species does not at all depend upon causal factors but upon transposition of identity alone and the latter can readily be explained simply in terms of spatio-temporal contiguity. Cf., however, *Avnei Nezer, Yoreh De'ah*, no. 75, sec. 7, who explains the distinction between the status of hatchlings of non-kosher species and the hatchling of an egg laid by a *treifah* in a different and more strained manner.

29. Cf., *Tosafot, Bekhorot* 7b, who express some equivocation with regard to such a distinction.
30. Note should be taken of one additional consideration. As reported by R. Shalom Mordecai Schwadron, *Da'at Torah, Yoreh De'ah* 60:5, R. Shlomoh Kluger, while serving as Chief Rabbi of Brody, was asked to rule upon an anomaly in a goose. Rabbi Kluger noticed that the goose was uncommonly fat. Upon questioning its owner, he discovered that it had been fattened by being fed pig meat and consequently he ruled that, quite apart from any problem associated with the anatomical defect it manifested, the goose was forbidden for that reason alone. *Da'at Torah, Yoreh De'ah* 60:4–7, follows that ruling in forbidding geese fattened on horsemeat. Those decisors assert that the controversy among early-day authorities is limited to animals raised on forbidden food other than meat. In such instances, they argue, the identity of the foodstuff is changed, e.g., fruit that has been consumed is metamorphasized into the flesh of the animal. However, they reason that if a goose

consumes horsemeat or flesh of a pig no intrinsic change takes place in the nature of the consumed meat. The meat that was consumed simply becomes the flesh of the animal that consumed it. Hence, they assert, even *Shakh* would concede that the geese fattened on the flesh of forbidden animals are impermissible.

Applying this consideration to transgenic animals or poultry, it would follow that, according to R. Shlomoh Kluger and Maharsham, since the gene of the non-kosher animal undergoes no change in transplantation, the recipient animal and its progeny would be forbidden, unless, of course, the principle of *zeh va-zeh gorem* is applicable. Cf., however, R. Moshe Feinstein, *Iggerot Mosheh, Oraḥ Ḥayyim*, I, no. 147, who draws no distinction between meat and other foodstuffs and rules that the digestive process destroys the identity and status of all foods.

31. Rabbi Sternbuch attributes the statement to *Teshuvot ha-Rambam* but does not cite a specific responum. R. Dov Eliach, *Me-Shulḥan Gevoha* (Jerusalem, 5754), *Va-Yikra*, p. 94, cites an anecdote reported in the name of R. Chaim Soloveitchick by R. Yissachar Dov of Retova in an unpublished source that serves to illustrate the same point. The identical anecdote concerning Rambam was earlier reported by R. Ya'akov Yosef ha-Kohen of Polennoye, *Ẓofnat Pa'aneaḥ*, ed. Gedalyah Negal (Jerusalem, 5749), p. 221, as having been related to him by his "teacher," apparently the Ba'al Shem Tov. *Be-Netivot Rabboteinu le-Bet Brisk* (Jerusalem, 5762), vol. II, *Parashat Shemini*, p. 17, reports that while in Warsaw R. Chaim came upon a work containing a reference to a responsum authored by Rambam as recounted by the Ba'al Shem Tov. The editor of *Be-Netivot Rabboteinu*, II, 18, note 24, cites an earlier reference to that responsum in *Degel Maḥaneh Efrayim, Parashat Ekev*, authored by a grandson of the Ba'al Shem Tov, as well as a report recorded in a work entitled *Shomer Emunim*. In actuality, the point is amply established by the statement of the Palestinian Talmud, *Ḥaggigah* 2:1, as cited in the text.
32. See, however, *Me-Shulḥan Gevoha, Va-Yikra*, p. 91, who reports that R. Yitzchak Zev Soloveitchik asserted that forbidden foods do not cause *timtum ha-lev* unless consumption of the foodstuff entails an actual halakhic infraction. Cf., *Teshuvot Ḥatam Sofer, Oraḥ Ḥayyim*, no, 83. *Teshuvot Rav Pe'alim*, IV,

Sod Yesharim, no. 6, similarly declares that no harm can result from inadvertent consumption of forbidden foodstuffs in situations in which such ingestion of a forbidden food could not have been foreseen. That view seems to be contradicted by the further statement of Rema, *Yoreh De'ah* 81:7; "Similarly, even a Jewish nursing woman should not eat forbidden things." *Taz*, *Yoreh De'ah* 81:12 and *Shakh*, *Yoreh De'ah* 81:25, explain that Rema is speaking of a woman who is halakhically permitted to partake of forbidden foods. They understood Rema as advising that, despite the permissibility of her conduct in this regard, she should not nurse an infant because of considerations of *timtum ha-lev*. R. Meir Simchah Ha-Kohen of Dvinsk, *Meshekh Ḥokhmah*, Deuteronomy 6:10–11, explains those verses as reflecting the concept that the phenomenon of *timtum ha-lev* is present even in situations involving no transgression.

Cf., R. Abraham Rubin, *Or Yisra'el*, no. 16 (Tammuz 5759), who cites Maharal of Prague, *Tiferet Yisra'el*, chap. 8, as asserting that *timtum ha-lev* is attendant only upon culpable transgression. This writer does not concur in that understanding of *Tiferet Yisra'el*. In that discussion, *Tiferet Yisra'el* develops the thesis that the dietary code is not predicated upon considerations of health. In that context Maharal comments that, were dietary laws designed to serve as health regulations, the Torah could not possibly have permitted forbidden foods in conjunction with war: "If the root of the prohibition is because of *mezeg ra*, whither did the prohibition go?" *Tiferet Yisra'el*'s point is only that the prohibition cannot be regarded as a health measure because, were the prohibition to be regarded in that light, since the nature of the foodstuff does not change, in time of war the prohibition would not have been suspended. Quite to the contrary, *Tiferet Yisra'el* must be understood as stating that otherwise forbidden foodstuffs may have deleterious effects even when they are permitted, e.g., in time of war. Cf., the earlier cited comments of *Meshekh Ḥokhmah*. See also R. Pesach Fried, *Or Yisra'el*, no. 18 (Tevet 5760).

Rabbenu Nissim of Gerodi, *Derashot ha-Ran*, *drush* 11, s.v. *ve-ani sover*, makes the interesting point that a food erroneously declared permissible by the *Sanhedrin* can cause no harm to a person who follows the *Sanhedrin*'s ruling. For a discussion of *timtum ha-lev* with regard to foods rendered permissible by reason of adulteration, see *Pitḥei Teshuvah, Yoreh De'ah* 116:10; R. Menasheh Klein, *Mishneh Halakhot*, VII, no. 104; and R. Yosef Yitzchak Lerner, *Shemirat ha-Guf ve-ha-Nefesh* (New York, 5748), introduction, chap. 13. Cf., *Mishneh Halakhot*, V, no. 101.

6

Palliation of Pain

Dr. Richard Chapman, a past president of the American Pain Society, reports that in only one in four of the approximately twenty-three million surgical procedures performed in the United States annually does the patient receive adequate relief. Put somewhat differently, three out of every four patients who undergo an operation in the United States can anticipate experiencing pain needlessly. Moreover, each year Americans incur more than sixty-five million traumatic injuries, including two million burns, and millions more are afflicted by diseases that cause acute pain.[1]

Of fifty million people in the United States who experience chronic pain, four in ten, i.e., forty percent, of those who suffer moderate to severe pain cannot find adequate relief. More than twenty-six million people twenty to sixty-four years of age have frequent or persistent back-pain and one in six Americans suffers from painful arthritis. *In toto*, many, many people experience a great deal of pain. But only about thirty percent of all patients who experience pain receive adequate pain relief. There are tens of millions of patients who experience pain that might be palliated but who, unfortunately, are not treated adequately.[2]

Professor Perry Fine, an anesthesiologist at the medical school of the University of Utah and associate director of a pain management center in Salt Lake City, explains why this is the case: Half the population may experience pregnancy.

Nature has decreed that only females can become pregnant. Males do not go through pregnancy—the motion picture "Junior" notwithstanding. Yet a hundred percent of board certified students must pass medical boards in obstetrics and gynecology. In contradistinction to pregnancy, one hundred percent of the population is at risk for pain. But how many physicians are required to demonstrate proficiency in pain management? The answer is that zero percent of medical students or of practicing physicians must undergo examination in pain palliation.[3] This situation is only now beginning to change in the United States. The Joint Commission on Accreditation of Health Care Organizations has formulated standards for pain management which formally went into effect on January 1, 2001. Although that development signals a marked improvement in a patient's prospects for receiving adequate pain relief, it is hardly a panacea.

I. THE OBLIGATION TO RELIEVE PAIN

The halakhic obligation to relieve pain must be examined first in terms of the general obligation with regard to palliation of pain and then with regard to treatment of pain in the terminally ill. The obligation to provide medical care in order to cure disease stems from a variety of sources. The Gemara, *Bava Kamma* 85a, cites the verse "And he shall surely cause him to be healed" (Exodus 21:19) as a grant of authority establishing licensure to practice the healing arts. Rambam, both in his *Commentary on the Mishnah*, *Nedarim* 4:4, and in the *Mishneh Torah*, *Hilkhot Nedarim* 6:8, adduces the verse "and you shall restore it to him" (Deuteronomy 22:2) as the source of the obligation to heal. Ramban, in his *Torat ha-Adam*,[4] finds that, in addition to whatever other obligations that may exist with regard to the treatment of the sick, the obligation of the physician to treat a suffering patient is inherent in the commandment "and you shall love your neighbor as yourself" (Leviticus 19:18). As a specific instance of the general obligation to manifest love and concern for one's neighbor, the obligation to heal encompasses not only alleviation of a threat to life or limb and restoration of impaired health but also extends to situations of lesser gravity that warrant medical attention for relief of pain and promotion of well-being. No one wishes to suffer pain; hence there is an obligation not to allow the pain of one's fellow to go untreated.

A latter-day authority, R. Yehudah Leib Zirelson, in his *Teshuvot Aẓei ha-Levanon*, no. 61, argues cogently that the obligations of rescue posited by the Gemara, *Sanhedrin* 73a, apply under non-life-threatening circumstances no less than in life-threatening situations. The verse "and you shall restore it to him" (Deuteronomy 22:2) mandates not only the return of lost property but, *a fortiori*, preservation of life as well. The verse, then, does not refer only to the return of objects of material value. Accordingly, declares *Aẓei ha-Levanon*, restoration of health to a person suffering from an illness is assuredly included in the commandment "and you shall restore it to him." *Aẓei ha-Levanon* further demonstrates that failure to provide a medical remedy, when available, entails violation both of the commandment "you may not hide yourself" (Deuteronomy 22:3), which, in its biblical context, refers to a person who comes upon lost property belonging to another, and the admonition "nor shall you stand idly by the blood of your fellow" (Leviticus 19:16). *Sifra, Kedoshim* 41, declares that those commandments establish an obligation making it incumbent upon an individual to act, if he is capable of doing so, in order to prevent his fellow from sustaining a financial loss. This obligation is recorded by Rambam, *Hilkhot Roẓeaḥ* 1:13; *Sefer ha-Ḥinnukh*, no. 237; and *Shulḥan Arukh, Ḥoshen Mishpat* 426:1. It similarly follows that a person is bound by the same commandments to prevent loss or deterioration of health if he possesses the requisite knowledge and skill to be of assistance in providing medical care. Failure to do so, concludes *Aẓei ha-Levanon*, would constitute transgression of those two negative commandments as well as of the positive commandment "and you shall restore it to him." The obligations requiring a person to restore his fellow to a state of good health should logically also mandate restoration to a pain-free state.

Indeed, a much earlier authority, R. David ibn Zimra, *Teshuvot Radvaz*, II, no. 628, declares explicitly that a person is obliged to come to the assistance of an individual in distress due to being weighed down by an excessive burden both because of the obligation to restore "the loss of his body" and because of the commandment "you shall not stand idly by the blood of your fellow." According to *Teshuvot Radvaz*, relief of pain and suffering is mandated not only by the commandment to restore that which has been lost but also by the admonition not to "stand idly by the blood of your fellow."[5]

Although it is quite apparent that alleviation of pain is integral to the physician's halakhic obligation to minister to the sick, unfortunately, such recognition is not reflected in the mores of the medical profession. Physicians, at least until recently, certainly have not regarded palliation of pain as a primary responsibility. An entirely different perspective emerges from the comments of R. Judah the Pious recorded in his *Sefer Ḥasidim*, no. 666, who declares that a person is punished for any pain or anguish he causes his fellow.[6] *Sefer Ḥasidim*, no. 676, further declares that a person is culpable for harm that he does to himself just as he is culpable for harm that he causes his fellow. The author of *Sefer Ḥasidim* proceeds to enumerate various forms of harm including physical and financial harm as well as "tearing his hair" as examples of prohibited forms of self-inflicted harm. Tearing one's hair is an example of self-inflicted pain and represents a form of pain that one dare not inflict upon others or upon oneself. Most striking is *Sefer Ḥasidim*'s concluding comment that a person who performs such an act "is not liable at the hands of man but his punishment is turned over to Heaven, as it is said,

'But your blood from your souls will I require' (Genesis 9:5)." Classical rabbinic sources regard this verse as the source of the prohibition against suicide. *Sefer Ḥasidim*, in an expansive interpretation of the verse, regards self-mutilation, negligence in exposing oneself to disease, as well as exposing oneself to pain, as constituting a form of demi-suicide. Any interference with the well-being of the human organism, according to *Sefer Ḥasidim*, represents a form of self-destruction; and self-destruction, *Sefer Ḥasidim* maintains, is prohibited not only in whole but in part as well.

It might, of course, be argued that suicide is limited to self-destruction by means of an overt act and that, according to *Sefer Ḥasidim*, strictures against infliction of harm are similarly limited to matters such as taking a knife and mutilating one's body or causing oneself pain in an active, overt manner, but that passive non-intervention in the face of pain might be acceptable. That, however, turns out not to be the case.

Rambam, *Hilkhot Shevu'ot* 5:20, codifies a presumption that a person cannot survive for a period of more than seven days without food. Consequently, a person who swears an oath to abstain from all food for seven days will face death before that time expires. Violation of an oath is required when necessary for purposes of preserving life. There is certainly no question that as soon as his life becomes endangered and he actually faces death by starvation, a person who has sworn to abstain from food must break his fast despite any oath he has taken. Rambam, however, adopts the position that since it can be predicted with certainty that the oath will not be fulfilled because of the threat to life that will certainly ensue, the oath must be regarded as a *shevu'at shav*, i.e., a vain oath. Swearing an oath that is vain because it cannot possibly be fulfilled is a punishable offense but the oath itself is a nullity. Accordingly, Rambam rules that such a person is subject to the statutory punishment for having sworn a vain oath, but since the oath itself is null and void *ab initio*, he need not wait to eat until his life is endangered because of imminent starvation; instead, he may partake of food immediately.

Rabbenu Nissim, in his commentary on *Shevu'ot* 25a, concurs with Rambam's ruling but for an entirely different reason. Rabbenu Nissim declares that a person who swears not to partake of food for a period of seven days has, in effect, taken an oath to violate a biblical law, i.e., he has sworn to put himself to death. An oath to commit a transgression does not give rise to license to commit that transgression. On the contrary, the oath is a nullity and the person is to be punished for having sworn a vain oath. An oath not to eat for seven days, declares Rabbenu Nissim, is a vain oath because it is in contravention of the biblical admonition "but your blood of your lives will I require," i.e., the prohibition against suicide. It should be noted that a person who starves himself to death commits suicide but does so only passively. Thus Rabbenu Nissim declares that passive suicide is also a proscribed form of self-destruction. Since the selfsame biblical verse that serves as a prohibition against active suicide also applies to passive suicide, it follows that the penalty provided for suicide in that verse applies to passive suicide as well.

Rabbenu Nissim's comments certainly establish unequivocally that the prohibition expressed in the phrase "but your blood of your lives will I require" applies equally to both overt acts and to passive acts. It is an elementary principle of logic that if A equals B and B equals C, then A must equal C as well. If, as *Sefer Ḥasidim* declares, infliction of pain is tantamount to demi-suicide, then even passive refusal to palliate pain, insofar as *Sefer Ḥasidim* is concerned, must also be regarded as prohibited on the basis of the verse "but your blood from your souls will I require." Thus, this biblical verse must be understood as commanding the patient to seek pain palliation. By the same token, the physician who provides such relief has, at the very minimum, performed the meritorious deed of assisting the patient in fulfilling a biblical obligation.

The obligation to seek relief of pain can be established on the basis of yet another source as well. The Gemara, *Ta'anit* 11a, records a controversy with regard to whether an individual who chooses to become a Nazarite is to be regarded as a *kadosh*, a holy individual, or whether he is to be regarded as a *ḥoteh*, a transgressor, because he denies himself the pleasures of the grape and its derivatives. The Gemara then proceeds to declare that, if a person who denies himself only wine is a transgressor, then, *a fortiori*, a person who fasts without good reason, i.e., a person who abstains from all food, is a transgressor. By the same token, if a person who merely denies himself the single pleasure of the fruit of the vine and its liquor is considered to have committed a transgression, then an individual who engages in self-mortification or who needlessly allows himself to remain in a state of pain is certainly a transgressor.

The Gemara further declares that, even according to the opinion that deems the Nazarite to have attained a state of holiness, a Nazarite can be deemed to be holy only if his self-denial does not cause him undue distress. If, however, the Nazarite's distress is severe ("*lo moẓi le-ẓe'urei nafsheih*"), all concede that he is a transgressor. *Shulḥan Arukh, Oraḥ Ḥayyim* 571:1, rules that a person who fasts but for whom the fast is onerous, i.e. "he is not healthy and strong," is a sinner. Similarly, a person is not permitted to assume the obligation of a non-mandatory fast if, as a result of abstaining from nourishment, his ability to engage in the "work of Heaven" will be diminished. Failure to seek palliation of pain is entirely comparable to failure to seek food and water. Such conduct, despite its passive nature, is sinful when the result is either severe and inordinate discomfort or diminution of the "work of Heaven."

The obligation to relieve pain is recorded in *Shulḥan Arukh*, albeit in a rather obscure and indirect manner. There is no section in *Shulḥan Arukh* that addresses palliation of pain explicitly. However, *Shulḥan Arukh* does record a ruling with regard to bloodletting of a father by his son. "Wounding" a father or mother, i.e., inflicting a trauma that causes bleeding, is ordinarily a capital crime. Nevertheless, Rema, *Yoreh De'ah* 241:3, rules that bloodletting, surgery or even amputating a limb of a parent is permitted but only when there is no other physician available. It is noteworthy that, in formulating that ruling, Rema does not justify bloodletting or performance of surgery by a son because the procedure is necessary to preserve a human life or even to cure a malady. Instead, Rema declares that the son may engage in bloodletting or a surgical procedure "if there is no other [physician] there to perform [the procedure] and the father is in pain." The implication of Rema's comment is, even if the procedure will have no effect upon the course of the underlying disease or malady, the son may nevertheless engage in an otherwise forbidden act of "wounding" simply in order to relieve the father's pain. If a son may treat the father under those circumstances solely in order to palliate pain, clearly, there must be an obligation to alleviate pain if it is in the power of the physician to do so.

Alleviation of pain and suffering is certainly commendable. Even in the absence of a particular halakhically mandated obligation, relief of pain should be aggressively pursued simply because it is the humane thing to do. The Psalmist declares of God: "and His mercy is upon all His creatures" (Psalms 145:9). The verse "And you shall walk in His ways" (Deuteronomy 28:9), declares the Gemara, *Shabbat* 123b, obliges man to emulate the ways of God. Rambam, *Hilkhot De'ot* 1:6, understands this obligation as requiring man to emulate the traits of the Deity: "Just as He is merciful, so be you merciful." The doctrine of *imitatio Dei* demands that a person act in a humane manner because, in doing so he shares, at least in a minuscule fashion, in the divine attributes.

II. PALLIATION OF PAIN IN THE TERMINALLY ILL

Palliation of pain in the terminally ill presents a much more difficult and complex issue. It is a much more difficult question because, in treating the terminally ill, palliation of pain may at times come into conflict with other *desiderata*. The preamble of the Declaration of Independence reveals that the Founding Fathers believed that "all men are endowed by their Creator with certain unalienable rights, among them life, liberty and the pursuit of happiness." Happiness is certainly a human value. But happiness is a dual-faced coin; sometimes it is positive, and sometimes it is found in the absence of a negative. Sometimes happiness is found in eating, drinking and making merry; but sometimes happiness lies simply in the alleviation of pain. Suffering is the antithesis of happiness and no one can be happy while in a state of anguish. Elimination of pain and suffering is one way of promoting happiness.

Life, liberty and happiness are human values. But there are times when those values come into conflict with one another. Sometimes there is a conflict between preservation of life and preservation of happiness, if happiness is defined as the elimination of pain. Sometimes the only way in which pain can be eliminated is by extinguishing life, either overtly through active euthanasia or passively by allowing the patient to die. In some circumstances the only effective pain palliation is eternal slumber.

Among American revolutionaries, Patrick Henry declaimed, "Give me liberty or give me death!" In doing so, he sought to give primacy to the value of liberty over other values, including life itself. Today, given the mores of contemporary society, the slogan might well be "Give me liberty *and* give me death!" In the bioethical context, the demand for death in the form of euthanasia or physician-assisted suicide is clothed in assertion of a right to liberty. However, the demand for liberty in the guise of patient autonomy is a demand for the right to choose death not necessarily because autonomy is perceived as the cardinal human value but often because of its instrumental value in assuring happiness in the form of alleviation of pain.

In Western culture there is general agreement with regard to delineation of moral values. Palliation of pain is a value in virtually all systems of ethics. Moral dilemmas occur when ethical values come into conflict with one another. Every ethical system must either establish a hierarchy of values so that a moral agent will know immediately which value must be given priority or else it must establish a set of canons or rules which will allow a moral agent to adjudicate between conflicting values. When ethicists talk about values, they do so with a *ceteris paribus* clause. All things being equal, we value motherhood and apple pie but, in the real world, it is seldom that all things are equal. The necessary result is that ethical values frequently come into conflict with one another. Relief of pain may, at times, present precisely such a dilemma. How is one to act when relief of pain can be achieved only at the cost of termination of life itself?

Robin Hood is a children's story and children perceive it as such. But a thoughtful adult who reads the story to his or her children must realize that it is not a children's story at all but a profound ethical treatise. The narrative, as everyone knows, recounts how Robin Hood steals from the Sheriff of Nottingham, but he does not steal because he is avaricious and wishes to enrich himself. Robin Hood steals because he is concerned for the plight of starving orphans and widows and he has no way to provide relief for them other than by appropriating property that belongs to the Sheriff of Nottingham. Now, Robin Hood recognizes full well that there exists a moral right to enjoyment of one's property; he accepts the binding nature of the commandment "*lo tignovu*—you shall not steal" (Leviticus 19:11). Presumably, the Sheriff of Nottingham not only accepts the commandment "*lo tirẓaḥ*—you shall not commit murder" (Exodus 20:13) but also recognizes the moral value reflected in "*lo ta'amod al dam re'ekha*—you shall not stand idly by the blood of your fellow" (Leviticus 19:16). The situation presents a conflict between two values—the preservation of life versus the preservation of property. And how is that conflict resolved? Apparently, the Sheriff of Nottingham thinks that the preservation of property represents a higher value than preservation of life, at least when the property to be preserved is that of the Sheriff of Nottingham.

All things being equal, the Sheriff of Nottingham would be happy to see the starving widows and orphans provided for, but not at his expense. Robin Hood, on the other hand, regards the preservation of the lives of starving orphans and widows to be a more compelling moral value than respect for the property of others. Both Robin Hood and the Sheriff of Nottingham subscribe to the same set of moral values, but each posits a different hierarchical ranking of those values so that, in the real world, when those values conflict, as they surely must, one acts in accordance with one value and the other acts in accordance with a different value.

It is noteworthy that one of the members of Robin Hood's band was Friar Tuck. One may ask, what was Friar Tuck's role in this group? It is not at all far-fetched to assume that Friar Tuck was present in the role of a professor of moral theology; he was there to give a *hekhsher shtempel*, an ecclesiastic imprimatur, to Robin Hood's value system as opposed to that of the Sheriff of Nottingham. Had a rabbinic figure been present rather than Friar Tuck, he would have adopted exactly the same position and would have ruled that preservation of life represents a cardinal value, and hence preservation of life takes precedence over preservation of property.[7] A rabbinic decisor, however, would have found it necessary to address the question of whether Robin Hood[8] and/or the beneficiaries of his largesse would have been obligated to make restitution to the Sheriff of Nottingham at such time as it became financially possible for them to do so.[9] Putting that point aside, preservation of life takes precedence even over promotion of happiness because, in the Jewish system of values, it is preservation of life which is the supreme value.

In some circles "vitalism" is a term of derision, but that should not be the case among Jews. On the contrary, it should be stated loudly and clearly that Jews are vitalists. We need not be ashamed of the fact that Judaism is a religion of vitalism and regards human life as being endowed with a value that far surpasses virtually all other values.

To state that preservation of life is a cardinal value is not to declare that life must be preserved in any and all circumstances. The few exceptions to the primacy of the preservation of life must be spelled out with precision. One such exception does exist, at least in theory, in the case of a patient who suffers intractable pain. In theory, there is no obligation, in the opinion of this writer, to treat a patient who suffers excruciating pain that cannot be palliated. Although active euthanasia cannot be countenanced in any circumstances, withdrawal of treatment is warranted in such situations, at least in theory.

There is a remarkable responsum authored by R. Moshe Feinstein, published in *Iggerot Mosheh, Yoreh De'ah*, II, no. 174, sec. 4. The issue concerned a requirement for the consent of next of kin for removal of an organ from a cadaver for the purpose of transplantation. To place the matter in historical context, the responsum was written at a time at which there was a furor with regard to autopsy practices in Israel. The demand was put forth that pathologists not be authorized by law to perform post-mortem examinations other than with consent of next of kin.

That proposal created a backlash. There was some agitation against the proposal even in rabbinic circles because, basically, insofar as Jewish law is concerned, autopsies are sanctioned in instances in which the information to be derived is necessary for *pikuaḥ nefesh*, i.e., in order to save a person's life. Preservation of life supercedes the dignity that must be accorded to a corpse reflected in the prohibition against desecration of the dead. Since it is the overriding consideration of preservation of life that governs, a life-saving organ, for example, may be recovered from the body without prior consent of the deceased during his lifetime. It would therefore seem that consent of next of kin is similarly not required.

At the time, rabbinic spokesmen took the position that consent of next of kin should be mandatory but that position appeared to many to be grounded in *Realpolitik* rather than in halakhic prerogatives. The argument was that since, in virtually all democratic countries, consent of kin is required, Israel should be no different. Basically, and for good reason, the rabbinic activists did not trust the medical establishment to perform post-mortem examinations only in situations of genuine *pikuaḥ nefesh* and, consequently, sought to establish a legal requirement for consent of next of kin as a means of preventing halakhically unjustified post-mortem procedures.

Iggerot Mosheh, however, asserts that consent of next of kin is required as an intrinsic matter of Halakhah. In support of that position he cites a rabbinic leniency with regard to conduct in the wake of a fire that breaks out on *Shabbat*. A corpse is regarded as *mukẓah* on *Shabbat* and ordinarily may not be moved. Nevertheless, the Gemara, *Shabbat* 43b, declares that it is permissible to remove a corpse in order to place the body outside the range of the fire. The Gemara justifies this exception to the rabbinic prohibition against moving a corpse on *Shabbat* on the grounds that *adam bahul al meto*, i.e., a person becomes extremely distraught when confronted by a situation in which a loved one is about to be incinerated before his very eyes. Therefore, the Sages sanctioned what would otherwise have been a violation of a rabbinic prohibition because of their recognition that the individual who becomes *bahul*, agitated and excited, is quite likely to transgress a halakhic prohibition in his agitation. Accordingly, they suspended the prohibition against the movement of *mukẓah* in order to assuage the quite normal agitation attendant upon such a situation.

Iggerot Mosheh, however, points to a psychological observation noted by *Tosafot*, *Shabbat* 44a. There is something remarkable in what the Gemara does not say. There is no similar dispensation for a person who has secreted his life's savings under his mattress and who now is confronted by a conflagration that is about to engulf the mattress. That individual is certainly agitated and in a state of stress. The banknotes hidden under his mattress are *mukẓah*. If he is not permitted to move them to a safe place, he may well become even more agitated, lose his head and in his confusion seek to preserve his fortune by seizing the money and transporting it through a public thoroughfare. Yet we find no dispensation to move the currency to a safe place even within a private domain. Even more striking is that, as recorded in the Mishnah, *Shabbat* 117b, with the exception of the quantity of food ordinarily consumed in the course of the *Shabbat* day, the Sages forbade a person to rescue even non-*mukẓah* items from a fire. The Gemara explains that they promulgated such an edict because of a fear that, if they were to permit a person to preserve his property from a conflagration even in a permissible manner, he might, in his agitation and confusion, unwittingly attempt to quench the flames.

Why did the Sages suspend the prohibition against moving a corpse in the case of fire but forbid the preservation of property that, in identical circumstances, could be rescued without any violation of Sabbath strictures whatsoever? It must be remembered that the prohibition against rescuing property from a fire on *Shabbat* remains in place even if as a result a person's entire fortune will go up in flames. The conclusion to be drawn, observe *Tosafot*, is that there are individuals who suffer far more distress at the sight of mutilation of the corpse of a loved one than they would experience upon the loss of their entire fortune. Accordingly, the Sages found it necessary to suspend the prohibition against moving an object that is *mukẓah* in situations in which a corpse would otherwise be ravaged by fire but did not do so, and indeed found it inadvisable to do so, when the prospect was only loss of a fortune.[10]

According to some authorities, it is a principle of Halakhah that a person is required to surrender his entire fortune for purposes of rescuing a person from death; according to other authorities, a person is obliged to expend only twenty percent of the value of his net worth in order to preserve the life of another.[11] However, no authority regards it as obligatory for any person to expend more than his entire fortune in such an endeavor.[12]

Limiting financial liability to the expenditure of no more than one's fortune may serve to negate an obligation to borrow funds in excess of one's net worth for such purpose. However, capping liability at the value of one's entire fortune establishes another ceiling as well. A person may not be called upon to expend money, but may find himself in a situation in which he is called upon to suffer intractable pain or emotional anguish of such severity that, if given the choice, he would cheerfully part with his entire fortune and go into debt in order to avoid the suffering. A person who would give more than his entire fortune in order to alleviate such pain, argues *Iggerot Mosheh*, need not accept the onus of such pain for purposes of rescuing the life of another. In effect, declares *Iggerot Mosheh*, a person may be obligated to expend his entire fortune in order to save a life, but not more than his entire fortune. Accordingly, he maintains, a person who would willingly surrender his entire fortune in order to prevent an autopsy or in order to prevent removal of an organ from the corpse of a loved one need not consent to such a procedure even in life-threatening circumstances. For some people, defilement of the corpse of a close relative may cause more anguish than the loss of an entire fortune. Consequently, rules *Iggerot Mosheh*, since a relative may legitimately object to a cadaveric organ transplant, informed consent of the relatives is required. *Iggerot Mosheh* quite understandably adds that, in cases of *pikuaḥ nefesh*, surviving relatives should be encouraged to give their consent and should be assured that to do so is extremely meritorious and constitutes a great *miẓvah*. Nevertheless, a relative who withholds consent is acting within his halakhic rights in refusing his cooperation.[13]

Further evidence demonstrating that some forms of suffering are more onerous than loss of an entire fortune may be adduced on the basis of a comment of an anonymous medieval scholar cited in *Shitah Mekubbeẓet*, *Ketubot* 33b, and identified simply as the author of the *kuntresin* or notebooks. The Gemara, *ad locum*, affirms that, as recorded in Daniel 3:13–23, Hananiah, Mishael and Azariah (referred to in Scripture as Shadrach, Meshach and Abed-nego)[14] did indeed accept martyrdom rather than transgress the prohibition against idolatry but that, had they been subjected to torture, they would have succumbed and worshipped the idol. *Tosafot* and other talmudic commentators object that idolatry is one of the three cardinal transgressions and, accordingly, one is obligated to suffer martyrdom under any and all circumstances rather than violate the commandment prohibiting idolatry. Those commentators advance various solutions to the problem based upon the general thesis that the act Hananiah, Mishael and Azariah were ordered to perform was not, in actuality, an act of idol worship.

The anonymous author of the *kuntresin* cited by *Shitah Mekubbeẓet* resolves the matter in an entirely different way. That authority argues that the obligation to suffer martyrdom derived from the verse "And you shall love the Lord your God . . . and with all your soul" (Deuteronomy 6:5) requires even the sacrifice of one's life in order to avoid an act of idolatry but does not require a sacrifice greater than that of the sacrifice of one's life. Torture, argues this authority, is more onerous than surrender of one's life and hence acceptance of torture is not demanded of a person even if it can be avoided only by an act of idolatry.[15] According to the author of the *kuntresin*, it is quite clear that excruciating pain need not be endured to avoid a transgression for which martyrdom need not be accepted. If such pain is more onerous than death, *a fortiori*, it must be regarded as more onerous than loss of all of one's material possessions.

Failure on the part of *Tosafot* and other early-day authorities to resolve their perplexity by advancing the view propounded by the author of the *kuntresin* certainly indicates their disagreement with that position. Those scholars apparently accept the notion that the obligation to suffer martyrdom entails an obligation to accept extreme and enduring pain. However, although they reject the notion that extreme pain need not be endured even in situations requiring surrender of one's life, there is ample reason to assume that they would concede that extreme pain is more onerous than expenditure of an entire fortune. Indeed, *Tiferet Yisra'el*, *Yoma*, *Bo'az* 8:3, cites the talmudic statement with regard to Hananiah, Mishael and Azariah as demonstrating that "great pain is more onerous than death" in arguing that there is no obligation to seek prolongation of life in circumstances of extreme pain.

It is thus clear from the comments of both *Tiferet Yisra'el* and *Iggerot Mosheh* that a patient who suffers intractable pain of a nature such that he would consider it well worth surrendering his entire fortune in order to avoid the torment does not have an obligation to accept such suffering for the purpose of prolonging his life.[16] The patient's obligation to preserve his own life requires expenditure of funds and for many authorities that obligation would require him to sign over his entire fortune if necessary to achieve that purpose but does not require expenditure of more than his entire fortune. Nor, it would seem, can such a burden be placed upon him by others. Accordingly, since the patient is under no obligation to accept ongoing intractable pain as the cost of prolonging his life, others do not have the right to impose such a burden upon him against his will. Of course, active euthanasia involving an overt act is prohibited even in such extreme circumstances, but passive withholding of treatment would be acceptable in cases of intractable pain of such magnitude.

Although it is subject to dispute, one explanation of the concept of a *goses*, i.e., a moribund patient as defined by Halakhah, and of why it is permissible to withdraw some types of treatment from a *goses* is based upon the notion that Halakhah postulates that a *goses* suffers some type of extreme metaphysical anguish. Halakhah does indeed recognize the phenomenon of metaphysical anguish at the moment of *yeẓi'at ha-nefesh*, the moment at which the soul departs from the body. Although the matter is open to dispute, some scholars maintain that such suffering is experienced not only at the moment of disassociation of the soul from the body but during the entire course of the terminal period. According to this hypothesis, justification for withholding treatment from a *goses* is based upon the consideration that metaphysical anguish during the period of *gesisah* involves expenditure of a non-monetary coin greater than the value of one's entire fortune. Such anguish is so great that the patient is not required, and cannot be expected, to suffer it with equanimity even for the purpose of prolongation of life.[17] Thus, treatment may be withheld because the patient need not accept pain of such magnitude for purposes of prolonging life.

It cannot be overly emphasized that the obligation of *pikuaḥ nefesh* in Jewish law is not limited to effecting a cure or even to enabling a patient to be discharged from a hospital; the obligation is equally binding even in situations in which it is clear that the patient will remain non-sapient and in which the patient's life will be preserved only ephemerally. There is an obligation to prolong life of even a terminally-ill patient and the quality of the life that is prolonged is not a determining factor in establishing the ambit of the obligation. Nevertheless, it remains true that, when the patient is afflicted by intractable pain such that the patient would cheerfully surrender even more than his entire fortune, there is no obligation to prolong the life of the patient. That, however, is true in theory; it is generally not true in practice.

Why is it not true in practice? Dr. Porter Storey reports that the findings of a study involving some two thousand terminally ill patients demonstrate that patients can be effectively and safely palliated by administrating narcotic analgesics provided that the dosages are carefully titrated against the symptoms.[18] Numerous other studies have been published over the past decade that indicate that narcotics can be administered for palliation of pain in a careful and sustained manner without risk to the patient. In an *amicus* brief submitted to the Supreme Court in *Washington v. Glucksberg*, the American Medical Association stated that "the pain of most terminally ill patients can be controlled throughout the dying process without heavy sedation or anesthesia."[19] A manual published by the Washington Medical Association reports that "adequate interventions exist to control pain in 90–99% of patients."[20] Oral information received from physicians prominent in the field of pain palliation indicates that 99% is probably a more accurate figure. In particular, chronic pain caused by various forms of carcinoma can be relieved and the patient should not be allowed to suffer unnecessarily. To be sure, there are cases in which pain may prove to be intractable, e.g., myeloma. One expert has informed me that some facial tumors involve certain sets of nerves that do not respond to pain inhibitors but even that gentleman conceded that such cases are extremely rare. Hence, it may be stated that, in the vast majority of cases, the point at which the patient need suffer this type of intractable pain is never reached. And, it must be remembered, in situations in which pain can be controlled there is a halakhic obligation to alleviate suffering by controlling pain.

III. RISK-TAKING FOR PAIN PALLIATION

Despite the plethora of medical evidence demonstrating that pain can be palliated with minimal risk of foreshortening the life of the patient,[21] it is widely presumed that pain relief is hazardous. Moreover, it is generally assumed that, despite the risk involved, it is halakhically acceptable to use methods of pain palliation that may shorten the life of the patient despite the fact that, as a general rule, Jewish law requires that the life of a patient be prolonged to the fullest extent possible.

There is discussion in halakhic literature of use of potentially hazardous analgesics even in situations that do not involve *pikuaḥ nefesh*, i.e., in situations in which the underlying disease presents no risk to the life of the patient but in which the medical condition does cause pain or discomfort. At least one authority, Rabbi Jacob Emden, *Mor u-Keẓi'ah* 328, discusses a proposed surgical procedure that he correctly or incorrectly understood as not required for alleviation of a life-threatening condition but that was being considered solely for purposes of pain palliation. The procedure in question seems to have been an operation for removal of gallstones. Referring to that procedure, R. Jacob Emden declares, "*Karov be-einai le'esor*—In my eyes it is close to being forbidden." Rabbi Emden's words are chosen with care: A matter that is "close to being forbidden" is not actually prohibited. Permissibility may not be obvious; permissibility may not even be beyond doubt. The proposed cause of action may perhaps not be commendable or even compatible with a halakhic value system, but it is not unequivocally forbidden. Although he refuses to encourage the procedure, R. Jacob Emden stops short of forbidding placing one's life at risk in order to obtain relief from pain.

The permissibility of self-endangerment for purposes of palliation of pain is evident from the earlier-cited ruling of Rema, *Yoreh De'ah* 241:3, permitting a son to perform surgery and even to amputate his father's limb in the absence of another qualified physician. As already noted, Rema justifies such intervention by a son, not because of fear that failure to intervene will result in the loss of the father's life, but because the father is in pain. Even today, surgical amputation of a limb involves a recognized degree of risk. In the sixteenth century, when Rema penned that ruling, the risk to life was quite high. On the basis of terminology employed by Rema, it is abundantly clear that he sanctions the hazardous surgical procedure simply to alleviate pain. In effect, Rema rules that one may assume certain risks even for the purpose of alleviating pain, despite the fact that the underlying pathology presents no danger to the patient. In actuality, a similar statement appears in the talmudic commentary of an earlier medieval authority, R. Menachem ha-Me'iri, *Bet ha-Beḥirah, Sanhedrin* 84a. Although Me'iri's commentary was not available to Rema, the principle formulated therein seems to have been well-known and accepted. Indeed, there seems to be no dispute with regard to the ruling formulated by Me'iri and Rema.

There is, of course, a general prohibition against self-endangerment derived from the verse "And you shall be exceedingly watchful over your lives" (Deuteronomy 4:15). The right to assume a measure of danger in order to escape pain is an exception to that prohibition. The theory upon which that exception is based is not spelled out by either Me'iri or Rema but such justification does not appear to be elusive. Dispensation, and hence the obligation, to practice medicine is derived from the verse "*ve-rapo yerape*—and he shall surely cause him to be healed" (Exodus 21:19). In its biblical formulation, the obligation to heal does not occur in the context of what is necessarily a case of *pikuaḥ nefesh*. The phrase "*ve-rapo yerape*" occurs in the biblical section dealing with the financial liability of a person who has committed an act of mayhem and is consequently called upon to make compensation for the physical danger caused by his battery. The injury suffered by the victim is not necessarily life-threatening. Since Scripture provides that the victim may recover damages, including medical expenses, the clear inference is that the physician may minister to the patient. What condition is the physician treating? The physician is caring for a patient who has suffered a non-terminal trauma. Yet Halakhah appreciates the fact that no therapy is entirely free of danger. Rabbenu Nissim, *Sanhedrin* 84b, observes, "All modes of therapy are a danger for the patient for it is possible that, if the practitioner errs with regard to a specific drug, it will kill the patient." Ramban, in his *Torat ha-Adam*, states even more explicitly, "With regard to cures there is naught but danger; what heals one kills another."[22] Since the physician is granted the right to treat even patients whose lives are not in danger even though the treatment is accompanied by an element of risk, and since palliation of pain is included in the physician's obligation *vis-à-vis* the patient, it follows that at least some hazards may be accepted even for the purpose of eliminating pain. Certainly, assumption of untoward risks for palliation of pain is not acceptable just as untoward risk is not acceptable in treatment of the underlying malady. Principles of prudence apply to pain relief just as they apply to therapeutic procedures having the potential of foreshortening life. Risks that are ordinary and usual and which would be accepted by a prudent person may be assumed in order to alleviate the pain that the patient suffers.

There are even stronger grounds to support risk-taking in the palliation of pain suffered by the terminally ill. Jewish law postulates a halakhic presumption that pain itself poses a danger of foreshortening life. Halakhah recognizes that *tiruf ha-da'at,* i.e., despondency, shock and emotional anguish, can cause death, or at least hasten the demise, of a dying patient. There are reports in the medical literature of a phenomenon known as "voodoo death," which is simply one form of *tiruf ha-da'at*, that may hasten death.[23] Similarly, *Mishnah Berurah*

328:13 rules that, if an infant is locked in a room on *Shabbat*, the door must be broken down without delay lest fear and shock cause the child to die.

If emotional anguish and agitation can hasten death, it should not be surprising that halakhic authorities recognize that physical pain, in some circumstances, may also hasten death. *Tosafot*, *Ketubot* 60a, s.v. *goneaḥ*, refer explicitly to "pain of a patient that approaches danger."[24] Accordingly, palliation of pain with a hazardous drug is a matter of weighing one risk against another risk.[25] Since Halakhah recognizes a license to assume risk for the alleviation of pain even in situations in which the patient is not terminal, *a fortiori*, in the case of the terminal patient for whom pain can hasten death, assumption of a prudent risk for relief of pain is certainly warranted.

Recent medical studies confirm that the halakhic presumption that severe pain is a causal factor of decreased longevity is empirically correct. One prospective, randomized, placebo-controlled study was primarily designed to assess the efficacy of pain relief in patients with unresectable pancreatic cancer. A total of 137 patients were randomized and blinded to receive either intraoperative chemical splanchnicectomy with alcohol block or placebo.[26] In what the authors of the report describe as "an unexpected finding" the study demonstrated a "highly significant improvement in actuarial survival" in the patients who received alcohol chemical splanchnicectomy.[27] As reported in the *New York Times Magazine*, a more recent study has shown that adequate pain treatment influences the survival of animals suffering from cancer. Rats afflicted with malignant tumors that were given morphine survived longer than those that did not receive treatment for pain.[28]

It should be added that if, in the course of judicious administration of analgesics, the patient does die, the death is a *davar she-eino mitkaven*, an unintended result giving rise to no halakhic or moral culpability.[29] Halakhah does not regard a calculated risk as an error of judgment and hence such misadventure does not constitute malpractice. Since reasonable assumption of risk is sanctioned by Halakhah, an untoward result carries with it no onus of transgression. Compelling arguments may be advanced in support of the position that even in the days of the Temple when, as indicated by *Shulḥan Arukh, Yoreh De'ah* 336:1, the physician who committed an act of manslaughter as a result of malpractice was subject to the penalty of exile to one of the cities of refuge, a physician who made a judicious determination to expose his patient to such a risk was not subject to any penalty.[30] Consequently, the physician need have no hesitation in palliating pain provided that he does so in a responsible and medically indicated manner.

Nevertheless, the right to palliation of pain is not unlimited. A rather enigmatic statement attributed to a highly respected and eminent halakhic authority is quoted in the literature to the effect that a physician may administer morphine even in a situation in which he knows in advance that at some undetermined time the patient will certainly die as a result.[31] The reason cited is that, in such circumstances, the death of a patient is a *davar she-eino mitkaven*, i.e., the physician has no intent to foreshorten the life of the patient. Although the patient's premature demise is a certainty, nevertheless, there is no *psik reisha*, or certainty, that any particular injection of morphine will cause death. Accordingly, it is argued, the principle of *davar she-eino mitkaven*, or the "double effect" principle, remains applicable. The statement itself is somewhat unclear and it is doubtful that this is really the import of the original statement.[32] If it is, this writer must respectfully but emphatically disagree.

The sources and arguments adduced in support of the permissibility of assuming certain risks in the treatment of pain apply only to situations in which resultant death is only a possibility, but not a certainty, even over a period of time. If, however, the resultant death of the patient is known to be a certainty, it seems to me that, according to Halakhah, administration of the drug is forbidden. The Gemara, *Sanhedrin* 78a, discusses a case in which a person is simultaneously beaten by ten people and a second case in which the victim is beaten by ten people *in seriam*. In both cases the victim dies as a result of the beating. In the case in which the blows are administered simultaneously none of the ten miscreants can be punished since no single person administered the fatal blow. However, the Gemara records a dispute with regard to culpability in the case in which the blows are administered in serial order. The controversy is whether the last person who administers the *coup de grace* is guilty of homicide. The technical controversy is whether causing the death of a person who has been placed in a terminal state by another human being rather than by Heaven, i.e., the terminal state is not the result of any physiological cause but is the result of an act of violence, constitutes homicide. Put somewhat differently, the issue is whether a supervening agent is to be punished for imminently causing the death of a *goses be-yedei adam*, i.e., a person who otherwise would die as a result of another perpetrator's already completed homicidal act.

There is no specific talmudic discussion of the possible exoneration of a person who administers ten lashes and thereby causes the death of his victim on the basis of the fact that the murderer could not know in advance which of the ten lashes will actually cause the death of the victim. Such a situation is hardly unusual since a person intent upon committing homicide by brute force is unlikely to know how many blows will be required to achieve that malevolent goal. If the perpetrator intends to commit homicide and has been properly admonished and informed that if the beating results in death he will be culpable, it would appear that the perpetrator is guilty of capital homicide even though it is impossible to predict in advance how many blows it will take before the victim actually dies. Indeed, the Gemara's explicit exoneration of the ten individuals who simultaneously administer ten blows implies that a single person who administers all ten blows would indeed be guilty of capital homicide.[33]

There is yet another pertinent source in the form of a comment of *Bereshit Rabbah*, 31:5, regarding the *dor ha-mabul*, the generation of the Deluge. Scripture declares "and the earth was filled with robbery" (Genesis 6:13). The Midrash amplifies this statement with the comment that those people were very crafty thieves. They knew that under the Noahide Code theft of property having the value of a *perutah* was a capital crime. To avoid culpability, they formed bands and sought as their victims persons in possession of *turmisin*, coins equal in value to half a *perutah*. Each thief would seize only one of those small coins, secure in the knowledge that there would be no recovery and no punishment. The net result was that the victim had no recourse against any one of the thieves but, since all of his coins were taken from him, he was left impoverished. Says the Midrash: "*Amar ha-Kadosh barukh Hu, 'Atem osim she-lo ke-shurah, ani oseh lakhem she-lo ke-shurah.'*" Translated literally, the Midrash declares: "The Holy One, blessed be He, said, 'You are acting out of line: I will also act out of line in punishing you." In effect, God declared, "You are taking advantage of loopholes and technicalities in order to accomplish goals that are clearly wrong and therefore I will respond accordingly. I will punish you even though what you have stolen is *de minimis*." Generally, *de minimis non cogit lex*, but the insignificant added over and over again can become highly significant. Even if repeated acts leading to an undesired result would be technically unpunishable in terms of the laws that apply to capital punishment, it is clear that acts that in the aggregate will certainly culminate in the taking of the life of a patient cannot be sanctioned in terms of Halakhah.

However, this discussion is largely theoretical. A recent report of the bioethics committee of the Montefiore Medical Center concludes with the statement: "The widespread belief that adequate pain control usually poses high risk of respiratory distress and a consequent hastening of death appears to be based more on longstanding myth than on medical fact." It is simply not the case that adequate pain control creates a certainty that sooner or later the drugs utilized for that purpose will extinguish the life of the patient. Yes, accidents can happen. Nevertheless, one of the leading specialists in pain palliation in the United States has commented to this writer that, in his decades of clinical practice, he has never heard of a single case of a death of a patient as a result of pain palliation—unless the death was intended by the physician. The "accidents," he assured me, are not accidental at all. Assuming that assurance to be exaggerated, it remains true that the certainty of a patient dying as a result of properly titrated pain medication is contrafactual. Hence the halakhic issue of the permissibility of performing a series of uncertain acts that in the aggregate will lead to certain death need not be adjudicated in the context of pain palliation.

Another concern that has been voiced is the fear that if high doses of pain medication are administered, the patient may become addicted to the pain medication. "Opiaphobia" is the word that has been coined to describe the fear of opiates. In actuality, that concern is without basis in fact. Clinical studies have shown that when terminally ill patients who are suffering great pain are treated with carefully titrated doses of narcotics the patients do not become addicted. Not only do they tolerate such doses of narcotics without ill effect but, for some unexplained reason, they do not become addicted to the opiates. In particular, patients suffering chronic pain associated with malignancies who are treated with narcotics for pain relief and who are subsequently cured of their malignancy do not remain drug dependent. This phenomenon is but one of the myriad wonders of the universe.

Moreover, fear of addiction in the terminally ill patient is misplaced. If addiction were indeed the cost of pain palliation of the terminally ill, the result would be well worth the price. Were the terminally ill patient to become addicted to narcotics, then he might indeed require opiates for the rest of his natural life. But surely, it is preferable to survive as a pain-free addict than to suffer intractable pain or not to survive at all.

To be sure, if high doses of opiates are administered to control pain the medication may suppress respiration with the result that the patient will then have to be placed on a ventilator. That is indeed unfortunate, but if it is necessary to provide artificial respiration in order to preserve the life of a patient he must be placed on a respirator. Let it be reiterated: Judaism espouses vitalism as a supreme value. From the vantage point of Judaism the primary goal and purpose of the healing arts is to prolong the life of a patient until such time as the Creator sees fit to reclaim that life. Of course, although life itself is an intrinsic goal, medical practitioners are also obligated to enhance the patient's quality of life to the extent possible. But only to the extent that achievement of that goal is compatible with preservation of life. When the two goals come into conflict, one dare not sacrifice human life because the quality of life that the patient or his family would desire is not attainable. The ultimate value is life itself.

A concluding comment that stems from a non-Jewish source appears to be entirely apropos. That comment reflects a rule that should govern halakhists and certainly should govern doctors in clinical practice. In the real world, there are many situations in which a doctor has to make a decision and he cannot always be certain that his decision is correct. There are cases in which a rabbinic decisor may not immediately know the answer, but he is called upon to render a decision and the situation does not permit procrastination. In the concluding sentences of his decision in *Application of the President and Directors of Georgetown College, Inc.*, Judge Skelly Wright remarks, "To refuse to act, only to find later that the law required action, was a risk I was unwilling to accept. I determined to act on the side of life."[34] A person called upon to make a decision involving a matter of life or death should govern himself by the aphorism "If I am to err, better to err on the side of life."

NOTES

1. SEE Donald McPhillips, "JCAHO Pain Management Standards Are Unveiled," *Journal of the American Medical Association*, vol. 284, no. 4 (July 26, 2000), p. 428.
2. One leading authority has intimated that, in economic terms, more than 400 million days of work were lost in 1986 because of chronic pain. Loss of earnings together with the cost of health care, compensation, litigation and quackery for that year were estimated at 79 billion dollars. See John J. Bonica, "General Considerations of Chronic Pain," *The Management of Pain*, ed. John J. Bonica, 2nd edition (Philadelphia, 1990), I, 182.
3. See McPhillips, "JCAHO Pain Management," p. 429.
4. *Torat ha-Adam, Kol Kitvei Ramban*, ed. R. Bernard Chavel (Jerusalem, 5724), II, 48.
5. See R. Ya'akov Yeshayah Blau, *Pitḥei Ḥoshen*, V (Jerusalem, 5748) 12:1, note 3, who, without citing *Teshuvot Radvaz*, declares that alleviation of suffering is subsumed in the latter obligation.
6. Causing pain or anguish to another is also prohibited according to the many authorities who regard the prohibition against causing pain to animals (*ẓa'ar ba'alei ḥayyim*) as also forbidding the infliction of pain or anguish upon humans. For a survey of those sources, see R. Betzalel Stern, *Be-Ẓel ha-Ḥokhmah*, IV, no. 125, and *Pitḥei Ḥoshen*, V, 2:1, note 6.
7. *Shulḥan Arukh, Ḥoshen Mishpat* 359:4, rules explicitly that, in a life-threatening situation, one may appropriate the property of another person in order to avert danger but only with intent to make restitution at some future time. That ruling is confirmed by Sema, *Ḥoshen Mishpat* 259:10; *Bi'ur ha-Gra, Ḥoshen Mishpat* 259:4; *Shulḥan Arukh ha-Rav, Hilkhot Gezeilah u-Geneivah*, sec. 2; and *Arukh ha-Shulḥan, Ḥoshen Mishpat* 359:3 and is also the opinion of *Yam shel Shlomoh, Bava Kamma* 6:27 and a host of later authorities. That position is based upon the analysis of

Bava Kamma 60b by *Tosafot, ad locum. Teshuvot ha-Rashba*, IV, no. 17, however, apparently maintains that in such circumstances, subsequent payment is not required.

Rashi, *Bava Kamma* 60b, is conventionally understood as maintaining that theft is not permitted even for the purpose of preserving life, while Me'iri, *Bava Kamma* 80a, is understood as asserting that, although normatively permitted, it is not an act of piety to appropriate the property of another person for such purpose. See, however, the discussion of Me'iri's comments presented by *Sedei Ḥemed, Ma'arekhet ha-Alef*, sec. 16. Rashi's position is accepted by *Teshuvot Binyan Ẓion*, nos. 167–168; *Sho'el u-Meshiv, Mahadura Kamma*, II, no. 174; and *Dvar Yehoshu'a*, II, no. 24. However, *Teshuvot Maharam Shik, Yoreh De'ah*, no. 347, asserts that even Rashi would concede that, as a matter of normative law, theft and subsequent restitution is permissible. *Teshuvot Zekher Simḥah*, no. 235, maintains that, in fact, Rashi understands the discussion in *Bava Kamma* 60b in the same manner as *Tosafot. Iggerot Mosheh, Yoreh De'ah*, I, no. 214, employs emphatic language in dismissing the conventional understanding of Rashi. For a comprehensive discussion of this issue, see Dr. Abraham S. Abraham, *Nishmat Avraham*, II, *Yoreh De'ah* 157:1, note 4(1).

8. For a discussion of the rescuer's liability for appropriation of property see this writer's *Contemporary Halakhic Problems*, IV (New York, 1995), pp. 309–314. In addition to the sources cited in that discussion, mention should be made of the comments of *Netivot ha-Mishpat* 340:6. The situation addressed by *Netivot* is that of a person who borrowed arms for use against enemy soldiers only to have those arms seized by the aggressor. The issue, of course, is the borrower's liability to the bailor. *Netivot* cites the statement of the Gemara, *Sanhedrin* 34a, to the effect that if a bystander who is intervening in order to rescue a potential victim from a pursuer breaks utensils belonging to a third party he is absolved from financial liability. *Netivot* argues that the borrower sought to defend not only himself but other potential victims as well and hence should not be liable and adds a comment to the effect that his privilege should not be diminished because he sought to preserve himself as well. Contrary to the position of R. Moshe Feinstein, *Iggerot Mosheh*, II, no. 63, *Netivot* does not regard the rescuer's immunity as limited to liability for tort damages but also to

other forms of liability such as liability arising from a bailment contract. Moreover, the Gemara declares that the pursuer is absolved from financial liability because "if you say [that he is liable] the result will be that no man will rescue his fellow man from a pursuer." That rationale does not seem to apply in situations in which the rescuer is himself among the endangered since no inducement is necessary to prompt a person to act when he is also among those whose lives are endangered.

9. *Nishmat Avraham*, III, *Ḥoshen Mishpat* 426:1, addresses the question of whether a person who is impoverished at the time of his rescue is obligated to compensate the rescuer if he acquires funds at some later time. R. Shlomoh Zalman Auerbach is quoted as stating that, unlike the situation with regard to a person who accepts alms, a lien attaches to the beneficiary with the result that he remains liable. It should however be noted that *Teshuvot Maharashdam, Yoreh De'ah*, no. 204, rules that a person lacking assets at the time of rescue cannot be held liable subsequently. See also sources cited by *Pitḥei Ḥoshen*, V, 12:5, note 11. For a detailed analysis of that question see this writer's "*Hoẓi Hoẓa'ot kedei le-Haẓil et Ḥaveiro ve-aḥar-kakh Nitasher ha-Niẓol*," *Bet Yiẓḥak*, XXXVII (5765), 532–538.

   Cf., also the ruling of Rema, *Yoreh De'ah* 252:12, regarding the liability of a captive for reimbursement of funds expended for his ransom. See also *Yam shel Shlomoh, Bava Kamma*, 6:15, regarding the liability of a captive whose life is in danger and the sources cited by *Pitḥei Ḥoshen*, V, 12:4, note 8, regarding the liability of an impoverished captive who subsequently acquires funds and of a captive of means who has no access to his fortune.

10. Cf., the discussions of R. Shlomoh Zalman Auerbach, *Minḥat Shlomoh*, I, no. 7, and Dr. Abraham S. Abraham, *Nishmat Avraham, Oraḥ Ḥayyim* 334:1.

11. For a discussion of this controversy, see this writer's *Bioethical Dilemmas: A Jewish Perspective*, I (Hoboken, NJ, 1998), 90–94.

12. This point was earlier noted by R. Abraham I. Kook, *Mishpat Kohen*, no. 144, sec. 17.

13. *Iggerot Mosheh*'s ruling with regard to the need for consent of family members for cadaveric organ donations is subject to question on extraneous grounds. A person need not accept pain that may be regarded as an expenditure of a sum greater than his entire fortune but it is far from clear that the

vicarious grief and suffering of another party is to be taken into account, particularly when such anguish is misplaced. For example, an unobservant parent may regard Judaism as a cult and be exceedingly distressed at the sight of a son donning phylacteries. The parent's anguish may be so inordinate that he or she is willing to offer a deprogrammer a sum in excess of her or his net worth in order to convince the child not to perform the *mizvah*. It is certainly the case that the parent's anguish, genuine as it may be, does not relieve the child of his obligation with regard to the *mizvah*. The situation with regard to organ donations is entirely similar. Relatives have no proprietary interest in the corpse of the deceased. The obligation of *pikuaḥ nefesh* that supercedes considerations of *nivul hamet* devolve upon medical practitioners who have the requisite skills to perform the necessary acts of rescue. It is difficult to understand why the misfounded emotional pain of the relatives of the deceased, who essentially have no standing or involvement in the matter, should serve to vitiate the obligation of medical practitioners.

14. For an explanation of the dual names, see Daniel 1:7.

15. Cf., *Midrash Rabbah, Shir ha-Shirim* 2:18: Said R. Ḥiyya bar Abba, "If a person will say to me 'Give your life in sanctification of the name of the Holy One, blessed be He,' I will give [my life] but only if they will slay me immediately; however, in a generation of [forced] apostasy, I could not bear [torture]."

16. The comments of Rabbenu Nissim, *Nedarim* 40a, sanctioning prayer for death in face of intractable pain are not relevant to this discussion for reasons discussed in this writer's *Judaism and Healing* (New York, 1981), pp. 142–143. See also, R. Shlomoh Zalman Auerbach, *Halakhah u-Refu'ah*, ed. R. Moshe Herschler, III (Jerusalem, 5743), p. 60, reprinted in Rabbi Auerbach's *Minḥat Shlomoh*, I, no. 91, sec. 24, and R. Shmu'el Eliezer Stern, "Be-Inyan Tefillah al Ḥoleh Mesukan," *Siaḥ Tefillah* (Jerusalem, 5759), p. 622; cf., however, *Tiferet Yisra'el, Yoma, Bo'az* 8:3 and *Iggerot Mosheh, Ḥoshen Mishpat*, II, no. 73, sec. 1.

17. For further discussion of this notion as well as of the general question of withholding of treatment from a *goses*, see *Bioethical Dilemmas*, I, 61–112.

18. Porter Storey, "It's Over, Debbie," *Journal of the American Medical Association*, vol. 259, no. 14 (April 8, 1988), p. 2095.

19. Brief of the American Medical Association *et al.*, as *amici curiae* in support of petitioners at 6, *Washington v. Glucksberg*, 117 S. Ct. 2258 (1997) (No. 96–110).
20. Albert Einstein, "Overview of Cancer Pain Management," *Pain Management and Care of the Terminal Patient*, Judy Kornell, ed. (Washington: Washington State Medical Association, 1992), p. 4. Another study indicates that when treated by skilled practitioners the pain of 98% of patients in hospice care can be relieved. See American Medical Association Council on Scientific Affairs, "Good Care of the Dying Patient," *Journal of the American Medical Association*, vol. 275, no. 6 (February 14, 1996), p. 475. See also C. S. Cleeland *et al.*, "Pain and its Treatment in Outpatients with Metastatic Cancer," *New England Journal of Medicine*, vol. 330, no. 9 (March 3, 1994), p. 592.
21. See T. D. Walsh, "Opiates and Respiratory Function in Advanced Cancer," *Recent Results in Cancer Research*, XXXIX (1984), 1115–1117; E. Bruera *et al.*, "Effects of Morphine on the Dyspnea of Terminal Cancer Patients," *Journal of Pain and Symptom Management*, vol. 5, no. 6 (December, 1990), pp. 341–344; M. Angell, "The Quality of Mercy" (editorial) *New England Journal of Medicine*, vol. 306, no. 2 (January 14, 1982), pp. 98-99. See also R. R. Miller and H. Jick, "Clinical Effects of Meperidine in Hospitalized Medical Patients," *Journal of Clinical Pharmacology*, vol. 18, no. 4 (April, 1978), pp. 180–189; and R. R. Miller, "Analgesics," *Drug Effects in Hospitalized Patients*, ed. R. Miller and D. J. Greenblatt (New York, 1976), pp. 133–164.
22. *Torat ha-Adam*, *Kol Kitvei Ramban*, II, 43.
23. See Walter B. Cannon, "'Voodoo' Death," *American Anthropologist,* New Series, vol. 44, no. 2 (April-June, 1942), pp 169–181, reprinted in *Psychosomatic Medicine*, vol. 19 (1957), p. 189.
24. See also the comment of R. Shlomoh Zalman Auerbach cited by R. Joshua Neuwirth, *Shmirat Shabbat ke-Hillkhatah*, I, 2nd edition (Jerusalem, 5739), 32:56, note 150. See also R. Eliezer Waldenberg, *Ẓiẓ Eli'ezer*, XII, no. 87.
25. This was clearly appreciated by R. Shlomoh Zalman Auerbach who is cited as stating that it is entirely possible that severe pain may pose a greater threat of foreshortening life than morphine. See R. Yitzchak Zilberstein, *Ateret Shlomoh*, VII (5762), 112–113.

26. See Keith D. Lillemoe, John L. Cameron, Howard S. Kaufman *et al.*, "Chemical Splanchnicectomy in Patients with Unresectable Pancreatic Cancer: A Prospective Randomized Trial," *Annals of Surgery*, vol. 217, no. 5 (May, 1993), pp. 447–55.
27. Ibid., p. 455. For a report of other studies see S. Staats, "The Pain-Mortality Link: Unraveling the Mysteries," *Assessment and Treatment of Cancer*, ed. R. Payne, R. B. Patt and C. P. Hill (Seattle, 1998), pp. 145-156 and *idem*, "Pain, Depression and Survival: Progress in Pain Research and Management," *American Family Physician*, vol. 60, no. 1 (July, 1999), p. 42.
28. See Melanie Thernstrom, "Pain, the Disease," *New York Times Magazine*, Dec. 16, 2001, p. 69.
29. For reference to authorities who would regard unintentional death as a *shogeg* rather than a *davar she-eino mitkaven*, see this writer's *Contemporary Halakhic Problems*, III (New York, 1989), pp. 7f.
30. See *Iggerot Mosheh*, *Even ha-Ezer*, IV, no. 31, s.v. *u-mah she-nizkar* and R. Yitzchak Zilberstein, *Halakhah u-Refu'ah*, ed. R. Moshe Hershler, II (Jerusalem, 5741), 193f., reprinted in *Emek Halakhah*: *Assia*, ed. R. Mordecai Halperin (Jerusalem, 5746), pp. 136f. The question of the circumstances in which a physician is liable to the penalty of exile is addressed at length by the present writer in "Medical Malpractice and Jewish Law," *Tradition,* vol. 39, no. I (Spring, 2005), 84–88.
31. See the statement attributed to the late R. Shlomoh Zalman Auerbach cited by R. Avigdor Nebenzahl, *Sefer Assia*, IV (Jerusalem, 5743), pp. 260–262, and his own difficulty with that statement. Cf. also, Abraham S. Abraham, *Halakhah u-Refu'ah*, ed. R. Moshe Hirschler (Jerusalem, 5741), II, 189; Dr. Mordecai Halperin, *Emek Halakhah*: *Assia* (Jerusalem, 5746), p. 310, and *idem*, "Modern Perspectives on Halakhah and Medicine," *Assia*: *Jewish Medical Ethics*, vol. 1, no. 2 (May, 1989), p. 157.
32. The basic assumption, *viz.*, that each discrete act in a series of acts is a *davar she-eino mitkaven* even if it is known with certainty that one of those acts will result in a forbidden effect, appears to be contradicted by *Mishnah Berurah* 328:151 and *Bi'ur Halakhah, ad locum. Mishnah Berurah* explains that the prohibition against Sabbath use of the type of suppository described by *Shulḥan Arukh*, *Oraḥ Ḥayyim* 328:49, is based upon

the following consideration: Since repeated acts of insertion and removal are needed in order to achieve the intended effect, tearing of anal hair in the course of at least one such act is a *psik reisha.* Thus, despite the fact that each insertion and removal is indeterminate insofar as plucking of hair is concerned, nevertheless, such acts are forbidden since, in the aggregate, removal of at least one hair is a certainty.

33. It has been argued that, on *Shabbat*, a person may perform a series of acts which will eventually lead to an unintended and unwanted effect which, if intended, would be forbidden. Since the person does not know which act will yield that effect each discrete act, it is argued, does not constitute a *psik reisha.* See this writer's *Contemporary Halakhic Problems*,V (Southfield, Michigan, 2005), 152–153.That situation, however, is readily distinguishable from homicide in that violation of *Shabbat* restrictions occurs only if the act is a *melekhet maḥashevet*, i.e., the particular act is designed to produce a forbiden effect.
34. *Application of the President and Directors of Georgetown College, Inc.*, 331 F.2d 1000, 1010 (Washington, D.C., 1964).

7

Stem Cell Research

I. THE PROBLEM

Other than the ongoing debate concerning the moral legitimacy of abortion, the heated controversy that erupted during the summer of 2001 regarding government funding of embryonic stem cell research is without parallel in bioethical discourse. The vehemence of the debate is such that each side accuses the other of gross insensitivity to the value of human life. Those who favor such research point to the potential for developing cures for diabetes, Parkinson's disease, senility and other life-threatening maladies and accuse their opponents of crass disregard for the lives that might be saved. Those who oppose research upon developing embryos assert that snuffing out nascent human life is as immoral as harvesting organs from terminally ill patients. By their lights, such research involves destroying some human lives in order to preserve others.

It should be emphasized that the controversy is limited to research involving utilization of stem cells derived from human embryos. Ongoing research involving stem cells obtained from the placenta or from adult cells does not pose a moral dilemma and may ultimately prove to be more fruitful than embryonic stem cell research.[1] However, many scientists believe that use of embryonic stem cells is crucial and is more likely to yield beneficial results.[2]

The moral issue is reducible to precisely the same set of issues upon which, for society at large, the abortion debate revolves. Is or is not a fetus or an embryo a human being? If yes, at what stage of gestation does it acquire that status? If the fetus or the embryo is indeed a human entity, rare is the ethicist who would sanction the overt destruction of a human being for any purpose, no matter how laudatory. If it is not a human entity, it is argued, no countervailing argument can prevail against the compelling moral value inherent in the preservation of human life.

Elsewhere,[3] this writer had examined in detail the diverse views of various rabbinic scholars with regard to feticide. To put the matter as succinctly as possible, destruction of a fetus by a non-Jew bound by the Noahide Code is a capital crime. For Jews, feticide is a form of non-capital homicide, at least according to Rambam; other authorities regard destruction of a fetus as an infraction of Jewish law but regard it as constituting a less serious transgression. For Rambam, an abortion can be considered only for the purpose of preserving the life of the mother from a threat posed by the fetus; for other authorities, an abortion may be performed for somewhat less compelling reasons as well.[4]

II. SCIENTIFIC RESEARCH

Stem cell research is certainly of no benefit to the mother, i.e., the donor of the ovum, whose life is not endangered. Hence, if feticide is a form of homicide, preservation of life cannot be invoked as a justification. Lesser prohibitions are suspended only in situations in which there is an identifiable danger as well as a direct cause and effect relationship between the otherwise forbidden act and the life-saving effect. The classic examples are those offered by R. Ezekiel Landau, *Teshuvot Noda bi-Yehudah, Yoreh De'ah, Mahadura Tinyana*, no. 210. If such is the medically prescribed therapy, a mother may—indeed must—build a fire and heat milk on the Sabbath on behalf of a seriously ill infant. But she may not make a fire or boil milk simply in order to be prepared for the unlikely eventuality that the child may become seriously ill during the course of the Sabbath day. An autopsy may be performed in the anticipation of obtaining information that may be useful in the life-saving treatment of an already ill, similarly afflicted patient but may not be performed with the hope that some item of information will be obtained that may be of benefit at some time in the future. Moreover, halakhic restrictions are suspended in anticipation of preserving life only in the case of a *refu'ah bedukah*, i.e., a therapeutic procedure known to be efficacious or with regard to which there is cogent reason to presume it to be efficacious.[5] Thus, the very nature of virtually all scientific research is such that Sabbath restrictions, for example, may not be disregarded in order to enhance the likelihood of success in such endeavors. Despite the fact that it may be predicted with certainty that a successful outcome of a research endeavor will save lives and hence the situation may be tantamount to that of a *ḥoleh le-faneinu*, nevertheless, at the research stage the endeavor almost by definition involves a *refu'ah she-einah bedukah*.[6] Hence no rabbinic authority has argued that a scientist may engage in activities prohibited on *Shabbat* in the course of conducting research on stem cells just as no one has argued that Sabbath restrictions are suspended for purposes of cancer investigation or the like. By the same token, no other prohibition may be ignored in order to engage in such research. Accordingly, stem cell research can be sanctioned by Halakhah only if it involves no infraction associated with the destruction of a fetus.[7]

Moral responsibility is readily perceived in the context of direct, proximate causal relationships. Obligations in less proximate situations are not at all obvious. For example, is a person obligated to develop life-saving skills so that he can succor others in time of need? Certainly, acquisition of such skills should be encouraged and is surely deserving of approbation. But is it incumbent upon any individual to acquire such skills? Society as a whole may well be obligated to train lifeguards and to post them at public beaches, but no individual need necessarily feel obligated to make this profession his life vocation. Similarly, the training and deployment of policemen, firemen, lifeguards, etc., in anticipation of potential emergencies is a social rather than a personal obligation.

A similar distinction may be employed in resolving dilemmas arising from conflicting moral duties. May a person on his way to a class in first-aid instruction ignore the plight of a dying man on the plea that he must perfect his skills which may enable him to rescue a greater number of persons at some future time? One's instinctive response is a clear-cut negative. No person may plead that engaging in an activity designed to advance future societal benefits provides justification for ignoring an immediate responsibility. Immediate needs create immediate obligations. Anticipated needs do not generate immediate, compelling obligations. The "here and now" test is a general rule of thumb which may be applied to most situations requiring an ordering of priorities.

The obligation of society at large is, however, much broader. This enhanced obligation is reflected in a statement of the Gemara, *Bava Batra* 7b, which is cited as definitive by *Shulḥan Arukh, Ḥoshen Mishpat* 163:1. Jewish law provides that the inhabitants of a city can compel one another to contribute the funds necessary for the erection of a wall around the city and for a door in the wall, as well as for bolts to secure the doors. Construction of the wall is designed to fortify the city against armed attack. Since the wall is constructed in order to preserve the lives of the inhabitants, all the townspeople may be compelled to contribute equally because all individuals derive equal benefit from the fortifications.

Were this an ordinary case involving an immediate danger to human life, each person would be required to do all in his power to erect the requisite fortifications. At best, he would have a cause of action against his fellow townspeople for reimbursement of funds expended on their behalf—but each person capable of doing so would be required to act on his own initiative and to act without delay. Such an individual obligation does not exist because, in the case in question, there is no imminent danger. Fortifications are erected, not to protect against present danger, but in anticipation of future contingencies.

Precaution against future dangers is not an individual obligation but a societal obligation. The obligations of society are not only greater than those of an individual but are qualitatively different as well. An individual must respond to an immediate danger. While every individual aware of the danger and capable of alleviating that danger is obligated to respond, such individuals, no matter how large their number may be, respond as individuals rather than as members of a society. However, no person is obligated to respond to an as yet nonexistent danger. The individual's responsibility to act is limited to a danger which is clear and imminent.

Society as a whole must see to it that there are lifeguards, physicians, and firemen trained to perform their functions and must provide facilities and incentives for the training of physicians. Any member of society may demand that a wall be built or that locks and bolts be provided. The individual who expresses a legitimate concern with regard to possible danger which may be alleviated and a legitimate way of doing so must be heard and his demands fulfilled. His demand is not for fulfillment of the duty of *pikuaḥ nefesh*, which is personal in nature, but for fulfillment of a societal obligation flowing from its social context. Individuals form societies in order to benefit from social amenities that they would experience extreme difficulty providing for themselves as individuals. Prevention of future danger is certainly such an amenity.

Development of therapeutic agents is no different from

erection of fortifications; both are designed to forestall future loss of life. So long as a *refu'ah bedukah*, i.e., a tried and tested therapy, does not exist there is no obligation to attempt a cure. Nevertheless, pharmaceutical research designed to develop what will become a *refu'ah bedukah* is no less of a social amenity than construction of thoroughfares and plazas and is quite properly the responsibility of society at large.

Elimination of health hazards, development of pharmaceutical agents and research designed to prevent and cure disease are entitlements that may justly be demanded by members of the body politic. Societies are established for the purpose of fulfilling such needs no less so than for the provision of social and recreational amenities. Such needs must be met by society by virtue of the reciprocal obligations into which its members have entered. But fulfillment of such obligations is not mandated by the *mizvah* of *pikuaḥ nefesh*. The differing nature of those diverse obligations is manifest in one striking manner: As noted earlier, halakhic strictures are suspended for purposes of *pikuaḥ nefesh*; they are not suspended for purposes of avoiding a future danger or for an activity that is not known to be causally connected to elimination of sickness. Thus, even on *Shabbat*, the physician may do whatever is necessary for the treatment of a seriously ill patient, but on *Shabbat* neither the patient nor the physician may engage in activities forbidden on the day of rest even in hopeful anticipation of hastening a discovery that may ultimately save countless lives.

Scientific endeavors designed for purposes similar to those of stem cell research are certainly laudable. Members of society may not only urge but may rightfully demand that the cost of such research be defrayed by the public treasury. But because they do not fall within the parameters of *pikuaḥ nefesh* no halakhic violation can be sanctioned even for the purpose of furthering those noble goals.

It is thus readily apparent that the prohibition against feticide would serve to prohibit destruction of a fetus even for purposes of scientific research. Accordingly, that consideration would appear to preclude the legitimacy of experimentation utilizing embryonic stem cells. Nevertheless, a number of considerations have been advanced which, if germane, would serve to establish that the procedures involved in embryonic stem cell research do not represent an infraction of the prohibition against feticide.

III. FETICIDE DURING EARLY PERIODS OF GESTATION

1. *Within the First Forty Days*

There is a significant difference of opinion among rabbinic authorities with regard to whether the prohibition against destroying a fetus is applicable within the first forty days of gestation.[8] There is at least one talmudic text which, upon first reading, seems to provide strong support for the permissive ruling. The Gemara, *Yevamot* 69b, records a declaration of Rav Ḥisda to the effect that the daughter of a *kohen* who becomes widowed shortly after marriage to an Israelite may partake of *terumah* during the first forty days following consummation of her marriage. Permission to eat *terumah* is a privilege accorded to an unmarried daughter of a *kohen* and to a widowed daughter who has borne no children to her Israelite husband. The concern in the case presented to Rav Ḥisda is that the widow, unknown to herself, may be pregnant with child, in which case *terumah* would be forbidden to her. Rav Ḥisda argues that, whether or not she is pregnant, the widow may certainly be permitted to eat *terumah* during the initial forty-day period. If the widow is not pregnant there is no impediment to her partaking of *terumah*; if she is pregnant the embryo is considered to be "mere water" until after the fortieth day of pregnancy. Accordingly, the widow may continue to eat *terumah* for a full forty days following her marriage. Rav Ḥisda's ruling appears to indicate that, in the eyes of Halakhah, fetal development within the initial forty days of gestation is insufficient to warrant according the fetus independent standing.[9]

Another source for this distinction is the Mishnah, *Niddah* 30a, which declares that a fetus aborted less than forty days following cohabitation does not engender the impurity of childbirth ordained by Leviticus 12:25.[10] Similarly, according to *Mishneh le-Melekh, Hilkhot Tum'at Met* 2:1, the defilement associated with a dead body is not attendant upon an embryo expelled during the first forty days of gestation. Furthermore, in the opinion of many authorities, a fetus cannot acquire property prior to the fortieth day of development.[11]

There are, however, sources indicating that the prohibition against destroying the life of a fetus is applicable even during this early period. In his *Torat ha-Adam*, Ramban notes that, according to the opinion of *Ba'al Halakhot Gedolot*, the Sabbath may be violated even during this forty-day period in order to preserve the life of the fetus.[12] The author of *Ḥavvot Ya'ir*, citing *Tosafot, Niddah* 44b, shows that the right to violate the Sabbath for the sake of saving a prenatal life is incompatible with permission to kill it deliberately.[13] It follows that, according to *Ba'al Halakhot Gedolot*, inducement of abortion during this period is forbidden. Responding to a specific inquiry, R. Meir Dan Plocki, *Ḥemdat Yisra'el* (Pietrkow, 5687), Indexes and Addenda, p. 17a, granted permission for termination of pregnancy within this forty-day period only when the life of the mother is threatened.

Drawing a parallel from the commandment against the kidnapping and subsequent sale of a person into involuntary servitude, R. Iser Yehudah Unterman, *No'am*, VI, 4f.,[14] cites the opinion of Rashi, *Sanhedrin* 85b, who maintains that this prohibition encompasses the sale of an unborn child as well. Although the fetus may not be considered a fully developed person, the kidnapper is culpable because he has stolen an animate creature whose status is conditioned by its potential development into a viable human being. Rabbi Unterman further notes that if the unborn fetus lacks human status it is excluded from the ambit of the injunction "And he [man] shall live by them" (Leviticus 18:5), which justifies violation of other precepts in order to preserve human life. Nevertheless, numerous authorities permit violation of the Sabbath in order to preserve fetal life. Rabbi Unterman views such permission as being predicated upon a similar rationale: anticipation of potential development and subsequent attainment of human status gives rise to certain privileges and obligations with regard to the undeveloped fetus. Consideration of future potential is clearly evidenced in the talmudic declaration, *Shabbat* 151b, "Better to violate a single Sabbath in order to observe many Sabbaths." Rabbi Unterman concludes that reasoning in these terms precludes any distinction that might otherwise be drawn with regard to the various stages of fetal development.

Surprisingly, there is one source that appears to rule that destruction of the fetus by Noahides, at least under some circumstances, does not constitute a moral offense. R. Isaac di Trani, *Teshuvot Maharit*, I, no. 99, writes: "I remember having seen in a responsum of the Rashba that he bears witness that Ramban rendered medical aid to a gentile woman in return for compensation in order that she might conceive and aided her in aborting the fruit of her womb."[15] It is of course inconceivable that an individual of Ramban's piety and erudition would have violated the injunction "Thou shalt not place a stumbling block before a blind person" (Leviticus 19:4) or that he would have actively assisted transgressors. Applying the line of reasoning adduced above, Rabbi Unterman draws the conclusion that there is a fundamental distinction between Jewish law and Noahide law with regard to the assessment of potential life. According to many authorities, Noahides are under no obligation to preserve the lives of their fellows, to "be fruitful and multiply" or to refrain from wasting the male seed.[16] They are forbidden to commit homicide and to take the life of "a man within a man" but bear no responsibility for the safeguarding and preservation of nascent life. It would appear, then, that Halakhah holds them accountable only for actual, in contradistinction to potential, life.[17] Accordingly, there is no objection to Noahides aborting, or to a Jew giving advice and rendering indirect assistance to Noahides in aborting, a fetus within the first forty days of gestation. Since during this initial period the embryo has not as yet developed distinctly recognizable organs or an independent circulatory system, argues Rabbi Unterman, it cannot be considered "a man within a man" and hence its destruction does not constitute murder under the Noahide dispensation. Ramban, Rabbi Unterman avers, sanctioned the performance of abortions by Noahides only within this forty-day period.[18]

Rabbi Unterman's distinction between Jews and Noahides with regard to termination of pregnancy within the first forty days following conception was anticipated by an earlier authority. In his *Ḥemdat Yisra'el*, Part I, p. 89b, Rabbi Plocki marshals evidence demonstrating that an embryo may be destroyed with impunity during the first forty days of its development based upon Rabbenu Tam's interpretation of the talmudic dispute recorded in *Yevamot* 12a concerning the "three [categories of] women" who may resort to contraceptive devices in order to prevent conception. Rabbenu Tam explains that the dispute concerns the insertion of a tampon *after* cohabitation. The *Tanna*, R. Meir, rules that the use of contraceptive devices by these women is mandatory since pregnancy would place their lives in jeopardy; the Sages assert that such action is not incumbent upon these women stating that the verse "The Lord preserves the simple" (Psalms 116:6) permits reliance upon divine providence to avert tragic consequences. However, according to Rabbenu Tam, the Sages permit the use of contraceptives after cohabitation reasoning that women are not commanded to refrain from "destroying the seed." *Ḥemdat Yisra'el* points out that fertilization most frequently takes place immediately following cohabitation. Contraception following cohabitation is then, in effect, not destruction of the seed but abortion of a fertilized ovum.[19] If abortion is forbidden even in the earliest stages of gestation, how then can Rabbenu Tam permit the use of contraceptive devices following cohabitation? *Ḥemdat Yisra'el* concludes that destruction of the embryo during the first forty days following conception does not constitute an act of feticide; rather, destruction of a fetus during that early period falls under the category of "destroying the seed." Since the opinion of those authorities who rule that women are also bound by the prohibition against "destroying the seed" is regarded as normative, *Ḥemdat Yisra'el*'s reasoning (as evidenced by his own remarks) finds practical application only with regard to Noahides. According to those authorities who maintain that the ban against destroying the seed does not apply to Noahides, the latter may be permitted to interrupt pregnancy during the first forty days of gestation.

Distinctions pertaining to the early period of gestation are echoed by numerous other authorities. R. Chaim Ozer Grodzinski, *Teshuvot Aḥi'ezer*, III, no. 65, sec. 14, writes, "It appears that a Noahide is not put to death for this and perhaps even with regard to an Israelite there is no biblical prohibition." *Torat Ḥesed, Even ha-Ezer*, no. 42, sec. 33, states explicitly that the prohibition against destroying an embryo within the first forty days following conception is rabbinic in nature. R. Joseph Rosen, *Teshuvot Ẓofnat Pa'aneaḥ* (New York, 5714), no. 59, comments, "Before the fortieth day there is not such a stringent prohibition according to many authorities." In an earlier collection of responsa, *Teshuvot Bet Shlomoh, Ḥoshen Mishpat*, no. 162, R. Solomon Drimer of Skole concludes that there is no prohibition against destroying an embryo less than forty days old and notes that in punishment for performing such a deed "even a Noahide is not put to death." Rabbi

Weinberg, in his original responsum, *No'am,* IX (5726), 213f., also concluded that it is permissible to induce abortion prior to the fortieth day of pregnancy, but later added in a note published in his *Seridei Esh*, III, no. 127, note 7,[20] that having read the contrary opinion expressed by Rabbi Unterman in *No'am,* VI, 8f.,[21] he reserves decision pending consultation with other halakhic authorities. The late Rabbi Moses Jonah Zweig of Antwerp, *No'am,* VII (5724), 48, concurs in the view that forbids abortions even during the first forty days of pregnancy other than on medical grounds.[22]

R. Moshe Feinstein, *Iggerot Mosheh, Ḥoshen Mishpat,* II, no. 69, sec. 3, cites *Ḥavvot Ya'ir* in stating emphatically that, for Jews, destroying a fetus is forbidden even within the first forty days of gestation. *Iggerot Mosheh* finds *Maharit*'s report to the effect that Ramban assisted gentile women in aborting their fetuses troubling in the extreme and, accordingly, finds Rabbi Unterman's assessment to be the only plausible explanation for such conduct. Acceptance of that explanation would necessarily lead to endorsement of Rabbi Unterman's distinction between Jews and gentiles with regard to abortion during the first forty days of gestation.

However, *Iggerot Mosheh* finds that distinction troublesome because he regards the prohibition against feticide to be subsumed within the prohibition against homicide. However, if a fetus within the first forty days is not yet a " 'man' within a man" according to the provisions of the Noahide Code, why should the fetus even during that early stage be regarded as a "man" for Jews?[23] In the same responsum *Iggerot Mosheh* points to other difficulties posed by *Maharit*'s responsum, including what *Iggerot Mosheh* describes as a contradiction between *Maharit*'s comments in the latter's responsa nos. 97 and 99. Accordingly, he dismisses *Maharit*'s latter responsum, and particularly the citation of the report that Ramban assisted in the abortion of non-Jewish fetuses, as a forgery interpolated in *Teshuvot Maharit* by an errant student. If it is indeed the case that there is no reliable evidence of Ramban's comportment in this regard, there is no evidence upon which to base a distinction between Jews and non-Jews insofar as destruction of a fetus within the first forty days of gestation is concerned. *Iggerot Mosheh* concludes his discussion with the comment that the matter requires further reflection.

2. *Subvisual Zygotes*

Elsewhere,[24] this writer has argued that there may be grounds to permit destruction of a nascent embryo in the earliest stages of development even according to the many authorities who do not accept the permissive view with regard to destruction of a fetus within the initial forty day period. A distinction may be drawn that is analogous to a legal concept that is well-known in the common law tradition: *De minimis non curat lex*. The notion that the law does not concern itself with trifles finds expression in Jewish law as well. Although, in Jewish law, the concept has extremely limited application in matters of jurisprudence, a closely related concept is of paramount importance within the context of religious law.

For example, Jews are commanded not to eat creeping animals, including marine creatures that live in an aquatic environment. If one takes a small drop of water, places it on a slide and examines it under a microscope, one will observe the presence of literally thousands of creeping organisms. The phenomenon has been observed by countless students in performing laboratory assignments in conjunction with introductory courses in biology. Nevertheless, Judaism does not forbid the drinking of a glass of water. But on what basis can the concomitant imbibing of the forbidden creatures be sanctioned? The answer must lie in the recognition that, insofar as such prohibitions are concerned, Jewish law concerns itself only with gross phenomena. A physical phenomenon that is subvisual is of no consequence. An organism that can be seen only under a microscope or by means of a magnifying glass is an organism of which Jewish law takes no cognizance; for the purposes of the Jewish legal system, it is as if the organism does not exist.[25]

Similarly, a broken letter in a Torah scroll, a *mezuzah* or in the biblical sections contained within *tefillin* renders such religious objects unfit for their ritual purpose. Yet, under high-power magnification it is immediately evident that all letters contain gaping chasms. The problem dissipates upon the recognition that a "break" in a letter is defined as a break that can be perceived with the naked eye by a person of normal eyesight.

If one applies this principle to the developing human organism, it yields the conclusion that legal cognizance can be taken of the organism only when it becomes visible to the naked eye. However, during its early stages of development, when the zygote is subvisual,[26] the law takes no cognizance of its existence. If so, it may well be argued that there is no prohibition associated with its destruction.

The application of the general principle regarding subvisual phenomena to stem cell research may be the subject of some disagreement. In a discussion of genetic manipulation of agricultural species, R. Shlomoh Zalman Auerbach, *Minḥat Shlomoh*, II (Jerusalem, 5759), no. 97, sec. 27, declares that pollination of one species with pollen of another species does not result in a fruit that would be halakhically classified as a hybrid. Thus, although Rabbi Auerbach affirms that the fruit of an *etrog* tree produced as the result of grafting a lemon branch may not be used on *Sukkot* for the purpose of fulfilling the *miẓvah* of the four species, he nevertheless regards pollination as an entirely different matter. Accordingly, rules Rabbi Auerbach, if an *etrog* is pollinated with the pollen of a lemon tree the resultant fruit is an *etrog* and may be used for fulfilling the *miẓvah*. Rabbi Auerbach declares that the prohibition against hybridization of species applies only to the planting or grafting of vegetative material that might independently yield fruit or a growing seed capable of germinating independently. Pollen can never grow into fruit; hence, for purposes of Halakhah, introduction of foreign pollen does not affect species identity. Again, it is quite obvious that such pollination conducted artificially by humans is not prohibited. Similarly, it follows that introduction of a gene of a foreign species is not forbidden as a form of hybridization since an isolated gene can never develop into a tree or into a plant.

However, an apparently contradictory statement by Rabbi Auerbach appears in a different volume, *Minḥat Shlomoh, Tinyana* (Jerusalem, 5760), no. 100, sec. 7. In that work Rabbi Auerbach writes that hybridization of trees is forbidden "even if the hybridization is [performed] only by means of injection of sap that, if planted in the ground, would not at all sprout." In context, Rabbi Auerbach's statement in *Minḥat Shlomoh, Tinyana* seems to be offered in order to establish a negative view regarding genetic manipulation of agricultural species.

In the latter discussion Rabbi Auerbach himself addresses the issue raised by the fact that genetic engineering involves manipulation of material that is not visible to the naked eye and dismisses that consideration with the remark that "since people engage themselves (*metapplim*) with these particles and transfer them from one species to another, this must be considered as visible to the eyes and not at all comparable to worms that are invisible."

According to a literal reading of Rabbi Auerbach's analysis, even random tinkering with genetic material for no practical or scientific purpose would trigger halakhic cognizance.

Rabbi Auerbach's cryptic statement, presented without sources or argumentation, is rather novel and, in a certain sense, halakhically counterintuitive. Conventional understanding of the principle under discussion is the common sense notion that the commandments of the Torah are to be defined in terms of perceivable phenomena within the ken of those addressed. Rabbi Auerbach introduces a new element, *viz.*, a *de minimis* notion defined other than in terms of perception. His argument certainly begs for elucidation.

However, Rabbi Auerbach's comments may be understood somewhat differently. It may be argued that Halakhah disregards subclinical phenomena only when they are freestanding. A microorganism will never be more than a microorganism; a subvisual break in a letter will never become anything other than a subvisual break in the letter. However, when such subvisual phenomena serve as causal factors yielding readily perceived effects, cognizance must be taken of such phenomena, he asserts, because they are, in effect, recognizable in their effects.[27]

The argument may also be understood as focusing upon intentional harnessing of subclinical phenomena in order to produce a desired effect. A theory ascribing halakhic cognizance based upon the intention or purpose of a procedure is, at least distantly, related to the halakhic category of *aḥsheveih*, roughly speaking, the principle, when applicable, that declares that an object lacking intrinsic value becomes endowed with value because of the intent of a person who utilizes the object for a subjectively valued purpose.

This formulation of Rabbi Auerbach's argument ascribes halakhic cognizance to subclinical phenomena only when a goal-oriented procedure is involved. The term "*metapplim*" employed by Rabbi Auerbach often has that connotation in modern Hebrew usage. That formulation of Rabbi Auerbach's argument commends itself for two reasons: 1) It narrows the area of halakhic innovation. 2) More significantly, it presents the argument as mirroring and applying a well-known halakhic concept, *viz.*, *aḥsheveih*.

Of course, taken literally, Rabbi Auerbach's distinction is predicated upon neither of these formulations but solely upon the phenomenon of human manipulation.

Regardless of how it is understood, if Rabbi Auerbach's position is regarded as correct, it might well be argued that a developing, albeit subvisual, zygote is regarded as a fetus for purposes of Halakhah from the moment of conception because of its potential for development into a viable human being.[28]

Be this as it may, the principle *de minimus non curat lex*, even if accepted in this context, is currently of little avail in addressing the issue of stem cell research. According to reports published in the media, destruction of the embryo in the course of such research takes place as late as on the fifth day of pregnancy when the embryo has grown in size to over 120 cells.

IV. STEM CELLS DERIVED FROM PARTHENOTES OR CHIMERIC EMBRYOS

There is, however, one form of embryonic stem cell research that may pose no moral quandary. In an article published in the February, 2002 issue of *Science* magazine, scientists associated with Advanced Cell Technologies Inc. report some success with embryonic cells obtained in a novel manner.[29] The researchers claim to have taken oocytes, i.e., unfertilized eggs, from a monkey and exposed them to chemicals that induced the cells to divide and to develop into fledgling embryos. Cell division usually occurs only when the ovum is fertilized by a sperm. Science has long known that cell division can also be asexually induced by means of electrical or chemical stimulation. That phenomenon is known as parthenogenesis. The company claims that it has begun development of the same procedure utilizing human oocytes with encouraging results.[30]

Unlike embryos created from the fertilization of an ovum by sperm, on the basis of experiments performed on mice and other animals, it is believed parthenogenic embryos will not survive even if returned to the mother's womb for gestation. If the parthenogenic embryo is not viable from the moment of its inception, destruction of such an embryo in the course of research may not constitute the destruction of a fetus or of potential human life.[31]

In a subsequent development, researchers at the Institute for Reproductive Medicine and Science, a fertility clinic associated with St. Barnabas Medical Center in West Orange, New Jersey, have proposed a novel method for obtaining embryonic stem cells from nonviable embryos. Fertility clinics routinely discard large numbers of embryos fertilized in vitro because they manifest abnormalities rendering it highly unlikely that they would survive if transferred to a woman's uterus. In a paper published in the July-August, 2002 issue of *Reproductive Biomedicine Online*[32] titled "Human Blastocysts from Aggregated Mono-Nucleated Cells of Two or More Non-Viable Zygote-Derived Embryos," Mina Alikani and Dr. Steen M. Willadsen report that they extracted cells from 107 such defective embryos and combined those cells to make thirty-six chimeric embryos, i.e., embryos that could not possibly survive for an extended period of time. Twelve of those embryos survived five or six days, by which time a cluster of stem cells had already developed. It is anticipated that those stem cells can be isolated and grown in a laboratory.

The claim that the discarded embryos from which such hybrids are derived are uniformly nonviable has been challenged by some scientists engaged in fertility research.[33] However, if the claim can be substantiated with regard to at least some aberrant embryos, the potential for deriving stem cells from hybridized nonviable chimeric embryos clearly exists and, as is the case with regard to parthenogenic embryos, destruction of such chimeric embryos may not constitute the destruction of a fetus or of a potential human life.

There is strong evidence suggesting that a *nefel*, a nonviable neonate, i.e., an infant suffering a congenital, physiological or anatomical anomaly that will cause it to die within the first thirty days of life, is not deemed to be a human being. The Gemara, *Shabbat* 136a, addresses the case of a *safek nefel*, i.e., an infant whose status as a viable neonate is a matter of doubt. If the infant is known to be nonviable there is no obligation to circumcise the child. Nevertheless, the Gemara declares that a "doubtful" *nefel* should be circumcised even on *Shabbat* despite the consideration that circumcision involves an act of bloodletting that is prohibited on *Shabbat* other than in conjunction with fulfillment of the commandment regarding circumcision. The Gemara justifies that pronouncement with the statement that if the infant is indeed a *nefel*, and hence no *mizvah* is fulfilled, the very fact that it is a *nefel* means that the act of circumcision is "merely [an act] of cutting flesh," i.e., the status of the *nefel* is equated with that of a cadaver. Since "wounding" or bloodletting on *Shabbat* is prohibited only with regard to a living organism, no such prohibition is attendant upon the circumcision of a *nefel*. In addition, the Gemara, *Shabbat* 135a, *Yevamot* 80a and *Bava Batra* 20a, compares an infant that cannot survive for a period of thirty days to an inanimate stone and declares that it may not be moved on *Shabbat*.

It would thus follow that just as a nonviable neonate is not considered to be a living person, a nonviable fetus or zygote is similarly not a developing human being.[34] It should further follow that there can be no violation of the prohibition against homicide or feticide in the destruction of an organism whose status is depicted as "mere flesh." It may also be noted in this context that the prohibition against bloodletting on *Shabbat* is a derivative of the prohibition against "slaughter." It is thus logical to assume that if circumcising the flesh of a *nefel* is not an act of "wounding" or bloodletting its destruction is similarly not an act of "slaughter." Accordingly, R. Moshe Sternbuch, *Be-Shevilei ha-Refu'ah*, no. 8 (Kislev 5747); R. Zalman Nechemiah Goldberg, *Teḥumin*, V (5744), 250; and Abraham S. Abraham, *Nishmat Avraham*, *Ḥoshen Mishpat* 425:1, assert that there is no prohibition against the destruction of a nonviable fetus.

It must, however, be noted that a disciple of *Noda bi-Yehudah*, R. Eleazer Fleckles, *Teshuvah me-Ahavah*, I, no. 53, who was consulted with regard to the destruction of a nonviable monster-like creature, ruled that the destruction of such life is biblically prohibited and is punishable by death at the hands of Heaven. It is quite possible that *Teshuvah me-Ahavah* would regard destruction of even a nonviable fetus as similarly interdicted. The weight that should be assigned to the opinion of *Teshuvah me-Ahavah*, particularly since it seems to stand in contradiction to the earlier-cited declarations of the Gemara, requires careful determination. Unfortunately, *Teshuvah me-Ahavah*'s statement has neither been analyzed nor cited by contemporary scholars.

V. DESTRUCTION OF A FETUS *EX UTERO*

Another argument in support of the permissibility of stem cell research involving destruction of a developing zygote is based upon the fact that the research is performed on nascent embryos that have been fertilized outside the mother's womb. The issue that must be analyzed is whether there is a prohibition attendant upon destruction of an embryo conceived and gestated in vitro, i.e., in a petri dish rather than in the uterus. The issue more commonly arises in the context of disposal of surplus conceptuses obtained in the course of in vitro fertilization. A normal, fertile woman is endowed from birth with an extremely high number of Graafian follicles. Typically, each month, beginning at puberty and continuing until menopause, a single Graafian follicle develops and becomes a mature ovum. When in vitro procedures are employed because of inability to conceive naturally, the infertile woman is treated with hormones in order to stimulate superovulation. For reasons that are not fully understood, the percentage of zygotes resulting from in vitro fertilization that successfully implant in the uterine wall is low. In order to enhance the likelihood of at least a single successful implantation, it is deemed advisable to introduce multiple fertilized ova into the uterus. At present, in order to avoid the possibility of an excessive number of fetuses, the usual practice is to implant three fertilized ova. However, superovulation usually yields more than that number of ova. Surplus fertilized ova are either frozen for possible later use,[35] donated to women whose fertility problem arises from lack of ovulation,[36] used for scientific purposes such as stem cell research[376] or discarded and destroyed.[38]

Several rabbinic scholars have adopted the position that there is no prohibition attendant upon destruction of a fetus conceived in a petri dish and gestating *ex utero*. The most prominent of those authorities is Rabbi Moshe Sternbuch, author of *Mo'adim u-Zemanim*. In an article that appeared in *Be-Shevilei ha-Refu'ah*, no. 8 (Kislev 5747), published by the Laniado Hospital in Netanya, Rabbi Sternbuch writes, ". . . the prohibition against abortion is [limited to destruction of the embryo] in the woman's uterus, for the [embryo] has the potential to develop and become complete in her womb and it is destroyed. But here, outside the womb, an additional procedure is required to implant [the embryo] in the woman's uterus and without that [procedure] it will . . . perish of its own accord and not reach completion . . . ." Rabbi Sternbuch cites no sources in support of the view that an embryo developing outside of the womb may be destroyed with impunity. A similar view is advanced without elaboration or citation of sources by R. Chaim David Halevy, *Assia*, vol. XII, no. 3–4 (Kislev 5750).

Ostensibly, one source that might be cited in support of such a conclusion is *Teshuvot Ḥakham Ẓevi*, no. 93. The Gemara, *Sanhedrin* 65b, reports that Rabbi Zeira commanded a *golem* created by utilization of incantations derived from *Sefer Yeẓirah* to return to dust. It is thus quite obvious that destruction of a *golem* does not constitute an act of homicide. *Ḥakham Ẓevi* suggests that a *golem* might indeed enjoy human status but that its destruction might nevertheless not constitute an act of homicide for an entirely different reason. Rabbinic exegesis presented by the Gemara, *Sanhedrin* 57b, renders Genesis 9:6 as "Whosoever sheds the blood of a man within a man, his blood shall be shed." The Gemara immediately queries, "Who is a 'man within a man'?" and responds, "It is a fetus within its mother's internal organs." Accordingly, argues *Ḥakham Ẓevi*, destruction of a *golem* does not constitute a prohibited form of homicide because the gestation of a *golem* is not in the mode of "a man within a man." Similarly, it might be argued, an embryo conceived in a petri dish and not yet implanted in a human uterus is also not "a man within a man" and hence its destruction involves no transgression.

Ḥakham Ẓevi's suggestion was rebutted by R. Gershon Leiner, popularly known as the Radzyner Rebbe, in his *Sidrei Taharot, Oholot* 5a, on the basis of what he considered to be a *reductio ad absurdum*. If *Ḥakham Ẓevi*'s criterion of "a man within a man," i.e., of issuance from a womb, is consistently applied, it would lead to the conclusion that a person who might have murdered Adam would not have been guilty of homicide since Adam had no mother.

More significantly, the exegetical interpretation of Genesis 9:6 cited by *Ḥakham Ẓevi* serves to establish a provision limited to the Noahide Code. That rendition of Genesis 9:6 as "a man within a man" serves to establish feticide as a form of capital homicide in the Noahide Code. However, feticide is certainly not a capital transgression in the Sinaitic Code. Presumably, the prohibition against feticide for Jews as a non-capital form of homicide according to Rambam and those who concur in his view, flows from the general prohibition "Thou shalt not murder" (Exodus 20:13).[39] Accordingly, there might be grounds for assuming that a Noahide does not incur capital punishment for destruction of an embryo fertilized in vitro but not for support of the position that a person born of in vitro fertilization may be destroyed with impunity by a Jew or for the position that there is no halakhic consideration forbidding a Jew to destroy a developing embryo while it is yet outside the human body.

Moreover, absent evidence to the contrary, there is no reason to assume that the exegetical interpretation "a man within a man" is designed to impose a limiting condition serving to exclude from the denotation of the verse what would otherwise be an act of culpable homicide. Rather, the exegetical interpretation should be understood as supplementary in nature, *viz.*, as adding to the ambit of the verse an act that would otherwise not be connoted by the literal meaning of the verse, i.e., the killing of a fetus who is "a man within a man." Accordingly, it is not only the killing of "a man within a man" that constitutes homicide but also the killing of "a man within a man" that constitutes homicide.

In any event, *Ḥakham Ẓevi*'s discussion cannot serve as a basis for distinguishing between a fetus *in utero* and a fetus *ex utero* because *Ḥakham Ẓevi* concludes that a *golem* lacks status as a Jew and perhaps even as a human being[39a] for other purposes as well.[40] Accordingly, even for *Ḥakham Ẓevi*, there is a more fundamental explanation for Rabbi Zeira's lack of reticence in destroying the *golem* and no evidence that *Ḥakham Ẓevi* accepted his tentative justification of R. Zeira's act as a normative thesis.

Acceptance of a distinction between *in utero* and *ex utero* gestation would lead to the conclusion that were the scenario depicted in Huxley's *Brave New World* not to remain within the realm of science fiction but to become a reality, a human being conceived in vitro and allowed to develop in a laboratory incubator for the full nine month period of gestation might be killed with impunity at any stage of his life. Such a conclusion is certainly counterintuitive.

It should also be noted that if, as discussed earlier, destruction of a developing fetus within the first forty days of gestation entails a violation of the prohibition against "destroying the seed," that prohibition applies with equal force to destruction of an ovum fertilized *ex utero*. The concept of "a man within a man" applied only to the prohibition against homicide but not to other relevant transgressions.

Moreover, there are sources indicating that active measures must be taken to preserve fetal life during all stages of pregnancy. The Gemara, *Yoma* 82a, describes in great detail the procedure to be followed in instances in which a pregnant woman manifests symptoms of great craving for a particular food. If she cannot otherwise be assuaged, she may be given the food she craves lest she suffer a miscarriage. Some medieval commentators regard the danger to be obviated to be danger to the life of the mother. Miscarriage, they assert, is tantamount to parturition and childbirth is statutorily defined as a life-threatening event. Despite the fact that a pregnant woman will sooner or later experience the danger of parturition, they maintain that the obligation to refrain from food on *Yom Kippur* is suspended in order to avoid unnatural preponing of that danger.

However, Ramban, cited by Ran, *Yoma* 82a, and Rosh, *Yoma* 8:13, maintains that the requirement to fast on *Yom Kippur* is suspended entirely for the purpose of preserving the life of the fetus. Ramban's position clearly reflects the view that there is an obligation to preserve fetal life. There is no obvious basis for assuming that nascent human life need not be preserved and may be destroyed with impunity simply because it is not sheltered in its natural habitat, i.e., because its development takes place outside the mother's womb.[41]

Among contemporary decisors, that view appears to be reflected in a ruling by R. Samuel ha-Levi Woszner, *Teshuvot Shevet ha-Levi*, V, no. 47. Rabbi Woszner expresses the opinion that Sabbath restrictions may not be breached for the sake of preserving the viability of a zygote that is the product of in vitro fertilization and that has as yet not been implanted in the uterus of the gestational mother. He does not argue that the status of a human life generated outside the mother's body is in any sense inferior to that conceived *in utero*. Rather, he argues that the vast majority of such zygotes are not viable and that Sabbath restrictions are not suspended to prolong the life of a nonviable fetus. Rabbi Woszner carefully adds the cautionary note that the empirical situation may change and that with advances in the development of reproductive knowledge and techniques any future halakhic ruling would reflect the changed reality. If so, it would appear that, even at present, overt destruction of a possibly viable zygote cannot be sanctioned. Nevertheless, in a letter appended by R. Abraham Friedlander to his *Ḥasdei Avraham*, II (Brooklyn, 5759), 317, Rabbi Woszner permits the destruction of surplus zygotes.

VI. PUBLIC POLICY AND STEM CELL RESEARCH

As noted in the introductory comments, federal funding of stem cell research has become a matter of passionate debate. The question of what position, if any, the Jewish community should adopt with regard to this issue has also become a matter of discussion. There are, however, a number of considerations that should inform public policy decisions that, in this writer's opinion, have not been sufficiently addressed.

The National Bioethics Advisory Commission was charged with making recommendations regarding governmental policy *vis-à-vis* stem cell research. *Ethical Lessons in Human Stem Cell Research*, the report and recommendations of the Advisory Commission, issued in January, 2000, does not really constitute the formulation of an ethical position and resultant recommendations. Indeed, it is certainly arguable that adjudication of ethical norms is no more the province of the federal government than is resolution of theological disputes. Rather, the report addresses matters of public policy that cannot and dare not be formulated in a moral vacuum.

In conjunction with its deliberations, the Advisory

Commission appropriately solicited the testimony of both ethicists and theologians. Not quite as appropriately, some of the experts consulted raised the shibboleth of separation of church and state, thereby betraying their own lack of understanding of the anti-Establishment Clause and/or the nature of government involvement in stem cell research. The issue is not—and never was—a proposed governmental ban on stem cell research akin to a governmental ban on abortion. Imposition of such a ban would indeed give rise to the question of whether or not such a policy, in effect, "establishes" a particular religious or moral belief. The issue confronting the Advisory Commission was not proscription of a certain avenue of research; the issue addressed was government encouragement and participation in such research in the form of federal funding. And that is a horse of a quite different constitutional color!

In public policy, no less so than in medicine, the fundamental principle must be: *Primum non nocere*—"First, do no harm." The Founding Fathers erected a wall of separation between Church and State in order to preserve the independence and integrity of religious institutions. The purpose was to shield religion from the pernicious and corroding influence of government. The notion of government funding designed to undermine the religious or moral convictions of even a portion of the populance would have been unthinkable.

The issue posed by stem cell research, in very blunt terms, is whether it is appropriate to use tax dollars in a manner that offends the religious sensibilities of some citizens. Deference to religious sensibilities in the form of non-involvement is not at all a constitutionally prohibited form of establishmentarianism; quite to the contrary, it is mandated by the spirit, if not the letter, of the First Amendment.

No ethicist would gainsay the moral value reflected in research designed to save human life. But, at the same time, no ethicist has called for federal funding of every project designed to preserve human life. Policymakers begin with the axiological principle that only a finite amount of sociological resources can be dedicated to such projects with the result that selection of projects to be funded must be determined on the basis of competing scientific, pragmatic, and—yes—moral considerations. Triage decisions are oftimes made in light of moral considerations.

No ethicist, at least to this writer's knowledge, is opposed to stem cell research *per se*. The opposition that has been voiced is to research that requires destruction of human life and is predicated on the position that human life begins at the moment of conception. Some ethicists regard any benefit derived from an evil or immoral action as itself immoral. Some are concerned that advancement of science may be regarded as exculpatory in nature and, thereby, in the popular mind, diminish the odium associated with the destruction of the conceptus. Some are concerned that awareness of the potential benefit to humanity may impact upon the abortion decision of a vacillating woman confronted by conflicting emotional and moral vector forces. Nascent human life, they argue, dare not be sacrificed even for the noble purpose of preserving other human life.

Regardless of one's personal faith commitment or moral viewpoint, one must recognize that the social contract that is the cornerstone of American democracy demands that proper deference be paid to opposing views in formulation of public policy and, in particular, in expenditure of public revenue collected from all citizens.

The recommendations of the Advisory Commission certainly reflect sensitivity to the challenge with which it was confronted. Thus, the Commission strongly recommended that research involving embryos specifically created for research purposes not be funded. For the same reason the Commission recommended that federal funds not be allocated for research involving transfer of a somatic cell nucleus into an oocyte since the procedure, in effect, results in the creation of a human organism.

At the same time, the Commission found no objection to federal funding of projects involving cadavaric fetal tissue, including fetal tissue obtained as a result of non-therapeutic abortions. It does, however, insist upon establishment of procedures to prevent fetal tissue donation from influencing the abortion decision. The Commission also endorses funding of research that will utilize embryos remaining after infertility treatment is completed provided that the donors have already decided to have those embryos discarded instead of donating them to an infertile couple or storing them. The Commission justified this recommendation with the comment, "If the decision to discard the embryos preceded the decision to donate them for research purposes then the research determines only how their destruction will occur, not whether it occurs."

The Commission has certainly endeavored to create a wall of separation between the scientific benefits of stem cell research and the morally contested actions that make the research possible. If effective safeguards are actually in place, it is certainly possible that the issue is entirely analogous to the question of whether it is morally acceptable to derive benefit from research upon the body of a homicide victim assuming, of course, that society assures itself that no homicide will ever be carried out in contemplation of such research. Certainly, Judaism posits no principle akin to a *Miranda* principle[42] that would categorically repudiate any scientific benefit derived from an antecedent immoral act.[43]

Commendably, the recommendations attempted to establish procedures designed to preclude the possibility that the research itself provide a motive or impetus for destruction of a fetus or embryo. Although the Commission's attempt to prevent research benefits from becoming a motivational consideration is salutary, the proposed procedures are only partially effective. The primary safeguard consists of divorcing consent to use the abortus from the decision to abort by refraining from soliciting such consent until the decision to abort has already been made. However, the decision to abort is not final until the deed is done. Not only is the decision morally and legally revocable, but there is significant evidence pointing to the phenomenon of vacillation and actual abandonment of plans to abort on the part of pregnant mothers. Intervening consent to use of the abortus for research designed to save human lives is as much of a concern with regard to a decision not to rescind consent as it is with regard to the original abortion decision. Only by delaying mention of possible research upon the abortus and solicitation of consent for such purposes until after the abortion is actually a *fait accompli* can this concern be assuaged.[44]

Use of surplus embryos obtained in attempts to overcome infertility presents an apparently insurmountable moral problem. Research is not performed upon already inanimate embryos. It is the research itself that causes destruction of the embryo. The argument that the embryos are in any event destined for destruction carries little moral weight. No ethicist would sanction the conduct of a transplant surgeon who plucks out the heart of a person already destined to be killed by a hired assassin. The fact that the putative victim faces imminent death does not vitiate an act of homicide. Morally, research upon the body of a homicide victim is light years removed from lethal research upon a living subject already marked for death. The excess embryos may indeed be destined for destruction whether or not the research is allowed to go forward, but they will not be destroyed with government funding. When the public coffers are used for such purposes society becomes implicated in the act of destroying nascent human life.

The present administration has endeavored to resolve the moral dilemma by limiting government spending to research utilizing cell lines already in existence at the time that approval of such research was announced, *viz.*, 9:00 p.m., August 9, 2001. Some cell lines are already in existence; others will no doubt become available without government funding or encouragement. The United States government, fearful that potential use in conjunction with federally funded research might encourage privately-funded development of additional cell lines by means that would entail destruction of embryos, refused to authorize use of newly-developed cell lines in federally-funded research. Limitation of government involvement to research using existing cell lines not only removes the government from implication in destruction of nascent life but also eliminates a federal imprimatur, implying that society has bestowed its blessing upon the procedure. The fear that such a perception may become a self-fulfilling prophecy is probably the most serious ethical issue in the current debate. Limiting government funding to research employing only existing cell lines serves to vitiate that concern.

In light of both the absence of a halakhic imperative to engage in stem cell research as well as the grave halakhic issues posed by destruction of even nascent embryos, the present policy of the United States government would merit, at the very minimum, the tacit support of the Jewish community. The inevitable association of the issue of stem cell research with the broader abortion controversy serves as an additional consideration auguring in favor of support of that policy.

Rambam, in a censored portion of chapter eleven of *Hilkhot Melakhim*,[45] questions why divine providence makes it possible for Christianity and Islam to flourish and capture the minds and hearts of so many devotees. Rambam asserts that those religions play a role in the divine blueprint for human history in promulgating and keeping alive the notion of the coming of the Messiah. Were Rambam writing today, he might well conclude that the function of preservation of belief in the coming of the Messiah has been assumed by the Chabad movement and find that the Catholic church now uniquely fulfills a different role in the transcendental divine plan, i.e., it tenaciously promulgates the notion of the sanctity of fetal life and the teaching that abortion constitutes homicide. Non-Jews who engage in that endeavor do so with divine approbation. Non-Jews engaged in fulfilling a sacred mission are surely deserving of commendation, applause and support.

NOTES

1. A team of American scientists has presented compelling evidence of success in isolating a stem cell from adult human bone marrow that can produce all tissue types, including blood, muscle and nerve tissue. They also isolated stem cells from adult mice and injected descendants of those cells into mouse embryos. The injected cells were found to be present in almost every tissue, including blood, brain, muscle, lung and liver. See Yuehua Jiang, Balkrishna N. Jahagirdar, R. Lee Reinhardt *et al.*, "Pluripotency of Mesenchymal Stem Cells Derived from Adult Marrow," *Nature*, vol. 418, no. 6893 (July 4, 2002), pp. 41–49.

   Stem cells have long been harvested from umbilical cord blood. More recently, researchers have found that deciduous teeth, i.e., "baby teeth," contain a rich supply of stem cells in their dental pulp. Those cells have been named SHED (Stem cells from Human Exfoliated Deciduous teeth). Such cells are long lived, grow rapidly in culture and have the potential to induce the formation of specialized dentine, bone and neuronal cells. See Masako Miura, Stan Gronthos, Mingrui Zhao *et al.*, "SHED: Stem Cells from Human Exfoliated Deciduous Teeth," *Proceedings of the National Academy of Sciences*, vol. 100, no. 10 (May 13, 2003), pp. 5807–5812.

2. Published in the same issue of *Nature* is an article reporting success in reversing the symptoms of Parkinson's disease in rats using embryonic stem cells derived from mice. See John-Hoon Kim, Jonathan M. Auerbach, Jose A. Rodriguez-Gomez *et al.*, "Dopamine Neurons Derived from Embryonic Stem Cells Function in an Animal Model of Parkinson's Disease," *Nature*, vol. 418, no. 6893 (July 4, 2002), pp. 50–56.

3. "Abortion in Halakhic Literature," *Contemporary Halakhic Problems*, I (New York, 1977), 325-371 and *Jewish Bioethics*, augmented edition, ed. Fred Rosner and J. David Bleich (Hoboken, N.J., 2000), pp. 155–196.
4. See *Contemporary Halakhic Problems*, I, 347–356 and *Jewish Bioethics*, pp. 167–174.
5. See this writer's "Experimental Procedures: The Concept of *Refu'ah Bedukah*," *Contemporary Halakhic Problems*, IV (New York, 1995), 203-217. For a critique of reliance upon these views see R. Moshe Feinstein, *Iggerot Mosheh, Ḥoshen Mishpat*, II, no. 69 and this writer's "Tay-Sachs Re-examined," *Contemporary Halakhic Problems*, I, 112–115 and *Jewish Bioethics*, p. 194, note 97.
6. For an analysis of the halakhic category of a *ḥoleh be-faneinu* see this writer's *Bioethical Dilemmas: A Jewish Perspective*, I (Hoboken, N.J., 1998), 154–156.
7. Stem cell research may present no problem according to R. Jacob Emden who regards abortion as permissible in the face of any "grave need" or according to those who understand *Maharit*'s view to be that abortion is prohibited because it represents "wounding" the mother rather than the fetus. Destruction of the developing embryo cannot be regarded as devoid of problems according to *Ḥavvot Ya'ir*, who regards the prohibition against feticide to be rooted in the ban against destruction of the male seed but does not expressly sanction such destruction in all instances of "grave need." Nor is destruction of the developing embryo nonproblematic according to those who understand *Maharit*'s view to be that abortion is forbidden because it represents "wounding" of the fetus. Moreover, although R. Eliezer Waldenberg, *Ẓiẓ Eli'ezer*, XIII, no. 102 and XIV, no. 100, was prepared to rely upon the rulings of *Maharit*, *Ḥavvot Ya'ir* and R. Ya'akov Emden in permitting therapeutic abortion designed to eliminate anguish on the part of the mother, that view was sharply rejected by the late R. Moshe Feinstein, *Iggerot Mosheh*, *Ḥoshen Mishpat*, II, no. 69. See *Contemporary Halakhic Problems*, I, 112–115, 354–356, 336-337 and p. 339, note 24 and *Jewish Bioethics*, pp. 173–174 and p. 188, note 25.
8. For a detailed review of sources dealing with this issue see *Contemporary Halakhic Problems*, I, 339–347 and *Jewish Bioethics*, pp. 163–167.

9. Those authorities who reject the distinction between the first forty-day period and subsequent stages of gestation presumably maintain that a fetus within the first forty days is not a "child" in the meaning of the verse "But if a priest's daughter be a widow or divorced and have no child" (Leviticus 22:13), i.e., the talmudic term "mere water" connotes only that during that early period the fetus is not sufficiently developed to be termed a "child" but does not define the fetus' ontological status for other halakhic purposes.
10. It is of interest to note that Aristotle, *De Historia Animalium*, VII, 3, declares that the male fetus is endowed with a rational soul on the fortieth day of gestation and the female on the eightieth. This distinction corresponds not only to the respective periods of impurity prescribed by Leviticus but also to the opinion of R. Ishmael in the Mishnah, *Niddah* 30a, who maintains that the prescribed periods of impurity correspond to the number of days required for the animation of the respective sexes and therefore declares that no impurity results from the miscarriage of a female embryo of less than eighty days. Aristotle's representation of animation as occurring on the fortieth or eightieth day, depending upon the sex of the fetus, was later incorporated in both Justinian and canon law. See Rabbi Immanuel Jakobovits, *Jewish Medical Ethics* (New York, 1959), p. 175.
11. *Shakh*, *Ḥoshen Mishpat* 210:2; *Teshuvot Ẓofnat Pa'aneaḥ*, (New York, 5714), no. 59; and R. Elchanan Wasserman, *Koveẓ Shi'urim*, II, no. 11, sec. 1.
12. *Torat ha-Adam*, *Sha'ar ha-Sakanah*, ed. R. Bernard Chavel, *Kitvei Ramban* (Jerusalem, 5724), II, 29; also cited by Rosh and Ran in their respective commentaries on *Yoma* 82a. See also *Korban Netanel*, *Yoma*, *Perek Yom ha-Kippurim*, sec. 13:10.
13. Reference by the late R. Moshe Yonah Zweig of Antwerp, *No'am*, VI (5723), 53, to an opinion by *Ḥavvot Ya'ir*, to the effect that there is no prohibition against abortion during this period is erroneous. *Ḥavvot Ya'ir*, in his introductory comments, calls attention to the fact that various stages of fetal development are recognized in different contexts, *viz.*, forty days, three months and independent movement of the fetal limbs, but quickly adds that it is not his desire to render judgment on the basis of "inclination of the mind or reasoning of the stomach." On the contrary, *Ḥavvot Ya'ir*'s failure to note such distinctions in the course of developing his own thesis

portends his rejection of such a distinction.

It may be of interest to note that this misconstrual of *Ḥavvot Ya'ir* is legend. *Sedei Ḥemed* cites with perplexity conflicting positions attributed to *Ḥavvot Ya'ir* with regard to this question by other sources and notes in resignation that he does not have access to the responsa of *Ḥavvot Ya'ir* and hence cannot determine which quotation is correct. Upon reading these comments, R. Solomon Abraham Rezechte wrote to the author of *Sedei Ḥemed* that he had indeed seen the words of *Ḥavvot Ya'ir* in the original and reported that the latter views the prohibition against feticide as binding during the early periods of pregnancy as well. See *Bikkurei Shlomoh* (Pietrkow, 5664), no. 10, sec. 35.

R. Weinberg's summary declaration in his *Seridei Esh*, III, no. 127, sec. 22 (p. 350), that such a prohibition does not exist even according to the *Ba'al Halakhot Gedolot*, who permits desecration of the Sabbath in order to save an embryo even within this forty-day period, is contradictory to the reasoning of *Ḥavvot Ya'ir*, as indicated by R. Weinberg himself *ibid.*, sec. 5 (p. 339). R. Weinberg argues that *Ḥavvot Ya'ir* fails to give consideration to the opinion of Ramban, who maintains that, despite the law against feticide, the Sabbath may not be violated on behalf of an unborn child. This allegation is readily refutable since *Ḥavvot Ya'ir* argues only that permission to violate the Sabbath in order to save a fetus logically entails a prohibition against destroying such a life, but not vice versa. It cannot be inferred from *Ḥavvot Ya'ir*'s comment that the absence of such permission necessarily entails license to destroy the fetus.

14. See also R. Iser Yehudah Unterman, *Shevet me-Yehudah*, I, 9f.
15. The authenticity of this quotation is highly questionable. R. Unterman, *No'am*, VI, 8, notes that he searched *Teshuvot ha-Rashba* in an unsuccessful attempt to locate this responsum. It seems probable that *Maharit*'s quotation is culled from responsum no. 120 of vol. I in the published text (Bnei Brak, 5718). That responsum deals with the permissibility of rendering medical assistance to Noahide women so that they may be enabled to conceive. In language similar to that quoted by *Maharit*, mention is made of Ramban's actually having done so in return for financial compensation. However, no mention

whatsoever is made of Ramban's having assisted in medical abortion. *Maharit* apparently had a variant textual version. Cf., also, R. Samuel Hubner, *Ha-Darom*, Tishri 5729, p. 33, who attempts to resolve the issue by suggesting an alternative punctuation of this quotation. R. Moshe Feinstein points to the absence of such a responsum in the works of Rashba as evidence that the responsum attributed to *Maharit* is itself a forgery. For other attempts to resolve the problems surrounding these two responsa see *Teshuvot Aryeh de-Bei Ila'i, Yoreh De'ah*, no. 19; R. Eliezer Waldenberg, *Ẓiẓ Eli'ezer*, IX, no. 51, chap. 3, sec. 1; and R. Ovadiah Yosef, *Yabi'a Omer*, IV, *Even ha-Ezer*, no. 1, sec. 7.

16. Regarding the question of whether Noahides are bound by the prohibition against onanism see *Tosafot, Sanhedrin* 59b; *Mishneh le-Melekh, Hilkhot Melakhim* 10:7; R. Naphtali Zevi Yehudah Berlin, *Ha'amek She'elah* 165:2; and *Teshuvot Ẓofnat Pa'aneaḥ* (New York, 5714), I, no. 30.
17. Examination of the phraseology of *Ḥemdat Yisra'el*, Indexes and Addenda, p. 17a, indicates that Rabbi Plocki also had such a distinction in mind. In cases of danger to the mother he permits abortion of embryos of less than forty days without further qualification and adds that there are grounds for permitting abortion at subsequent stages of development provided this procedure is performed by a Jewish physician. Rabbi Unterman fails, however, to note the comments of R. Jacob Zevi Jalish in his *Melo ha-Ro'im, Sanhedrin* 57b, who expresses a contrary view.
18. For a discussion of how this thesis may serve to explain the Septuagint's puzzling mistranslation of Exodus 21:22–23 see *Contemporary Halakhic Problems*, I, 344, note 40 and *Jewish Bioethics*, p. 190, note 43.
19. *Ḥemdat Yisra'el*'s argument is predicated upon a faulty biological premise. Fertilization takes place in the Fallopian tube and subsequently the fertilized ovum descends into the uterus. A tampon inserted into the vagina does not penetrate beyond the cervical os. Contraception following cohabitation is designed to prevent sperm which have not already done so prior to insertion of the tampon from penetrating beyond the vagina. Thus there is no possibility of destroying an already fertilized ovum. Cf., *Teshuvot R. Akiva Eger*, no. 72.
20. Rabbi Weinberg's responsum discussing abortion of fetuses

suffering congenital anomalies was originally published as an article in *No'am*, IX (5726), pp. 193–215, and was reprinted in the third volume of *Seridei Esh* with a number of added notes.

21. R. Unterman's opinion was actually expressed much earlier in his *Shevet me-Yehudah*, I, 50.
22. See also R. Samuel Engel, *Teshuvot Maharash Engel*, VII, no. 85, who, after drawing a distinction between the first forty days and the subsequent periods of pregnancy, concludes with the statement "but it is difficult to rely upon this."
23. *Iggerot Mosheh*'s perplexity stems from his presumption that the prohibition against feticide as applied to Jews is derived from the prohibition in the Noahide Code on the basis of the principle recorded in *Sanhedrin* 59a: "There is nothing forbidden to a Noahide that is permitted to a Jew." *Iggerot Mosheh* also assumes that this presumption is inherent in the comments of *Tosafot*, *Sanhedrin* 59a, s.v. *lekka mid'am*.

    That presumption cannot be correct according to Rambam as his position is understood by the many scholars who maintain that Rambam rejects the principle of *mi ikka midi*. Those scholars must maintain that, for Rambam, the prohibition against feticide is subsumed in the commandment "Thou shall not murder" (Exodus 20:13), while capital punishment for feticide is excluded by the verse "And the person who smites any soul of man shall die" (Leviticus 24:17) on the grounds that a fetus is not a "soul" (*nefesh*) in the full sense of the term as is indeed the case with regard to a *tereifah*.

    Thus, if there is validity to the position that a fetus within the first forty days of gestation is excluded from the Noahide prohibition, according to Rambam such exclusion must be based upon the premise that the term "man" (*adam*) in Genesis 9:6 refers only to a fetus that has acquired a "form" of a "man." Accordingly, the exclusion is limited to the Noahide prohibition derived from Genesis 9:6 but not to the prohibition addressed to Jews, "Thou shalt not commit murder," in which no such exclusion occurs.

    Since Rambam's position must be understood in this manner, there is no reason to postulate that *Tosafot* disagree. In invoking the principle of *mi ikka midi*, *Tosafot*, in context, may be understood not as declaring the source or basis of the governing prohibition, but as identifying the particular aspect of feticide that is the subject of *Tosafot*'s discussion, i.e., prohibition of the destruction of the fetus even for the purpose of preserving the life of the mother. It is that particular application of the provision, rather than the fundamental prohibition against feticide, that *Tosafot* in their query assert should be transposed to the law and applied to Jews as well. Feticide itself, *Tosafot* might freely concede, is explicitly prohibited to Jews on the basis of Exodus 20:13, but a ban against sacrifice of the fetus even when it threatens to cause the death of the mother can be suggested only on the basis of *mi ikka midi*.

24. "Artificial Procreation," *Bioethical Dilemmas*, I, 210–211.

25. See R. Israel Lipshutz, *Tiferet Yisra'el, Avodah Zarah* 2:6 and R. Yechiel Michal Epstein, *Arukh ha-Shulḥan, Yoreh De'ah* 83:15 and 84:36. See also R. Abraham Danzig, *Ḥokhmat Adam* 38:8; *idem, Binat Adam*, sec. 34; R. Shlomoh Kluger, *Teshuvot Tuv Ta'am va-Da'at, Mahadura Tinyana, Kuntres Aḥaron*, no. 53; R. Zevi Hirsch Shapiro, *Darkei Teshuvah, Yoreh De'ah* 18:20; R. Eliezer Waldenberg, *Ẓiẓ Eli'ezer*, VIII, no. 15, chap. 14, sec. 10; and R. Moshe Feinstein, *Iggerot Mosheh, Yoreh De'ah*, II, no. 146; *idem, Iggerot Mosheh, Even ha-Ezer*, III, no. 33; R. Pesach Falk, *Teshuvot Maḥazeh Eliyahu*, no. 91 and *Assia*, vol. 9, no.1 (Tammuz 5742), pp. 26–27. See also *Eliyahu Rabbah, Oraḥ Ḥayyim* 648:24; *Sha'arei Teshuvah, Oraḥ Ḥayyim* 648:5; *Sha'ar ha-Ẓiyyun*, 648:49; Rabbi Y. Mashash, *Teshuvot Mayim Ḥayyim, Oraḥ Ḥayyim*, no. 269; and R. Ovadiah Yosef, *Teshuvot Yabi'a Omer*, IV, *Yorah De'ah*, no. 20, sec. 8. and no. 21, secs. 4–5 and 7. Cf., also, R. Yom Tov Lipman Heller, *Ma'adanei Yom Tov, Halakhot Ketanot, Hilkhot Tefillin* 9:40; R. Dov Berish Weidenfeld, *Teshuvot Dovev Meisharim*, I, no. 1 and *hashmattot*; R. Yonah Mintzberg, *She'erit Yisra'el, Oraḥ Ḥayyim* nos. 11–12; and R. Benjamin Aryeh ha-Kohen Weiss, *Teshuvot Even Yekarah*, II, no. 32. Cf., however, R. Iser Zalman Meltzer, *Hashkafah ve-He'arot*, appended to R. Yechiel Michal Tucatzinsky, *Sefer Bein ha-Shemashot*, p. 153; R. Betzalel Zolti, *Mishnat Ya'aveẓ, Oraḥ Ḥayyim*, no. 66; and R. Moshe Sternbuch, *Mo'adim u-Zemanim*, II, no. 124 and VIII, no. 124. See also R. Elyakim Dworkes, *Be-Shevilei ha-Halakhah*, II (Jerusalem, 5752), 50–62 and *idem, Be-Shevilei Ha-Parashah* (Jerusalem, 5762), pp. 545–548.

26. At the eight-cell stage the developing zygote is roughly half

the size of a period that appears at the end of a sentence in the *New York Times*. I am not quite certain whether something of that size is to be characterized as an object that can be perceived by the naked eye. If it is not to be classified as something perceivable by the naked eye, it may well be the case that, at that stage of development, Halakhah takes no cognizance of the zygote and regards it as non-existent for purposes of the prohibition against destroying an embryo or of the prohibition against destroying the male seed.

27. An analogous, but by no means identical, concept is reflected in the talmudic controversy regarding whether or not *yesh shevaḥ eẓim be-pat*, i.e., whether or not forbidden wood consumed as fuel is present and halakhically recognized in its enhancement of the dough in causing it to become baked. The principle *yesh shevaḥ eẓim be-pat* is employed in the context of prohibited benefit rather than in the context of species identity. The issue is whether the "*shevaḥ*" or "enhancement" of the bread attributable to the wood used as fuel in its baking is halakhically deemed to be recognizable in the bread. If yes, the bread is deemed to be *asur be-hana'ah*, i.e., an object from which benefit may not be derived just as benefit may not be derived from the forbidden wood.

   In any event, the notion that "the enhancement of the wood can be perceived in bread" serves to transpose the halakhic identity of the wood to the bread but not vice versa. Thus the pollen might be perceived in the fruit and the zygote in the embryo but not the fruit in the pollen or the embryo in the zygote. That point is actually made by *Ḥokhmat Adam* 38:8, *Binat Adam*, sec. 34. The author of *Sefer ha-Brit* had written that vinegar may not be consumed because of the presence of microscopic organisms that cause the fermentation process. The sole solution, argued *Sefer ha-Brit*, is to boil the vinegar, a process presumed to cause those organisms to rise to the surface so that the vinegar may then be skimmed.

   Binat Adam takes strong exception to that ruling in contending that Halakhah takes no cognizance of subclinical phenomena. In the process, *Binat Adam* advances a possible argument in favor of the position of *Sefer ha-Brit*, *viz*., the microscopic organisms will eventually become "worms" and hence their potential condition confers upon them present status as worms. *Binat Adam* proceeds to dismiss that argument by means of a *reductio ad absurdum*. Aristotle postulated that a homunculus, i.e., a "little man," is subclinically present in every sperm. Similarly, argues *Binat Adam*, a chicken must be present in every egg. If so, consumption of eggs should be forbidden! But that is clearly not the case, concludes *Binat Adam*, for "the Torah forbade only what has become actual, not that which is [merely] potential."

28. See also R. Samuel ha-Levi Woszner, *Teshuvot Shevet ha-Levi*, VII, no. 122, who asserts, in a different context, that an entity not discernible as a living organism but which will eventually develop in size is for that reason encompassed in the prohibition against eating non-kosher creatures. Most authorities maintain that a minuscule organism that is perceived merely as a "black dot," but not as a living creature, is a prohibited creeping thing. See this author's "New York Water," *Tradition*, vol. 38, no. 4 (Winter, 2004), pp. 78–79. *Shevet ha-Levi,* however, maintains that such creatures are not forbidden unless they are recognizable as living creatures by virtue of their motion or if they are members of a species that eventually develops to a recognizable size.
29. See Jose B. Cibelli, Kathleen A. Grant, Karen B. Chapman *et al.*, "Parthenogenetic Stem Cells in Nonhuman Primates," *Science*, vol. 295, no. 5556 (February 1, 2002), p. 819. See also "Stem Cell Research: Primate Parthenotes Yield Stem Cells," ibid., pp. 779-780, and *New York Times*, February 1, 2002, p. A23.
30. See *Science*, p. 780.
31. If a reliable method of deriving stem cells from human parthenotes is perfected, therapeutic cloning in which a potentially viable embryo is created would be unnecessary for the treatment of females having oocytes.
32. *Reproductive Biomedicine Online*, vol. 5, no. 1 (July-August, 2002), pp. 56-58, *at* http://www.rbmonline.com/Article/656.
33. See Gina Kolata, "Hybrid Embryo Mixture May Offer New Source of Stem Cells for Study," *New York Times*, June 4, 2002, p. F3.
34. Cf., *Teshuvot Radvaz*, II, no. 695, who rules that it is forbidden to hasten the death of a fetus whose mother has died in childbirth.

35. Freezing fertilized ova even in perpetuity presents no halakhic problems. Even according to the authorities cited later in this text who maintain that an embryo may not be allowed to perish, there appears to be no halakhic impediment to maintaining an embryo in a state of suspended animation.
36. Assuming there is a maternal-filial relationship between the genetic mother and the child, anonymous donation which entails suppression of maternal identity would serve to bar such donations. See this writer's "Surrogate Motherhood," *Bioethical Dilemmas*, I, 253–254.
37. In vitro fertilization presents other halakhic issues, particularly with regard to semen procurement. See *ibid.*, pp. 249–251.
38. It is precisely because of a concern for destruction of fertilized ova that German federal law strictly regulates fertility clinics and prohibits physicians from fertilizing more ova than will be implanted at any one time.
39. See *supra*, note 23.

39a. See *supra*, p. 22.

40. See also R. Joseph Rosen, *Teshuvot Ẓofnat Pa'aneaḥ* (Jerusalem, 5728), II, no. 7.
41. This also appears to be the view of R. Mordecai Eliyahu, *Teḥumin*, XI (5750), 272.
42. In *Miranda v. Arizona*, 384 U.S. 43 (1966), the U.S. Supreme Court ruled that tainted evidence in the form of an improperly obtained confession may not be admitted as evidence in judicial proceedings.
43. For a fuller discussion of this issue see this writer's "Utilization of Scientific Data Obtained through Immoral Experimentation," *Contemporary Halakhic Problems*, IV, 218–236.
44. For a fuller discussion of this issue see this writer's "Fetal Tissue Research: Jewish Tradition and Public Policy," *Contemporary Halakhic Problems*, IV, 171–202.
45. Those passages have been restored in the more recently published *Rambam la-Am* (Jerusalem, 5715) and Frankel editions of the *Mishneh Torah* (Jerusalem-Bnei Brak, 5759), as well as in the single volume indexed edition edited by Zevi Preisler (Jerusalem, 5746). Those sections also appear in the Yale Judaica Series translation, *The Code of Maimonides: The Book of Judges*, translated by Abraham M. Herschman (New Haven, 1949).

8

Hazardous Medical Procedures

I. CONVENTIONAL RISKS: *SHOMER PETA'IM*

As a general rule, Jewish law forbids self-endangerment. The talmudic dictum "Never should a person stand in a place of danger" (*Shabbat* 32a and *Ta'anit* 20b) is predicated on the biblical admonition "and be exceedingly watchful with regard to your lives" (Deuteronomy 4:15). An entire section of the *Shulḥan Arukh, Yoreh De'ah* 116, is devoted to an enumeration of actions and situations that must be avoided because they present an element of risk. Some activities, for example, standing beside an unstable wall or drinking water that has been left uncovered into which a serpent might have deposited venom, are uniformly banned even though the danger is remote. Other matters are subject to *ad hoc* determination.

However, the definition of "danger" in this area of Halakhah is far from simple. Life is fraught with danger; there are few, if any, activities that are totally risk-free. The rule determining acceptable assumption of risk is formulated by the Sages of the Talmud, *Shabbat* 129b, *Yevamot* 12b, *Ketubot* 39a and *Niddah* 31a, as "Since many have trodden thereon, '*shomer peta'im Ha-Shem*—God preserves the simple' (Psalms 116:6)." The concept encapsulated in that dictum is that any activity routinely undertaken by members of society and not perceived by them as hazardous is permitted despite the inherent danger. To the extent that a person is found worthy, divine providence is extended to the "simple" who comport themselves in blissful oblivion of the danger inherent in commonplace activities. However, providential guardianship is not made available to the foolhardy who assume risks shunned by prudent members of society. Risks ignored by people in general fall below the threshold of "danger" of which Jewish law takes cognizance.[1]

The concept embodied in the dictum *shomer peta'im Ha-Shem* is not difficult to fathom. Willfully to commit a daredevil act while relying upon God's mercy in order to be preserved from misfortune is an act of hubris. It is sheer audacity for a person to call upon God to preserve him from calamity which he can himself avoid. Therefore, one may not place oneself in a position of recognized danger even if one deems oneself to be a worthy and deserving beneficiary of divine guardianship. That principle is clearly reflected in the statement of the Gemara, *Shabbat* 32a, indicating that a person dare not endanger himself in anticipation "that a miracle will be performed on his behalf."

Yet, at the same time, it is universally recognized that life is fraught with danger. Crossing the street, riding in an automobile, or even in a horse-drawn carriage, for that matter, all involve a statistically significant danger. It is, of course, inconceivable that such ordinary activities be denied to man. Such actions are indeed permissible since "the multitude has trodden thereon," i.e., since the attendant dangers are accepted with equanimity by society at large. Since society is quite willing to accept the element of risk involved, any individual is granted dispensation to rely upon God who "preserves the simple." Under such circumstances the person who ignores the risk is not deemed to be presumptuous in demanding an inordinate degree of divine protection; on the contrary, he acts in the manner of the "simple" who perceive no problems. An act which is not ostentatious, which does not flaunt societally accepted norms of behavior and does not draw attention to itself, is not regarded by Halakhah as an unseemly demand for divine protection. The risk involved may be assumed with impunity by an individual who desires to do so.

Accordingly, although hazardous medical procedures, when permitted, are discretionary rather than mandatory,[2] nevertheless, a person requiring medical attention for a serious condition cannot plead that he is not required to seek treatment because of the danger inherent in the taxi ride to the doctor's office or to the emergency room of a hospital. The risk of fatality as a result of a motor vehicle accident is certainly real and omnipresent; however, in our society, awareness of that risk is generally suppressed.

Risks of the nature encompassed by the principle "God preserves the simple" may not only be assumed by oneself but may be imposed upon others as well. For example, circumcision performed on a cloudy day was thought by the Sages of the Talmud to entail a risk beyond that associated with circumcision when performed at other times. Nevertheless, as recorded by the Gemara, *Shabbat* 129b and *Yevamot* 72a, the practice was permitted "since many have trodden thereon." The practice was permitted not only as a discretionary assumption of risk for oneself but represents a risk that may also be imposed by a father or a *mohel* upon a newborn infant. Since circumcision on the eighth day is a *mizvah* and may be delayed only in the presence of genuine danger, assumption of that risk is mandatory. Halakhah simply does not regard a hazard that is commonly accepted with equanimity as a halakhically cognized "danger." It follows that, in a medical context, a physician may expose a patient to commonly accepted risks even without specific authorization.[3]

As is evident from the discussion of R. Jacob Ettlinger, *Teshuvot Binyan Ẓion*, no. 137, there is, however, one factor that serves significantly to limit the type of risk that may legitimately be assumed on the basis of *shomer peta'im Ha-Shem*. Jewish law provides that those who return safely from a sea journey or from a trip across the desert must offer a *korban todah*, a thanksgiving sacrifice. That offering is brought in gratitude for having been delivered from danger. In our day, in the absence of the sacrificial order, this deliverance is acknowledged in the public recitation of *birkat ha-gomel* which is a *birkat hoda'ah*, i.e., a blessing of thanksgiving. In light of the recognized danger inherent in travel of such nature, *Binyan Ẓion* questions the permissibility of taking such journeys in the first place. He responds by drawing a distinction between an immediate danger and a potential or future danger. Immediate danger must be eschewed under all circumstances; future danger may be assumed if, in the majority of cases, no harm will ensue. One who embarks upon a sea voyage or caravan excursion is in no immediate danger, although at some point in the course of travel danger may arise. Since, in the majority of cases, no harm will befall the traveler, the risk of future danger may be hazarded. It is for this reason, asserts *Binyan Ẓion*, that the Sages, invoking the verse "God preserves the simple," rule that a woman belonging to one of the classes of women enumerated in a Baraita cited by the Gemara (*Yevamot* 12b and 100b, *Ketubot* 39a, *Nedarim* 35b and *Niddah* 45a) whose lives may be endangered by pregnancy is permitted to engage in normal coital relations without any restrictions whatsoever. Justification for assuming the risks involved in pregnancy follows an identical line of reasoning: Intercourse itself poses no hazard. The jeopardies of pregnancy lie in the future and may be assumed since, in the majority of instances in which such risks are present, no harm will result. However, were the danger to arise in the majority of instances, the activity could not be countenanced.

In formulating a distinction between an immediate danger and a danger that may arise only in the future, *Binyan Ẓion* also cites the distinction posited by the Gemara, *Berakhot* 33a, between the danger posed by a scorpion versus a danger represented by a serpent. The Mishnah, *Berakhot* 30b, declares that a person should not interrupt his *shemoneh esreh* prayer even if a serpent is coiled around his heel. The Gemara, however, limits that ruling to the type of danger represented by a serpent in stating that a person should indeed interrupt his prayer if threatened by a scorpion. Rambam, in his *Commentary on the Mishnah, ad locum,* explains that the distinction lies in the fact that in the majority of instances serpents do not bite.

Because of the general rule that all risk to life is prohibited even in cases in which it is quite evident that an untoward result will occur only in a minority of instances, *Binyan Ẓion* is troubled by the Mishnah's admonition to ignore the presence of a scorpion. *Binyan Ẓion* resolves the problem by noting that, in the situations described by the Gemara, both the serpent and the scorpion appear to be calm and tranquil. Indeed, *Tosafot, ad locum*, comment that if the serpent appears to be agitated the prayer should be interrupted. *Binyan Ẓion* asserts that the distinction lies in the fact that, although placing oneself in a situation fraught with imminent danger is always forbidden, assumption of a risk that will materialize only in the future is prohibited only if death will result in a majority of instances. The persons described both by the Mishnah and the Gemara are in no immediate danger since both reptiles appear to be placid. Serpents do become aroused on occasion but that danger lies in the future and since it occurs only in a minority of situations, asserts *Binyan Ẓion*, it may be ignored. On the other hand, the scorpion is much more aggressive and generally does bite; hence it is forbidden to assume the risk of the scorpion biting even though the danger is not immediate.

R. Aryeh Balhuver, *Teshuvot Shem Aryeh*, no. 27, addresses the same questions raised by *Binyan Ẓion* but fails to draw a distinction between imminent danger versus future danger. *Shem Aryeh* declares that sea voyages are inherently dangerous and are indeed forbidden if undertaken solely as pleasure jaunts. *Shem Aryeh* draws that conclusion from his understanding of the Gemara, *Mo'ed Katan* 14a, regarding a person who, after having traveled "without permission," returns from his voyage. Unlike other persons who have legitimate reason for not cutting their hair in preparation for the festival who are permitted to cut their hair on *ḥol ha-mo'ed*, the traveler is forbidden to cut his hair on *ḥol ha-mo'ed* because he embarked on his voyage "without permission." In disagreement with earlier commentators, *Shem Aryeh* understands the reference to a voyage undertaken "without permission" as connoting a pleasure trip that is prohibited because of an attendant danger. In fact, the Palestinian Talmud, *Mo'ed Katan* 3:1, declares even more explicitly that it is forbidden to undertake a sea voyage. *Korban Edah, ad locum,* qualifies the thrust of that statement in explaining that the prohibition to which the Gemara refers is limited to the three-day period preceding *Shabbat*. *Shem Aryeh*, however, understands the admonition as reflecting simply an instantiation of the general prohibition against self-endangerment.

According to *Shem Aryeh*'s analysis of the discussion recorded in *Mo'ed Katan* 14a, the same journey is expressly permitted by the Gemara when undertaken for purposes of earning a livelihood; if the journey is undertaken, not for purposes of assuring basic sustenance, but in order to increase one's wealth, the permissibility of the voyage is a matter of talmudic dispute. *Shem Aryeh* permits activity involving an inherent danger, e.g., sea voyages, for purposes of earning a livelihood or when undertaken for what is considered to be "a need of the world" even when the attendant danger is immediate.

According to *Shem Aryeh*, intercourse by members of the three classes of women enumerated by the Baraita is permitted despite the potential dangers of pregnancy because such activity is "the way of the world." *Shem Aryeh* equates "the need of the world" with earning a livelihood. The Gemara, *Bava Meẓi'a* 112a, interprets Deuteronomy 24:16 as declaring that a workman deserves prompt payment of his wages because he accepts the danger to his life entailed by his labor in anticipation of receiving his earnings (*eilav hu nosei et nafsho*).

Nevertheless, *Shem Aryeh* does not sanction activity involving an inherent danger simply because it is undertaken for the purpose of fulfilling a *mizẓvah* even if the danger lies in the future unless the danger is minor (*lo shekhiaḥ hezeika*). The distinction between a scorpion and a serpent, he asserts, is that in the case of a serpent the danger is minor while in the case of a scorpion the danger is significant and hence must be eschewed even for the sake of fulfilling a *mizvah*. Even a remote danger is forbidden, according to *Shem Aryeh*, when undertaken for a frivolous purpose.

R. Eliyahu Klatzkin, *Imrei Shefer*, no. 29, takes direct issue with *Binyan Ẓion*'s thesis. The distinction between a serpent and a scorpion is explained by *Imrei Shefer* on the basis of *Kohelet Rabbah* 10:14. Commenting upon the verse "If the serpent bites before it is charmed" (Ecclesiastes 10:11), the Midrash depicts the serpent as exclaiming, "Is it possible that I do anything unless it is told to me from on high?" and proceeds to declare: "Said R. Abba bar R. Kahana, 'A serpent never bites unless it is whispered to him from above.' R. Simeon bar Yoḥa'i taught, 'The serpent breached the fence of the universe; therefore he became the executioner for all breachers of fences.' " Thus, the distinction between a scorpion and a serpent is self-evident: Scorpions are inherently dangerous whereas serpents do no harm other than when deputized to do so as instruments of divine providence. Accordingly, a person engaged in prayer faces no danger since retribution will not be exacted while he is engaged in performing a *mizvah*.

Basing himself upon the same statement of the Palestinian Talmud cited by *Shem Aryeh*, *Imrei Shefer* asserts that a minor degree of danger is warranted for purposes of earning a livelihood or in order to perform a *mizvah*. *Imrei Shefer* maintains that the principle "God preserves the simple" applies to imminent danger no less so than to future danger but is limited to matters involving only a low probability of loss of life.

Imrei Shefer further cites an anecdote recorded by the Gemara, *Shabbat* 90, indicating that eating dates may be dangerous because of the possible presence of minuscule creatures that may cause perforation of the esophagus. On the basis of that narrative *Imrei Shefer* concludes that, other than in conjunction with a frivolous undertaking, a risk may be assumed for any cogent purpose, provided that the danger is both minor and cannot be completely obviated. Accordingly, he contends that the three classes of women permitted to engage in natural intercourse may do so only because there was no contraceptive measure known to be totally effective. In such situations, he contends, assumption of a low degree of risk is permissible in reliance upon the principle "God preserves the simple." However, when the attendant risk can be eliminated totally, asserts *Imrei Shefer*, no degree of danger is permissible.

Unlike *Shem Aryeh*, *Imrei Shefer* assumes that only a remote danger (*lo shekhiaḥ hezeika*) may be assumed for purposes of earning a livelihood.[4] Hence *Imrei Shefer* is forced to conclude that sea voyages represent only a remote danger and, even when the danger is remote, such voyages are forbidden when undertaken for frivolous purposes. In contradistinction to *Binyan Ẓion*, both *Shem Aryeh* and *Imrei Shefer* are in agreement that even a remote danger is not acceptable when undertaken for a frivolous purpose.

Presumably, according to *Shem Aryeh*, therapeutic endeavors, in addition to serving as a means of fulfilling a *miẓvah*, represent a "need of the world" and are justified despite attendant risk. However, according to *Imrei Shefer*, the permissibility of assuming such risk in situations in which there is significant danger is not immediately clear. According to *Binyan Ẓion*, whose opinion is probably the most authoritative, use of a medication or of any substance that has been statistically determined to foreshorten life in the majority of users cannot be automatically sanctioned simply on the basis of "the multitude has trodden thereon." That is the case even if the danger lies far in the future and even if longevity anticipation is compromised only marginally.[5]

II. HAZARDOUS RISKS

The narrative recounted in II Kings 7:3–4 describes the quandary of four leprous men. Samaria was besieged by the Syrian army and there was hunger in the city. The lepers outside the gates of the city realized that they faced death from starvation. Crossing into the camp of the enemy, where provisions were available, would entail the risk of immediate death by violence. However, the possibility existed that, because of their piteous affliction, the Syrians might not treat them as potentially dangerous enemies but would spare their lives as an act of mercy and, in addition, provide them with nourishment. The four lepers assumed this calculated risk. Despite the danger, they reasoned, "And now go and let us fall into the camp of the Syrians; if they save us alive we shall live; and if they kill us we shall die" (II Kings 7:4). To their surprise, they found that the Syrian hordes had fled, leaving behind not only food and drink but treasure as well.

The Gemara, *Avodah Zarah* 27b, cites this narrative in support of a rule formulated with regard to seeking medical ministration at the hands of pagan practitioners. The idolaters of antiquity were regarded by the Gemara as potential murderers and, for that reason, various restrictions were placed upon social intercourse with them, including a prohibition against availing oneself of the medical services of pagan physicians. The Gemara qualifies that restriction by limiting it to situations in which the patient's condition, if allowed to remain untreated, is not necessarily terminal. However, in situations in which the affliction would otherwise inevitably lead to the death of the patient, the Gemara permits the patient to assume the risk of death at the hands of the pagan physician. The reasoning is that, since, if the malady is allowed to take its natural course death would be inevitable, the patient has little to risk in exposing himself to the danger of being killed. As authority for sanctioning the assumption of such risk the Gemara cites the biblical narrative of the four lepers. Facing death as a result of near-term starvation, they assumed the risk of imminent death at the hands of the enemy in the hope of avoiding starvation. To the objection that such a course of action involves the possible loss of the brief period of time the individual would certainly survive until overcome by the ravages of hunger, the Gemara responds, "*Le-ḥayyei sha'ah lo ḥaishinan*—We are not concerned with ephemeral life."

Tosafot, in their commentary *ad locum*, hasten to point out that it is by no means the case that Jewish law regards ephemeral life as devoid of moral significance.[6] Quite to the contrary, euthanasia or the foreshortening of the life of a terminally ill person by even the briefest period of time is a capital crime. Sabbath strictures and the like are set aside, when necessary, in order to prolong life even ephemerally. The Gemara, *Yoma* 85a, clearly prescribes that a victim trapped under the debris of a fallen wall is to be rescued even on *Shabbat* despite the fact that as a result of such efforts his life will be prolonged only by a matter of moments. Accordingly, *Tosafot* comment that the Gemara's declaration regarding *ḥayyei sha'ah* must not be understood as an absolute assessment but rather as a comparative balancing of *ḥayyei sha'ah* versus normal longevity anticipation. Thus, the Gemara declares that, as a matter of prudence, the gamble of *ḥayyei sha'ah* in the hope of a complete recovery is halakhically warranted.

The most obvious application of this principle is in the case of a patient confronted by a life-threatening malady for which the only available medication may prove to be toxic. R. Jacob Reischer, *Teshuvot Shevut Ya'akov*, III, no. 75, describes a patient diagnosed as suffering from a terminal illness that, without intervention, would cause him to die "within the same day or [within] two days." The physician advised that a medication was available but that the medication would either cure the patient or cause his imminent demise. *Shevut Ya'akov* ruled that the medication might be administered but only upon consultation with multiple physicians and in accordance with the judgment of at least a two-thirds majority of the physicians consulted and even then only upon the acquiescence of "the wise man [i.e., the halakhic authority] of the city." The basic consideration underlying *Shevut Ya'akov*'s ruling is a straightforward application of the principle enunciated by the Gemara, *Avodah Zarah* 27b, i.e., a brief period of longevity anticipation may be jeopardized in the hope of achieving a complete cure. Similar rulings permitting endangerment of *ḥayyei sha'ah* are recorded by R. Shlomoh Eger, *Gilyon Maharsha, Yoreh De'ah* 155:1 and 336:1; R. Jacob Ettlinger, *Teshuvot Binyan Ẓion*, no. 111; R. Me'ir Posner, *Bet Me'ir, Yoreh De'ah* 332:1; and R. Abraham Danzig, *Ḥokhmat Adam, Binat Adam*, no. 73 (93).

The stipulation of *Shevut Ya'akov* that the potential efficacy of the drug be determined on the basis of the opinion of a significant majority of medical experts reflects the application of an amplified principle of majority rule not only to questions of law but also to questions of fact. But why the need for confirmation of the decision by the local halakhic authority? The rabbinic scholar certainly possesses neither scientific expertise nor insightful medical judgment beyond the ken of expert physicians. The rabbinic role in such decision-making requires careful elucidation.[7] But, regardless of its basis, the requirement for rabbinic endorsement of what is essentially a medical determination certainly implies that *ḥayyei sha'ah* may not always be placed in jeopardy in the hope of achieving a cure.

An apparent contradiction to the principle that one may endanger *ḥayyei sha'ah* in the hope of achieving a cure is found in R. Judah the Pious, *Sefer Ḥasidim*, no. 467. This source describes a folk remedy consisting of "grasses" or herbs administered by "women" in treatment of certain maladies which either cured or killed the person so treated within a period of days. *Sefer Ḥasidim* admonishes that the women who administer such remedies "will certainly be punished for they have killed a person before his time." R. Shalom Mordecai Schwadron, *Orḥot Ḥayyim, Oraḥ Ḥayyim* 328:10, resolves the contradiction by stating that the instances discussed by *Sefer Ḥasidim* involved situations in which there was clearly a possibility for cure without hazardous intervention. According to that analysis, *Sefer Ḥasidim* sets forth the common-sense approach that hazardous procedures dare not be instituted unless conventional, non-hazardous approaches have been exhausted.

III. DEGREE OF ACCEPTABLE RISK

In none of the earlier-cited sources does one find discussion or even consideration of the statistical probability of prolonging life versus the mortality rate or the odds of shortening life. Yet, certainly, in weighing the advisability of instituting hazardous therapy, the relative chance of success in achieving a cure as opposed to that of a fatal outcome is a factor to be considered. Nevertheless, in early rabbinic discussions of the issue there is no explicit reference to the role of statistical probability of prolonging life versus the odds of shortening life or of the mortality rate of the contemplated procedure. Later discussions are hardly univocal with regard to this question.

R. Ze'ev Wolf Leiter, *Bet David*, II, no. 340, permits intervention even if there exists but one chance in a thousand that the proposed drug will be efficacious, whereas there are nine hundred and ninety-nine chances that it will hasten the demise of the patient. A diametrically opposed view is presented by R. Joseph Hochgelehrnter, *Mishnat Ḥakhamim*, as cited by R. Chaim Ozer Grodzinski, *Teshuvot Aḥi'ezer*, II, *Yoreh De'ah*, no. 16, sec. 5.[8] *Mishnat Ḥakhamim* refuses to sanction hazardous therapy unless there is at least a fifty percent chance of survival. In effect, according to *Mishnat Ḥakhamim*, the issue of whether the act is to be considered an act of homicide or an act of rescue is to be determined on the basis of the presumed result in at least fifty percent of similar cases. That view is also espoused by R. Eliezer Waldenberg, *Ẓiẓ Eli'ezer*,

X, no. 25, chap. 5, sec. 5.[8] Much earlier, R. Moshe Sofer, *Teshuvot Ḥatam Sofer, Yoreh De'ah*, no. 76, refused to sanction hazardous medical procedures in which the prospect of effecting a cure was "remote" but offered no statistical criteria with regard to the upper limit of mortality risk that may legitimately be assumed.

The position of *Mishnat Ḥakhamim* is contested by *Teshuvot Aḥi'ezer* who rules that a fifty-percent chance of success is not a requirement but nevertheless requires, as did *Shevut Ya'akov* before him, that prior rabbinic approval be obtained on each occasion that such therapy is initiated. R. Moshe Feinstein, *Iggerot Mosheh, Yoreh De'ah*, III, no. 36, asserts that the view of *Mishnat Ḥakhamim* is more compelling but nevertheless defers to the ruling of *Teshuvot Aḥi'ezer*. Earlier, in *Iggerot Mosheh, Yoreh De'ah*, II, no. 58, he ruled that, when death is imminent, a hazardous procedure may be instituted so long as there is a "slim" chance (*safek raḥok*) of success, even though the chances of survival are "much less than even" and it is in fact almost certain that the patient will die. A former Chief Rabbi of Israel, R. Iser Yehudah Unterman, *No'am*, XII (5730), 5, maintains that medical risks are warranted "when there is hope for a cure even if, in most cases, [the procedure] is not successful and will shorten life."

Tiferet Yisra'el, Bo'az, Yoma 8:3, raises a quite different question in discussing the permissibility of prophylactic inoculations which are themselves hazardous. In the situation described, the patient, at the time of treatment, is at no risk whatsoever. The fear is that he will contract a potentially fatal disease, apparently smallpox. The inoculation, however, does carry with it a certain degree of immediate risk. *Tiferet Yisra'el* justifies acceptance of that risk, which he estimates as being "one in a thousand," because the statistical danger of future contagious infection is greater.

It is difficult to determine whether there exist nuances of disagreement between these authorities. Is the merely "remote" chance of success that *Ḥatam Sofer* refuses to sanction greater or lesser that the "one chance in a thousand" that *Tiferet Yisra'el* and *Bet David* find acceptable? Is the acceptable "slim chance" described by *Iggerot Mosheh* a greater or lesser risk than the "remote" chance that *Ḥatam Sofer* finds unacceptable? More fundamentally, what is the underlying principle employed by these authorities in determining the degree of risk that may be sanctioned?

At least one contemporary author differentiates between various cases on the basis of the nature of the risk involved rather than on the basis of anticipated rates of survival. Rabbi Moshe Dov Welner, *Ha-Torah ve-ha-Medinah*, VII–VIII (5716–5717), 314, argues that hazardous procedures may be undertaken despite inherent risks only if the therapeutic nature of the procedure has been demonstrated. For example, a situation might present itself which calls for administration of a drug with known curative potential but which is also toxic in nature. The efficacy of the drug is known but its toxicity may, under certain conditions, kill the patient. The drug may be administered in anticipation of a cure despite the known statistical risk. The same statistical risk, argues Rabbi Welner, could not be sanctioned in administering an experimental drug whose curative powers are unknown or have heretofore not been demonstrated. This, he maintains, is why *Sefer Ḥasidim* censures the practice of administering dangerous herbs as was the custom of women in his day. According to Rabbi Welner, it was not the risk *per se* which was found to be objectionable. Use of the herbs in question was simply not accepted medical practice. Since the efficacy of such potions had not been demonstrated, risk to the life of the patient precluded their use. The same distinction is applied by Rabbi Welner in determining the propriety of novel surgical procedures. Surgical hazards are acceptable only when the technique is known to be effective. Experimental surgery employing untried techniques does not justify exposure to risk.

Insofar as disagreement between the authorities cited does exist, such disagreement is limited to the permissibility of instituting potentially hazardous therapy.[9] It must be emphasized that procedures which involve any significant risk factors are always discretionary rather than mandatory.[10]

The position of those authorities, and indeed the general parameters within which hazardous medical procedures may be legitimately undertaken, must be understood in the context of the halakhic attitude toward risk-taking in general.

As is manifestly evident from the discussion of the Gemara, *Avodah Zarah* 27b, acceptance of a clearly perceived risk in conjunction with medical treatment is halakhically acceptable. As has been discussed earlier in conjuction with palliation of pain,[11] R. Jacob Emden, *Mor u-Keẓi'ah* 328, describes the surgical procedure for the removal of gallstones or kidney stones which he viewed as designed not to eliminate a threat to life but to alleviate excruciating pain and, in that context, *Mor u-Keẓi'ah* grapples with the issue of acceptance of risk for purposes other than preservation of life. A modern-day example would be performance of a sympathectomy, a major surgical procedure designed, not to cure any disease, but to sever a nerve in order to control pain. *Mor u-Keẓi'ah* seeks to discourage risk-taking for palliation of pain with the comment that those who submit to such surgery "do not act correctly" because "in my eyes it is close to being forbidden (*karov le-issur*)." "Close to being forbidden," but not actually forbidden. Presumably, *Mor u-Keẓi'ah* recognizes that palliation of pain is a therapeutic endeavor. *Mor u-Keẓi'ah,* presumably, also maintains that at least some measure of risk may be assumed with regard to the treatment of even non-life-threatening medical conditions.[12]

Risks for the purpose of palliation of pain were certainly sanctioned by earlier rabbinic scholars. R. Moses Isserles, known as Rema, the sixteenth-century author of authoritative glosses to the *Shulḥan Arukh*, appears to sanction hazardous procedures designed solely to alleviate pain. In light of the scriptural prohibition against smiting or assaulting a parent (Exodus 21:15), *Shulḥan Arukh, Yoreh De'ah* 241:13 rules that a son should not "wound" his father even for medical reasons. Thus, in treating a parent, a son is cautioned not to remove a splinter, perform bloodletting or amputate a limb. Rema comments that, if no other physician is available and the father is "in pain," the son may perform bloodletting or an amputation on behalf of his father. A similar statement is contained in the earlier thirteenth-century commentary of Me'iri, *Sanhedrin* 84b. The phraseology employed by these sources clearly indicates that the contemplated procedures were designed to mitigate pain rather than to preserve life. There can be little question that, at the time those works were authored, the amputation of a limb was accompanied by a significant risk to the life of the patient. It is evident that such procedures were sanctioned despite the hazards involved.

The permissibility of placing a life in danger when the patient is not afflicted by a life-threatening malady does, however, require justification. The great value placed upon preservation of life augurs against placing oneself in a situation of risk. Nevertheless, it is certainly the case that medical intervention is permitted in order to restore a patient to good health even in the absence of danger to life.

Authority for the practice of medicine is derived by the Gemara, *Bava Kamma* 85a, from the verse "and he shall cause him to be thoroughly healed" (Exodus 21:19). In context, the scriptural reference is to the treatment of the victim of a battery whose wounds may or may not be life-threatening. It is beyond dispute that an aggressor is liable for medical expenses even if the wound inflicted is not potentially lethal. It follows that the physician is permitted, and indeed obligated, to treat patients who suffer from afflictions which are not life-threatening. This is certainly the case when the treatment itself poses no danger. However, Ramban, in his *Torat ha-Adam*, observes that all medications are hazardous for, as he puts the matter, "With regard to cures, there is naught but danger; what heals one kills another."[13] Even a patient whose life is not in jeopardy may be treated; every medical treatment carries with it an element of risk; ergo, risks may be assumed in the treatment of even non-life-threatening conditions.

The underlying rationale that serves both to justify medical risk-taking as well as to establish the limits placed upon the degree of risk that may be assumed may be found in the nature of a person's relationship to his life and body. Judaism teaches that a person does not have a proprietary interest in his life or in his body. Life belongs to the Creator of the universe who bestows life upon man in causing the soul to enter the body. In the words of the morning prayer: "You created [the soul]; You fashioned it; You preserve it within me; and You will take it from me...." In the interim, during the course of his lifetime, man is a bailee charged with nurturing and preserving both soul and body.

Bailment is one area in which Jewish law adopts a reasonable man standard. A bailee has a duty of care requiring him to safeguard the bailment entrusted to him. The standard of care to which he is held *ke-de-natri inshi* (as people safeguard),[14] i.e., the quality of care a prudent person would exercise with regard to his own property.[15] In order to preserve his property and maintain it in serviceable condition even a prudent person would be prepared to accept a certain measure of risk. A bailee may act in a comparable manner with regard to property entrusted to him by others. The same is true with regard to preservation of life and health. Prudent risks are warranted in order to ensure normal longevity anticipation and restoration of health, i.e., the proper functioning of the body for its divinely ordained purposes.

The notion that man has the status of a bailee with regard to his life and his body and that as a bailee he is held to a standard of care *ke-de-natri inshi*, literally, "as people safeguard," rather than to either a higher or lower standard of care serves, in this writer's opinion, to justify not only assumption of prudent risks but also to explain why acceptance of such risks is discretionary rather than obligatory.

With regard to their own financial resources, some people are conservative by nature; others are more open to assuming calculated risks for potential gain. Innate fiscal conservatism allows some individuals to invest funds only when they perceive virtually no chance of loss of capital; others, following their natural instincts, eagerly venture capital in pursuing investments which, although prudent on balance, involve an element of risk. Neither policy is "right" and neither is "wrong." A bailee is permitted the same order of leeway, so long as he acts within the bound of prudence in managing funds entrusted to him for purposes of investment. He is required simply to safeguard the bailment *ke-de-natri inshi*—in the manner in which people safeguard their own fortunes.

Man, as a bailee, is granted the same discretion with regard to decisions concerning prolongation versus possible foreshortening of life. Some individuals are by nature highly conservative; others are more open to risk. But all are acting *ke-de-natri inshi*, in a manner in which similarly inclined people would act. In choosing a bailee, a bailor may well wish to assess the nature and predilections of his prospective bailee. It is for that reason that some people choose to invest their money only in investment funds guided by highly conservative managers, while others seek to maximize their return by choosing growth funds managed by persons whose fiscal outlook is aggressive. Still others will balance risks by investing a portion of their resources in conservative funds and a portion of their resources in aggressive growth funds. The same disparate patterns of behavior are exhibited by individuals engaged in making choices involving medical risks.

The Creator did not fashion man with a single temperament; rather, He endowed some individuals with a highly prudent nature and others with a more venturesome temperament. To each the Creator entrusted the precious gift of life with full cognizance, and even the desire, that each is likely to exercise vigilance in accordance with his individual temperament in protecting the precious treasure entrusted to him. Thus, each person is given authority to exercise discretion, subject to established parameters, in making necessary medical decisions. And, in possibly arriving at conflicting decisions, each individual is acting *ke-de-natri inshi* and thereby fulfilling the divine mandate with which he is charged.[16]

The risks that are acceptable are not simply those that would be undertaken by a reasonable and prudent person with regard to his own property. A person might well be unconcerned by the prospect of the loss of a particular item and hence not be inclined to spend time and effort to assure its preservation. Not so a bailee *vis-à-vis* bailed property. The bailee must safeguard the property on behalf of the bailor who has entrusted it to him in order to assure its preservation.[17] Since man is but the steward of both his life and body, the fiduciary nature of his responsibility requires that any risk assumed be prudent *vis-à-vis* preservation of the interests of the bailor, i.e., the Creator of all life. A physician is uniquely qualified to diagnose illness, to offer a prognosis and to evaluate the relative risks and benefits attendant upon medical intervention versus those of non-intervention. Whether or not assumption of the attendant risk is prudent when measured against potential benefits is a value judgment rather than a medical determination.

Recognition that the decision to accept or to reject such procedures reflects a moral judgment based upon a halakhically predicated value system serves to explain *Shevut Ya'akov*'s demand that any decision of such nature be endorsed by a rabbinic scholar. It is the rabbinic decisor rather than the physician who may be presumed to be sensitive to the role of individual persons within the divine scheme of creation and to be mindful of the need for measured assessment of the prospects for maximization of longevity.[18]

IV. DEFINITION OF *ḤAYYEI SHA'AH*

In his glosses to *Shulḥan Arukh*, R. Shlomoh Kluger, *Ḥokhmat Shlomoh*, *Yoreh De'ah* 155:1, postulates that the concept of *ḥayyei sha'ah* is not relative in nature but should be understood as connoting at least a limited, if not an ephemeral, period of time. He impliedly assumes that a perfectly healthy person has no right to jeopardize his anticipated life span for the sake of a potential increase in longevity. In seeking to understand the risks that may legitimately be assumed in the hope of achieving a cure he declines to define *ḥayyei sha'ah* as the residual period of life, regardless of duration, remaining to a person afflicted by an illness that, if left untreated, is terminal in nature. *Ḥokhmat Shlomoh* dismisses that definition on the grounds that all mortals will die of one cause or another; hence, the fact that the specific cause of eventual death has been identified should not create a novel halakhic situation. In effect, *Ḥokhmat Shlomoh* argues that all persons suffer from a terminal condition known as life. Nevertheless, he remains convinced that *ḥayyei sha'ah* connotes a qualitative type of life that is different from ordinary longevity anticipation. *Ḥokhmat Shlomoh* candidly concedes that he has no direct evidence pointing to a definition of *ḥayyei sha'ah*.[19] Nevertheless, he points to another halakhic category from which he seeks to derive a definition by way of analogy.

Halakhah posits a category known as "*treifah*" in a number of diverse areas of Jewish law. A *treifah* is a person or an animal suffering from a fatal congenital anomaly of certain specified organs or a person who, or an animal that, has sustained a trauma resulting in the loss or perforation of one of those specified organs and, as a consequence, death will follow. To give but several examples of the implications of *treifut*: the meat of an animal that is a *treifah* is non-kosher; an animal that is a *treifah* may not be offered as a sacrifice; the murder of a human being who is a *treifah*, although assuredly forbidden, does not constitute capital homicide. Although the physical criteria that establish the various forms of *treifut* are quite complex, a common factor is present in each of the various conditions that are deemed to establish *treifut* in man or beast, *viz.*, it may be anticipated that the person or animal suffering from that trauma or anomaly will not survive for a full twelve-month period. Taking the concept of *treifah* as his model, *Ḥokhmat Shlomoh* asserts that *ḥayyei sha'ah* should also be defined as longevity anticipation of less than twelve months. Much later, *Iggerot Mosheh, Yoreh De'ah*, III, no. 36, independently formulated the same definition of *ḥayyei sha'ah*.[20]

R. Abraham I. Kook, *Mishpat Kohen*, no. 144, sec. 3, somewhat equivocally advances the identical definition of *ḥayyei sha'ah*, but with one significant qualification. The Gemara, *Ḥullin* 42a, records a dispute with regard to whether it is indeed the case that a *treifah* cannot be anticipated to survive for a period of twelve months. According to the talmudic opinion that *treifah ḥayyah*, i.e., that a *treifah* may well survive for a longer period, the sole determining criterion of *treifut* is that the cause of death is already present and, even if death is remote, the process of dying has already begun. That line of reasoning was, of course, rejected by *Ḥokhmat Shlomoh* as tenuous, but then *Ḥokhmat Shlomoh* fails to explain why such reasoning should not be accepted according to the opinion that maintains that *treifah ḥayyah*. Moreover, *Mishpat Kohen* himself concedes that the twelve-month definition of *ḥayyei sha'ah* is open to criticism "on many grounds" and that the paradigm of *treifah* is but a *remez*, i.e., a hint or allusion, for delineation of *ḥayyei sha'ah*.

The categorization of *treifut* cannot serve as a conclusive source for establishing the limits of *ḥayyei sha'ah* for a number of reasons. The first reason is reflected in the controversy regarding *treifah ḥayyah*, or *treifah einah ḥayyah*, i.e. whether a *treifah* can or cannot survive for a twelve-month period. According to the normative view that maintains that a *treifah* cannot survive for twelve months, there are two separate factors common to all *treifot*: 1) the cause of death is already present; and 2) survival for a minimum of twelve months cannot be anticipated. According to the view that maintains that *treifah ḥayyah, treifut* is defined solely on the basis of the first criterion, i.e., the cause of death is already present. What basis, then, is there for assuming that *ḥayyei sha'ah* is also determined on the basis of both criteria, since, according to one opinion, presence of the cause of future death is, in and of itself, a sufficient criterion for establishing *treifut*?

A far more telling objection arises from a more exact analysis of the nature of *treifut*. An animal experiencing a terminal physiological disorder, e.g., kidney failure, is not a *treifah*, even though its demise may be imminent. Euthanasia committed upon a terminally ill patient riddled with disease is a capital transgression. The category of *treifah* is restricted to the presence of particular anatomical anomalies that are congenital in nature and to excision or perforation of specific organs of the body as a result of trauma. Humans and animals afflicted by disease or physiological disorders, no matter how advanced or how devastating, and regardless of the organ affected, are not included in the category of *treifah*. The concept of *ḥayyei sha'ah* connotes a brief or ephemeral period of life-expectancy without reference to the reason for the cause of diminished life expectancy. Accordingly, there can be no hard and fast correlation between categorization as a *treifah* and the definition of *ḥayyei sha'ah*. Undoubtedly, it is this fundamental distinction between the two halakhic concepts that prompted *Mishpat Kohen* to dismiss the comparison as aught but a "hint" or "allusion."

Acceptance of the definition of *ḥayyei sha'ah* advanced by *Ḥokhmat Shlomoh* and *Mishpat Kohen* and the resultant conclusion that risk-taking is never warranted when a patient is expected to survive for more than a year even in the absence of intervention leads to a conclusion that is counterintuitive. Consider the situation of a patient afflicted with a slowly developing, but definitely lethal, form of leukemia. Assume that it can be determined with a high degree of probability that, if left untreated, the patient will survive for thirteen months. Assume also that the sole therapy available to this patient is a bone marrow transplant which, if successful, will cure the leukemia and restore the patient to good health but which carries with it a significant risk of death due to tissue incompatibility or as a result of infection contracted during the period of suppression of the patient's white blood cell count.

According to the thesis propounded by *Ḥokhmat Shlomoh* and *Mishpat Kohen*, the potentially hazardous bone marrow exchange could not be sanctioned because the thirteen-month longevity anticipation is, qualitatively speaking, not mere *ḥayyei sha'ah*. Consequently, the patient refuses the transplant. A bit more than one month later the patient finds himself in the same severe straits only now, since it is one month later, the remaining survival period is less than twelve months. Since the period of remaining life expectancy is presently less than twelve months, the bone marrow transplant may, at this point, be undertaken in good conscience. However, since it is now one month later and the disease has progressed markedly, the likelihood of a cure is much lower. It turns out that applying the rule as formulated by *Ḥokhmat Shlomoh* and *Mishpat Kohen* does not guarantee twelve months of life but only a single month of life. The notion that a patient must delay therapy while the chance of successful intervention plummets may not offend the technicalities of the principles applied in such dilemmas but it is certainly counterintuitive.[21]

The position advanced by *Ḥokhmat Shlomoh* is apparently contradicted by another renowned rabbinic scholar, R. Israel Lifschutz, *Tiferet Yisra'el, Yoma, Yakhin* 8:3. *Tiferet Yisra'el* reports that, subsequent to the development of the smallpox vaccine, he was informed that, although the vaccine was highly effective in preventing smallpox epidemics, inoculation carried with it a small but significant risk of death. *Tiferet Yisra'el* observes that assumption of that risk for the sake of averting a statistically greater danger is justified. However, according to the position espoused by *Ḥokhmat Shlomoh*, the risk of death assumed by an as yet perfectly healthy individual could not be categorized as endangerment of only *ḥayyei sha'ah*. Thus, even in situations of possible imminent contagion, administration of the smallpox vaccine in an age in which the associated danger loomed as a significant risk would not appear to be consistent with the view of *Ḥokhmat Shlomoh*. It would appear to be the case that smallpox vaccination can be sanctioned only upon expanding the definition of *ḥayyei sha'ah* to encompass not only situations in which the cause of death is already present, a position rejected by *Ḥokhmat Shlomoh*, but to include also situations in which the cause of death is merely a statistical possibility.

Similar halakhic issues arise with regard to other prophylactic procedures. During the early part of the twentieth century, it was common practice for missionaries dispatched to remote areas of Africa to undergo prophylactic appendectomies. Approximately seven percent of the population of the United States will at some time in their lives be afflicted with appendicitis.[22] Precise mortality rates for untreated appendicitis are not available but are certainly very high. Before the age of sulfonamides and antibiotics and in situations in which medical evacuation was not a possibility, the desire to limit the avoidable risk of death as a result of a perforated appendix was entirely cogent. Even taking into account the high risks associated at that time with anesthesia and perioperative infection, the statistical balance of risk versus benefit certainly augured in favor of the procedure. In our own age, some oncologists suggest that patients with a family history of breast cancer who are known to be carriers of the BRCA gene consider undergoing prophylactic bilateral mastectomy. It is highly unlikely that the risks associated with that procedure are either ignored or perceived as negligible in our society. Even if a genetic predisposition or a statistical probability is to be equated with a present danger,[23] the as yet unafflicted patient is highly unlikely to die within twelve months. In such circumstances, surgical procedures that present a recognized danger do not represent the gamble of mere *ḥayyei sha'ah* as defined by *Ḥokhmat Shlomoh* and *Mishpat Kohen.*

V. *ḤAYYEI SHA'AH* DEFINED IN TERMS OF LIFE-QUANTA

The Gemara, *Yoma* 85b, cites the verse "and he shall live through them" (Leviticus 18:5) as establishing preservation of life as a paramount value. Mandatory suspension of *Shabbat* restrictions as well as of other halakhic strictures for the sake of prolongation of life for even the briefest of periods demonstrates that preservation of every moment of life is a paramount value. It seems to this writer that the willingness of Halakhah to sanction the risk of *ḥayyei sha'ah* does not compromise that value but is, in actuality, a reflection of precisely that underlying value.

Let us imagine a casino featuring a roulette wheel bearing only the numbers one through ten.[24] The house accepts ten-dollar wagers on any one of the numbers and pays one hundred dollars to the winner. The statistical probability is that a person who spends an evening placing bet after bet upon the turning of the wheel will leave the casino no richer and no poorer than when he entered. Depending upon one's perspective, the player has either wasted his time or has engaged in an innocent pastime.

Let us imagine also a casino featuring a roulette wheel bearing only the numbers one through nine. The house accepts ten-dollar wagers on any of the numbers and pays one hundred dollars to the winner. On eight out of nine turns of the wheel the player will lose, but the player has one chance out of nine of winning one hundred dollars. The statistical probability is that if he places bet after bet he will be ahead by ten dollars for every nine spins of the wheel. A player who takes advantage of such an opportunity is not a gambler but a shrewd entrepreneur. A player offered not simply marginal odds in his favor for modest gain but favorable odds for the opportunity to "break the bank" and walk away with all of the funds in the cashier's booth is offered a proposition that few reasonable men would refuse.

Imagine the more likely scenario in which the casino has a roulette wheel bearing the numbers one through eleven. The casino accepts ten-dollar wagers on each of the numbers and returns one hundred dollars to the winner. The statistical probability is that a player will expend one hundred and ten dollars in order to recoup one hundred dollars while the casino owner will earn a ten-dollar profit for every eleven turns of the wheel. The proprietors of the casino are not gamblers but schrewed businessmen; the players are fools throwing away their money.

Roulette gambling and gaming in general represent enterprises entered into for the express purpose of enhancing the number of banknotes in one's pocket. Money is risked for the sake of acquiring more money. Medical risks are assumed for an analogous reason: limited longevity anticipation is wagered in the hope of a return in the form of a longer longevity anticipation. The period of time placed at risk and the enhanced period of life to be gained may be described as life-quanta. The function and goal of medical intervention is maximization of life-quanta. Such intervention often involves the gamble of ephemeral longevity anticipation, a period of time that may be described as life-certain quanta, in an attempt to restore normal longevity anticipation which, in turn, may be described as representing life-possible quanta. In some situations the prospective gain and the chance of realizing that gain may be so great as to make the choice seem compelling. But that need not necessarily be the case. The gambling paradigm assumes that the opportunities for repeated wagers are open-ended. Humans do not enjoy the proverbial nine lives of a cat; each person has but one life. A person who has only one ten-dollar bill and no prospects of acquiring more will be extremely cautious in wagering that ten-dollar bill even when the odds of winning are weighted heavily in his favor.

The medical intervention risk-benefit calculus reflects two factors, *viz.*, the number of life-certain quanta at risk versus the anticipated gain of life-quanta as well as the recognition that normal longevity anticipation is extremely desirable but largely unquantifiable. In the classic cases discussed by the Gemara and in rabbinic responsa the precise length of normal longevity anticipation is not a factor. Those situations involve persons who, if left untreated, will succumb to disease within a predictable and relatively short period of time but, if intervention is successful, the result will be a normal life span. Clearly, the presumption is that the life-possible quanta of normal longevity anticipation are much greater than the life-certain quanta that will be enjoyed by the patient in the absence of intervention.

If the notion of risking *ḥayyei sha'ah* is understood, not as reflecting an intrinsically inferior quality of life, but as an expression of the balancing of life-certain quanta against life-possible quanta, the duration of certain survival is relevant only in terms of formulating a comparative risk-benefit calculation. Accordingly, a ten percent mortality risk might legitimately be accepted in the treatment of a malignancy that will lead to death, for example, within one to two years but for which treatment, if successful, will add many years of life.

A similar calculus can be applied to assumption of risk in conjunction with prophylactic procedures. In such cases, however, the calculations are much more complex and involve statistical probability rather than relatively firm medical prognoses. Thus, if it is established that there are cogent medical reasons for advising some carriers of the BRCA gene to undergo prophylactic mastectomy, the first step in assessing the halakhic propriety of the procedure is to determine the statistical probability of a carrier developing breast cancer over the course of a lifetime. The next step would be to establish the average age at which carriers of the BRCA gene who do develop breast cancer will succumb to the disease. The mastectomy candidate's present age should be subtracted from the average age of demise as statistically predicted. Assume, then, using statistics that are entirely hypothetical but convenient for purposes of illustration, that the woman in question has a one in five chance of succumbing to breast cancer twenty years in the future as opposed to longevity anticipation of forty years subsequent to successful bilateral mastectomy and that the surgery itself presents, at the most, a one percent risk of imminent mortality. Since twenty percent of all BRCA carriers in this hypothetical will survive only twenty years, rather than forty years, twenty out of every one hundred such women will lose twenty years of life. Thus, failure to intervene represents a twenty percent chance of a loss of twenty years of life, or a net loss of forty-eight months of life-quanta. The surgical risk represents a one percent loss of forty years of life or a net loss of 4.8 months of life-quanta. The sacrifice of 4.8 months for a gain of forty-eight months is readily justified in terms of maximization of life-quanta.

A theory of such nature must have been the basis of *Tiferet Yisra'el*'s endorsement of smallpox vaccination. Present danger as a result of vaccination was extremely small, albeit not nil. Statistical danger of smallpox contagion lay in the future but was far greater. Even absent methods for calculating precise statistical probability, it would have been readily apparent to *Tiferet Yisra'el* that the goal of maximizing life-quanta augurs in favor of vaccination. Prophylactic appendectomies for persons about to establish residence in areas in which subsequent medical or surgical intervention is precluded can similarly be justified on the basis of a relative life-quanta analysis.

VI. MINIMAL *ḤAYYEI SHA'AH* VERSUS ENHANCED *ḤAYYEI SHA'AH*

The question of whether a person may risk *ḥayyei sha'ah*, not in anticipation of a cure and hence a normal life span, but simply for prolongation of life, i.e., a longer period of *ḥayyei sha'ah*, is not addressed explicitly in the various codes of Jewish law. Nevertheless, *Iggerot Mosheh, Yoreh De'ah*, III, no. 36, rules that a person may jeopardize *ḥayyei sha'ah* only when it may reasonably be anticipated that, if the procedure is successful he will survive for at least twelve months. The same view is again expressed in *Iggerot Mosheh, Ḥoshen Mishpat*, II, no. 75, sec. 3.

There is, however, one early source that seems to address this issue in a few brief words and to formulate an entirely different view. Ramban, in his *Torat ha-Adam*, explains the phrase employed by the Gemara, *Avodah Zarah* 27b, "*Le-ḥayyei sha'ah lo ḥaishinan*" as meaning, "we are not concerned with possible [loss of] *ḥayyei sha'ah* in the face of more life (*ḥayyei tuva*)."[25] This writer does not understand the phrase "*ḥayyei tuva*" as connoting a normal life span but as meaning quite literally "more life."[26] If so, Ramban clearly affirms the principle that brief *ḥayyei sha'ah* may legitimately be hazarded, at least in some circumstances, in the hope of achieving a longer period of *ḥayyei sha'ah*.

Formulation of a life-quanta calculus also presents a vehicle for addressing the issue of limited *ḥayyei sha'ah* versus enhanced *ḥayyei sha'ah*, i.e., acceptance of the risk of the loss of a brief period of life on the part of a person afflicted by a terminal illness, not for the sake of a cure, but for the purpose of prolongation of life before succumbing to the ravages of that fatal disease. If justification of the risk of *ḥayyei sha'ah* is predicated upon the notion that it represents the gamble of a qualitatively less valuable form of life against the value of an intrinsically more valuable form of life, i.e., normal longevity, the risk of *ḥayyei sha'ah* for a marginally longer period of *ḥayyei sha'ah* could not be justified. If, however, the justification of the risk-taking involved in *ḥayyei sha'ah* is the maximization of life-quanta, the risk of *ḥayyei sha'ah* for a significantly longer period of *ḥayyei sha'ah* is readily justifiable.

A simple, but all too frequent, example lies in the case of a person suffering from terminal cancer who has developed an intestinal obstruction. Let us assume that it is known with certainty that, barring surgical intervention, the patient will survive no more than three days. If the obstruction is removed the patient may reasonably be assured of survival for a period of thirty days before succumbing to the effects of the underlying malignancy. The patient's general medical profile is such that he is deemed to have a thirty-three and one third percent chance of death during the course of surgery or shortly thereafter.

If presented with three such medically identical patients and surgery is performed upon all three, two of the patients will survive for a total combined life-quanta of sixty days. One patient will die immediately for a loss of a period of three days of life-quanta. Net life-quanta gained by a patient who successfully undergoes surgery will be sixty days minus three days, or fifty-seven days. To be sure, absent surgery, each of the patients would have lived three days. Nevertheless, taking into account the loss of three days of life in each of the two instances of unsuccessful intervention, the net gain as a result of surgical intervention will be fifty-one days. On balance, such a risk is entirely prudent.

The purpose of determining a risk-benefit calculus is to establish a means of distinguishing between prudence and foolhardiness. Medical prognoses with regard to survival periods are far from precise. Even more significantly, in any individual situation it is impossible to determine which choice will yield greater life-quanta. Hence, on this analysis, in all such circumstances, the decision to intervene and the decision not to intervene are, both halakhically and morally, equally acceptable.

As guardian of the body and soul, of the treasure of life entrusted to man, a person is duty-bound to avoid unnecessary risk and danger. In the course of daily life man has been granted license to engage in commonplace activities trusting that *shomer peta'im ha-Shem*. Activities that are not routine in nature require more careful scrutiny. Ofttimes during a person's lifetime occasions arise when medical intervention becomes a necessity. Attendant medical decision-making requires careful assessment of potential danger. Some forms of intervention are, relatively speaking, risk-free and hence mandatory; others border on the foolhardy and are to be eschewed; yet others require judicious balancing of potential benefit against possible harm. Discretionary intervention in the latter cases may be undertaken with the prayer to the Guardian of all life that the carefully considered decision of the wise also merit providential blessing.

NOTES

1. It is on the basis of this consideration that R. Moshe Feinstein, *Iggerot Mosheh, Yoreh De'ah*, II, no. 49, peremptorily dismisses the contention that cigarette smoking constitutes a violation of Jewish law. In that brief responsum, but seven and a half lines in length, *Iggerot Mosheh* does little more than cite the various talmudic references to *shomer peta'im ha-Shem*. To be sure, in earlier periods in Jewish history, the Sages promulgated decrees against specific forms of activity that they regarded as hazardous. *Tosafot, Beiẓah* 6a, describe the prohibition against drinking uncovered water, a practice forbidden lest a snake had previously partaken of the water and had deposited poisonous venom therein, as the subject of a *davar she-be-minyan*, a formal rabbinic decree. The hazards of cigarette smoking are quite probably greater than those of drinking uncovered

water. Had smoking been prevalent in days gone by and the hazards of tobacco been known, the Sages of the Talmud might well have deemed it wise to ban smoking. Thus *Iggerot Mosheh*'s responsum reflects the unexceptionable observation that, in the absence of biblical grounds and in the absence of a rabbinic decree either in the past or in the present, it cannot be maintained that a popularly accepted practice constitutes a violation of Halakhah because of an element of attendant danger. For a review of the controversy concerning smoking see this writer's "Smoking," *Tradition*, vol. 16, no. 4 (Summer, 1977), pp. 121–123.

It must be noted, however, that there is little question that *Iggerot Mosheh*'s responsum, written in 1964, accurately reflects the societal reality of that time, i.e., smoking was known to be fraught with danger but was nevertheless a path well trodden by the multitude. However, it is more than likely that, at present, that condition no longer obtains. See also *infra*, note 5.

2. See *infra*, note 10.
3. For an application of this principle in another context see the letter of R. Joseph Shalom Eliashiv quoted in *Am ha-Torah*, vol. II, no. 3 (5742), p. 102.
4. R. Ezekiel Landau, *Teshuvot Noda bi-Yehudah, Mahadura Tinyana, Yoreh De'ah*, no. 10, forbids hunting undertaken for sport because of the danger inherent in that activity but permits hunting for the purpose of earning a livelihood. *Noda bi-Yehudah* seems not to regard that danger as remote but nevertheless permits assumption of the attendant risk for the purpose of earning a livelihood.
5. Cigarette smoking might at first glance appear to be analogous to the situations ruled upon by *Binyan Ẓion*. No danger is present at the time the act is performed. The health hazards posed by smoking lie in the future. To be sure, certain physiological changes occur immediately upon inhalation of cigarette smoke, but such changes assume clinical significance only when they develop into symptoms of smoking-related illnesses. However, in light of presently available evidence, it appears that the cumulative risks of lung cancer, cardiovascular disease and respiratory illnesses will, in the aggregate, foreshorten the lives of the majority of smokers. If the majority of smokers do indeed face premature death as a result of cigarette smoking there is, according to *Binyan Ẓion*'s thesis, no halakhic basis for

sanctioning the practice even though the multitude continues "to tread thereon." That is so even if longevity is reduced only marginally.

6. Jewish teaching thus stands in stark contradiction to the Catholic view expressed by the seventeenth-century Spanish Cardinal, Juan de Lugo, in his *De Justitia et Jure*, Disp. 10, n. 30: "The duty of preserving one's life . . . does not include the duty of using means that will prolong life so briefly that they may be considered morally as nothing." See this writer's, "The Obligation to Heal in the Jewish Tradition," *Jewish Bioethics*, ed. Fred Rosner and J. David Bleich, 2nd ed. (Hoboken, N.J., 2000), pp. 16–18.
7. See *infra*, note 18 and accompanying text.
8. As a practical matter, although it may not be difficult to establish the possibility of therapeutic efficacy, it may be extremely difficult and even impossible to quantify the probability of success as more or less than fifty percent. For example, the four lepers described in II Kings had rational grounds to believe that feelings of pity might be evoked in the enemy, but what basis might they have had for assuming that the chances of mercy were at least fifty percent? Cf., R. Moshe Feinstein, *Iggerot Mosheh, Yoreh De'ah*, II, no. 36.
9. See *infra*, note 16 and accompanying text.
10. See *Iggerot Mosheh, Yoreh De'ah*, III, no. 36, s.v. *u-be-dvar*. *Iggerot Mosheh*, however, does assert that if the chances of success are greater than fifty percent the procedure is obligatory. *Iggerot Mosheh* cites no evidence in support of that view and says only that it is "*mistaber*" ("logical" or "reasonable"). However, in light of the fact that the principle of *rov* is not applicable in restricting jeopardization of *ḥayyei sha'ah*, despite the paramount value of every moment of life, there seems to be no compelling reason to assume that the same principle can, in other circumstances, require such jeopardization of *ḥayyei sha'ah*. It is because every moment of life is of infinite value that even discretionary jepardization of *ḥayyei sha'ah* requires justification. See *infra*, section V. As will be explained, those considerations do not serve to render assumption of such risk mandatory. Rabbi Feinstein's view is reiterated in *Iggerot Mosheh, Ḥoshen Mishpat*, II, no. 74, sec. 5.
11. See *supra*, p. 182.
12. Cf., however, R. Eliezer Waldenberg, *Ẓiẓ Eli'ezer*, IV, no. 12,

sec. 1, s.v. *ve-lakhen,* who somewhat tentatively forbids self-endangerment unless it is certain that, absent intervention, the patient will die. See also *Iggerot Mosheh, Yoreh De'ah,* II, no. 36, s.v. *ve-hineh,* who regards it as self-evident that it is forbidden to perform a hazardous medical procedure on behalf of a patient who would otherwise suffer chronic pain and remain bedridden for life.

Cf., however, *Ẓiẓ Eli'ezer,* XIII, no. 87, who notes that, in a terminally-ill patient, extreme pain may serve to hasten death. See also the comment of R. Shlomoh Zalman Auerbach cited by R. Joshua Neuwirth, *Shmirat Shabbat ke-Hilkhatah,* I, 2nd ed. (Jerusalem, 5739), 32:56, note 150 as well as *supra,* chap. 6, "Palliation of Pain," pp. 184–185.

13. See *Kol Kitvei ha-Ramban,* ed. R. Bernard Chavel (Jerusalem, 5723), II, 43.
14. See *Bava Meẓi'a* 93b. The phrase "*ke-derekh ha-shomrim*—in the manner of bailees" employed by the Mishnah, *Bava Meẓi'a* 42a, has the same connotation.
15. See *Shulḥan Arukh, Ḥoshen Mishpat* 291:13.
16. Cf., *Iggerot Mosheh, Yoreh De'ah,* III, no. 36, who explains the discretionary nature of such decisions in terms of a notion of at least limited proprietorship of one's body. In this writer's opinion, the problem requiring resolution does not compel establishment of a notion of limited proprietorship.
17. See *Shulḥan Arukh, Ḥoshen Mishpat* 291:14. See also *Ginat Veradim, Ḥoshen Mishpat, klal* 1, no. 5 and R. Ya'akov Yeshayah Blau, *Pitḥei Ḥoshen,* II, 2:1, note 3.
18. Another reason for requiring rabbinic endorsement of a decision to institute hazardous therapy may be gleaned from comments made in an entirely different context by R. Chaim Pelaggi, *Ḥikkekei Lev,* I, *Yoreh De'ah,* no. 50. *Ḥikkekei Lev* accepts the view of Rabbenu Nissim, *Nedarim* 40a, who states that it is permissible, and even praiseworthy, to pray for the death of a patient who is gravely ill and in extreme pain but expresses an important caveat with regard to such prayer. According to *Ḥikkekei Lev,* only totally disinterested parties may take any action, including prayer, which might lead to a premature termination of life. Husband, children, family, and those charged with the care of a patient, according to *Ḥikkekei Lev,* may not pray for death. The considerations underlying this reservation are twofold in nature: (1) Persons who are

emotionally involved, if they are permitted even such non-physical methods of intervention as prayer, may be prompted to perform an overt act that would have the effect of shortening life and thus be tantamount to euthanasia. (2) Precisely because of their closeness to the situation, they are psychologically incapable of reaching a detached, dispassionate and objective decision in which consideration of the patient's welfare is the sole controlling motive. The human psyche is such that the intrusion of emotional involvement and subjective interest preclude a totally objective and disinterested decision.

There is no reason to assume that a physician will, or should, distance himself emotionally from the treatment of his patient. Unable to be completely dispassionate, the physician may well be inclined to accept an unwarranted risk if there is even a remote chance of achieving a cure. Alternatively, frustration at being unable to cure the patient may engender despair and hence the physician may fail to take proper cognizance of the value of even limited residual longevity. It is not easy for the physician to transcend his emotional involvement in the care of his patient, his personal and professional interest in achieving a cure or his frustration when confronted by lack of success. Those factors, singly or in combination, may well color his judgment. In contradistinction, as is the case with regard to a judge sitting in a capital case, the rabbinic decisor is charged with reaching a dispassionate conclusion based solely upon the facts of the case untinged by emotional or psychological factors.

19. Rashi, *Avodah Zarah* 27b, s.v. *ḥayyei sha'ah*, comments: ". . . and perhaps he will live a day or two days." R. Abraham I. Kook, *Mishpat Kohen*, no. 144, sec. 3, categorizes that comment as contextually explanatory rather than as normatively definitive. Accordingly, *Mishpat Kohen* dismisses the position of his interlocutor who sought to define *ḥayyei sha'ah* as a period of no more than twentyfour hours.
20. *Iggerot Mosheh, Ḥoshen Mishpat*, II, no. 75, sec. 2, posits the same distinction for purposes of triage decisions.
21. Positing a definition of *ḥayyei sha'ah* as longevity anticipation of no more than twelve months leads to a quandary in many contemporary decision-making situations. Scholars such as *Shevut Ya'akov* and *Mishnat Ḥakhamim* address situa-

tions in which the degree of danger is manifest. In such cases the physician may well be able to assess the length of potential survival in an individual patient. But what of the case of the patient suffering from an aortic aneurysm? Left unattended, such a patient may survive for years and even decades; on the other hand, the aneurysm may rupture momentarily. There is simply no way to assess the longevity anticipation of any such individual patient in order to determine whether, without intervention, he will or will not survive for more than twelve months. Whether or not *Ḥokhmat Shlomoh* and *Mishpat Kohen* would accept statistical evidence establishing the probability of a mean survival period of more or less than twelve months as a basis for decision-making in such instances is a question that cannot readily be answered.

The identical issue presents itself with even greater force with regard to diagnostic procedures. For example, a patient suffering from blocked cardiac vessels requires angioplasty or bypass surgery. Assume that the patient may be suffering from a form of coronary disease such that, absent intervention, survival will be less than twelve months. However, the existence of a blockage can only be established on the basis of an angiogram, a procedure which does present a quantifiable risk. If the patient is afflicted with coronary disease and will survive less than twelve months, all authorities would endorse use of an angiogram as a diagnostic measure. However, if the patient is found to be free of coronary disease or to be afflicted by a relatively mild cardiac condition, it turns out that he has risked not *ḥayyei sha'ah* but a normal life span. If the thesis of *Ḥokhmat Shlomoh* and *Mishpat Kohen* is accepted, hazardous diagnostic procedures of such nature do not appear to be justifiable.

22. See D. Mike Hardin, Jr., "Acute Appendicitis: Review and Update," *American Family Physician*, vol. 60, no. 7 (November 1, 1999), p. 2027.
23. See this writer's *Bioethical Dilemmas: A Jewish Perspective*, I (Hoboken, N.J., 1998), 154–156.
24. The analogy presented herein as well as the notion of maximization of life-quanta as a basis for decision-making were earlier formulated in this writer's "Baby Jane Doe and Baby Fae," *Bioethical Dilemmas*, I, 333–337.

25. *Kol Kitvei ha-Ramban*, II, 38.

26. Cf., however, Avraham Steinberg, *Encyclopedia Halakhatit Refu'it*, V (Jerusalem, 5756), 3, who understands Ramban as sanctioning the risk of *ḥayyei sha'ah* only for *ḥayyei olam*, i.e., normal longevity anticipation. In this writer's opinion Ramban abjured use of the phrase "*ḥayyei olam*" or of the phrase "*ḥayyei kiyyum*" and advisedly employed the phrase *ḥayyei tuva* in order to negate the notion that *ḥayyei sha'ah* may be risked only in anticipation of gaining a normal life span.

9

The Case of the British Conjoined Twins

Over a period of weeks during the summer of 2000, British newspapers published a series of reports concerning the heart-rending case of conjoined twins, neither of whom would have been able to survive unless one were sacrificed to save the other.

The parents live in Gozo, a smaller sister island of Malta and one of the group of islands that constitute the Republic of Malta. The presence of conjoined twins in the mother's uterus was discerned by ultrasound when the mother was four months pregnant. Because of the comparatively poor medical facilities on the island of Gozo the parents traveled to Britain, which has a reciprocal medical arrangement with Malta, in order to avail themselves of the services of Britain's National Health Service. Earlier, two other sets of conjoined twins were sent to Britain from Malta within a period of twelve months. Unfortunately, all four of those infants failed to survive. Since the total incidence of all forms of twins physically connected to each other by some part of the body is generally accepted as being approximately one in fifty thousand births, the birth of three sets of conjoined twins within less than two years in a country having a total population of 367,000 is striking.

The mother was treated at St. Mary's Hospital in

Manchester. Because of the medical anomalies present in the fetuses as well as the fear that the smaller of the twins would not survive birth, the parents were offered the option of an abortion, a procedure that is apparently illegal in Malta in any pregnancy. The parents, who are Roman Catholic, refused to consider termination of the pregnancy as an option. The twins, who were girls, were delivered on August 8, 2000, by Caesarian section at 42 weeks.

In order not to intrude upon the privacy of the family, a British family court judge ordered that the parents not be identified. For the purpose of judicial proceedings the twins were given fictitious names: the larger, stronger twin was referred to as Jodie; the smaller, weaker twin was referred to as Mary.

The twins were ischiopagus, i.e., joined at the ischium, the bone which forms the lower back portion of the pelvis. The lower ends of the two spines were fused and the spinal cords were joined. The bodies were also fused from the umbilicus to the sacrum. The twins had four lower limbs which protruded at an acute angle to the spine at the center of their shared torso. Internally, the twins had separate hearts, lungs, livers and kidneys but shared a bladder that emptied through two separate urethra. The smaller, weaker twin had an insufficiently developed brain. Mary was in a chronic persistent hypoxic state and was suffering an acute shortage of oxygen which was likely to have a damaging effect on her metabolism and to have led inevitably to the death of cells throughout her body.

There were two crucial anatomical problems: 1) Although each twin had a separate and anatomically normal four-chambered heart, Jodie's aorta fed into Mary's aorta with the result that the arterial circulation ran from Jodie to Mary. The venous return passed from Mary to Jodie through a united inferior vena cava and other venous channels in the united soft tissue. 2) Although she had lungs, Mary was incapable of respiration. Thus, since Mary's lungs and heart were too deficient to oxygenate and pump blood through her body, she was dependent upon Jodie's ability to circulate blood for both of them through a common aorta. The danger was that Jodie's heart would not be able to sustain the double burden indefinitely and would eventually fail. Separation of the twins would have required clamping and then severing the common aorta with the resultant imminent death of Mary.

Physicians at St. Mary's Hospital sought to separate the twins, but the parents refused to consent. According to testimony before the High Court, the parents objected to the separation both because they believed that the matter had to be left in God's hands and because, even if the separation was successful, Jodie would require additional surgery and further extensive medical cure that was not available in their homeland. The father, who had been unemployed for some time, and the mother could not afford to remain in England and could not bring themselves to surrender the child to foster care even if that were feasible. The hospital applied to the High Court for an order permitting the surgical separation to proceed despite the absence of parental consent. That petition was granted[1] on August 25, 2000, on the ground that severing the aorta should be regarded as withholding an extraneous blood supply and hence—although the aptness of the analogy was denied by the Court—should be regarded as the equivalent of disconnecting a heart-lung machine, i.e., as merely the withholding of treatment rather than as a positive act of homicide. The parents were supported in their objection to separation of the twins by the Roman Catholic bishop of Gozo and by the Archbishop of Westminster as well as by the Pro-Life Alliance. The latter two were granted permission to make written submissions in the form of amici briefs. The appellate court disagreed with the reasoning of the lower court but nevertheless, on September 22nd, in an extremely lengthy opinion, confirmed the order.[2] The surgery was performed on November 9, 2000, and Jodie survived the procedure.

A detailed analysis of the precedents and of the legal reasons advanced by the various justices in concurring opinions is beyond the scope of this undertaking.[3] Suffice it to say that courts in the United States do not regard themselves as empowered to overrule medical decisions of parents unless those decisions are determined to be clearly unreasonable.[4] As will be shown, a conclusion to that effect does not appear to be compelled by the circumstances of this case.

The halakhic issues involved in separation of conjoined twins were discussed by this writer in the Fall, 1996 issue of *Tradition* in connection with the Halsey twins who were then the focus of media attention and the much earlier Philadelphia case involving conjoined twins born to a devout Jewish couple. An amplified treatment of those issues was subsequently published in *Bioethical Dilemmas*, I (Hoboken, N.J.,1998), 283–328. The present discussion will be limited to an endeavor to show which of the earlier discussed considerations are germane to the present case and how, because of the distinctive facts of the case, this case may be distinguished from the earlier considered instances of conjoined twins.

On the basis of available reports, Jodie and Mary must be considered to have been separate and individual persons and indeed no one has suggested otherwise. Despite fusion of the spines, joined spinal cords and a continuation from one twin to the other of the sheath covering the spinal cord, the twins had separate nervous systems as evidenced by the fact that they apparently reacted independently to pain stimuli. As indicated in our earlier treatment of the topic, that phenomenon is the crucial indicator of whether the twins constitute a single organism or two separate persons. Accordingly, separation and removal of the smaller twin cannot be halakhically construed as the amputation of a harmful appendage.

I. THE LAW OF THE PURSUER

From the perspective of Halakhah, separation of the twins represents the sacrifice of one for the purpose of preserving the life of the second. Except in the rarest of circumstances, Jewish law forbids the taking of one life in order to preserve another. That prohibition is predicated upon the underlying premise that each life is of infinite value and hence rescue of a life, or even of many lives, cannot serve to exculpate an act of homicide. As expressed in the talmudic formulation, "*Mai ḥazit de-dema didakh sumak tefei dilma dama de-hahu gavra sumak tefei*—What makes you consider your life to be sweeter; perhaps the life of your fellow is sweeter?" The selfsame principle applies even in situations in which sacrifice of a single life will result in the rescue of multiple lives and also applies—albeit, as will be shown, with a narrow exception—in situations in which the life that might be sacrificed will ultimately be lost even if there is no intervention. In effect the applicable rule is: "Better two deaths than one murder." Although there are exceptions to the general rule that the taking of human life is forbidden, no life can be extinguished unless the applicability of an exception is clear and unequivocal; in cases of doubt the applicable principle is *shev ve-al ta'aseh*, i.e., passive non-interference.

The chief exception to the rule banning intervention is in the case of a *rodef*, i.e., a "pursuer" engaged in an activity that will result in the loss of the life of another individual.[5] The rule applicable in the case of a *rodef* is not limited to situations of unjust aggression; the law of the *rodef* applies regardless of whether the *rodef* acts intentionally or unintentionally. Accordingly, in the case of the British conjoined twins, a *prima facie* argument can be formulated to sanction surgical intervention on the grounds that Mary was a *rodef* threatening the life of Jodie. Despite the fact that they shared a common blood supply, Mary was compelling Jodie to pump blood through her body, an activity Jodie would not have been able to sustain without forfeiting her own life.

That argument, however, might fail for three separate reasons:

1. The mandate to eliminate a "pursuer" does not apply in situations of mutual pursuit. In the Philadelphia case, for example, the twins shared a single heart that, had it been assigned to either twin, would have enabled that twin to survive. But, since the heart was in the common possession of both, each was an aggressor *vis-à-vis* the other. In the present case, no vital organs were shared. Medical testimony indicated that, if the twins were to be separated, Mary's own heart and lungs would not sustain life. Thus, while Mary posed a threat to the life of Jodie, Jodie posed no reciprocal threat to Mary. Quite to the contrary, Jodie was prolonging her sister's life since, had Mary been born a singleton, she would already have expired.

2. The law of *rodef* is not automatically triggered by virtue of the aggressor's intention. Quite apart from having the intention to destroy the life of the victim, the aggressor must be capable of successfully carrying out that intention. As pointed out elsewhere,[6] the degree of certainty that, absent intervention by another person, the *rodef* will succeed in accomplishing his malevolent goal that is required to justify such intervention is a matter of dispute among latter-day authorities. Although R. Elijah of Vilna, *Bi'ur ha-Gra, Ḥoshen Mishpat* 338:74, appears to apply a looser standard, R. Chaim Ozer Grodzinski, *Teshuvot Aḥi'ezer*, I, no. 123, sec. 2, requires an "*umdena*" or assessment of probable success on the part of the *rodef*, while R. Moshe Feinstein, *Iggerot Mosheh*, *Ḥoshen Mishpat*, II, no. 69, sec. 2, requires an "*umdena gedolah karov le-vadai*—an assessment approaching certainty." The same standard of certainty is required in cases of nonvolitional aggression. On the basis of the medical testimony cited by the appellate court in its decision it would seem that there existed an *umdena* that Jodie would die if she were not separated from her sister but it is not clear whether or not that assessment "approached certainty."

3. As has been quite cogently documented by the late R. Baruch Dov Povarsky, *Bad Kodesh*, IV, no. 52, s.v. *ve-sham'ati*, the rule of *rodef* is not at all applicable in cases such as this. The Gemara, *Sanhedrin* 72b, presents the case of a hydroencephalic fetus whose head is too large to emerge from the mother's birth canal without causing fatal hemorrhaging to the mother. The fetus is clearly a "pursuer" in the sense that its passage through the birth canal is factually an act of mortal aggression against the mother while, since the infant can survive the delivery, the mother is not a "pursuer" *vis-à-vis* the child. Nevertheless, once the child is "born," an event defined as delivery of the major portion of either its body or its forehead, intervention is forbidden. Despite the fact that the infant is a *rodef*, its life is not forfeit because "*me-shemaya ka radfi lah*—It is Heaven that pursues her." That formulation means simply that the law of *rodef* does not apply in a situation in which the danger is the result of the workings of nature as distinct from a danger resulting from a human act even though such an act may be nonvolitional. In all cases of conjoined twins, the hazard to life is the result of anatomical malformation that occurs in the course of cell division and therefore it is Heaven that is the aggressor. Hence mortals may not rely upon the rule of *rodef* in order to intervene for the purpose of eliminating one life in order to save another.

II. THE PHILADELPHIA CASE

R. Moshe Feinstein's oral ruling in the Philadelphia case permitting the separation of conjoined twins who shared a single six-chambered heart is well known. At the time, that ruling caused raised eyebrows for the reasons outlined above. Indeed, as reported in the letters to the editor section of *Tradition*, vol. 31, no. 4 (Summer, 1997), pp. 80–82, a number of rabbinic decisors disagreed with that ruling.

This author has attempted to explain Rabbi Feinstein's ruling on the basis of the latter's own analysis of the law of *rodef* as formulated by him in *Iggerot Mosheh, Yoreh De'ah*, II, no. 60, in an entirely different context. Rabbi Feinstein rejects the conventional distinction between the usual *rodef* and aggression "at the hands of Heaven." Instead, on the basis of a parallel statement in the Palestinian Talmud, he understands that phrase as reflecting the rule that the law of *rodef* is not applicable in situations of mutual aggression. Rabbi Feinstein further endeavors to demonstrate that the inapplicability of the law of *rodef* in cases of mutual aggression is limited to situations in which each aggressor is engaged in a qualitatively comparable act. However, in a situation in which one aggressor is intent upon taking a life that, in terms of objective halakhic criteria, is superior to the life threatened by the other aggressor, the qualitatively inferior life of that *rodef* may be extinguished in order to preserve the halakhically superior life.

Although, according to Rambam, feticide is a form of homicide, the life of a fetus is inferior to the life of a person already born because, for Jews, feticide does not lead to capital punishment. Similarly, the life of a *treifah* is inferior to the life of an anatomically normal person because the murderer of a *treifah* does not incur the death penalty. A *treifah* is a person with a congenital anomaly that will cause death within twelve months or who has sustained a trauma that will cause death within a twelve month period. Thus, according to Rabbi Feinstein, in the case of mutual aggressors, the nascent life of a fetus may be destroyed in order to preserve the mother and the life of a *treifah* may be extinguished to preserve an anatomically normal person. Applying this line of reasoning to the case of the Philadelphia twins, if it is presumed that one of the twins was a *treifah*, that twin might be sacrificed in order to save the "normal" twin.

However, in the present case, reliance upon Rabbi Feinstein's ruling, as it is understood by this author, is problematic for a number of reasons:

1. The assumption ascribed to Rabbi Feinstein to the ef-

fect that an infant who possesses a congenitally malformed heart is a *treifah* requires clarification. An obvious source for that position is the eighteenth-century ruling of R. Yonatan Eibeschutz in a celebrated controversy between himself and R. Zevi Ashkenazi.

A young woman eviscerated, soaked and salted a chicken but failed to find a heart. She consulted R. Zevi Ashkenazi who, as recorded in his *Teshuvot Ḥakham Ẓevi*, nos. 74, 76 and 77, ruled that the animal was kosher. *Ḥakham Ẓevi* reasoned that, since it is impossible for any creature to survive without a heart for even a brief period of time, it must be assumed that the chicken, which had thrived and developed in a normal manner, must indeed have been endowed with a heart. The absence of a heart, declared *Ḥakham Ẓevi*, must assuredly be attributed to the predatory nature of a cat that undoubtedly had been in close proximity. Not content with simply ruling with regard to the case presented to him, *Ḥakham Ẓevi* further announced that "even if witnesses will come and testify that they saw with open eyes that nothing was removed from the body of the chicken, it is certain that their testimony is false for it is contrary to reality." In sharp disagreement, R. Yonatan Eibeschutz, *Kereti u-Peleti* 40:4, declared that the testimony of credible witnesses cannot be dismissed peremptorily but rather "it must be assumed that there was some piece [of tissue] which does not appear as a heart but which is designed to fulfill the functions of the heart, but yet the chicken is *treifah* since it is not a normal heart." Thus, *Kereti u-Peleti* clearly regards an animal born with an anomalous heart to be a *treifah* because it lacks a normal heart.

However, *Ḥazon Ish*, *Yoreh De'ah* 4:14, takes issue with *Kereti u-Peleti* in arguing that the chicken thus described is kosher despite the cardiac anomaly that may have been present. *Ḥazon Ish* argues that, although removal of the heart does indeed render the animal a *treifah*, there is no source for a ruling that an anomaly of the heart similarly renders the animal a *treifah*. Moreover, there is no clear indication that *Kereti u-Peleti* would regard a six-chamber heart in the same light as a mere piece of tissue that fulfills the function of a heart.

Granting, *arguendo*, that a six-chamber heart is sufficiently anomalous to be recognized as a *treifah* by *Kereti u-Peleti*, it does not automatically follow that Mary's anatomical anomalies rendered her a *treifah*. Essentially, Mary's organs were structurally intact and uncompromised save for the fact that her aorta and vena cava were joined to those of her sister. In effect, she possessed an elongated aorta and an elongated vena cava. Although she was apparently incapable of independent respiration, Mary's lungs seemed to have been anatomically normal. A patient who must be maintained on a respirator is not thereby rendered a *treifah*. It is certainly arguable that the linkage of Mary's circulatory system to that of her sister did not involve a gross structural anomaly and hence the danger to her life is, for purposes of Jewish law, to be defined as physiological in nature as distinct from anatomical. Accordingly, since the anatomical integrity of none of Mary's vital organs had been compromised, she could not be adjudged to be a *treifah* and hence Rabbi Feinstein's ruling, as understood by this writer, is rendered inapplicable.

2. However, the dispute between *Ḥazon Ish* and *Kereti u-Peleti* occurs in the context of the status of an animal. Although as evidenced by Rambam's undisputed rulings in *Hilkhot Ma'akhalot Assurot* 4:9 and *Hilkhot Sheḥitah*, chaps. 5 and 6, the talmudic enumeration of the various *treifot* is exhaustive, nevertheless, insofar as human *treifot* are concerned, Rambam, *Hilkhot Roẓeaḥ* 2:8, asserts that, in every era, the particular anomalies or traumas that render a human being a *treifah* are to be assessed in accordance with the medical knowledge of the day. Thus Rambam rules that a human being is not to be considered a *treifah* (and his murderer must be executed) unless "it is known with certainty that this [person] is a *treifah* and the physicians declare that this wound has no

cure in a human being or he will die as a result of it unless something else kills him [sooner]."[7] Rambam's categorical statement regarding medical assessment of human *treifot* indicates both that a wound or anomaly that would render an animal a *treifah* does not necessarily render a human being a *treifah* and also that a wound that will cause death in man renders a human being a *treifah* even though, with regard to animals, it is not one of the enumerated *treifot*.

Accordingly, although the absence, perforation or presence of an anomalous aorta or vena cava does not render an animal a *treifah*, it is arguable that, according to Rambam, the presence of an anomaly in one of those structures that will cause death within twelve months would serve to render a human being a *treifah*. In the present case, however, it is not at all clear that Jodie's ultimate demise should be described as the result of a malfunction of a defective aorta since an elongated aorta is not, in and of itself, a defect. Rather, death would have resulted from the burden placed upon a normal heart, a cause that may be described as physiological rather than anatomical.

Rambam's definition of the halakhic concept of *treifut* as applied to humans is far from universally accepted. According to those who disagree with Rambam, a person is deemed a *treifah* only if he suffers from one of the talmudically enumerated anomalies or has experienced the perforation or excision of one of the group of identified vital organs.[8] Since Mary did not manifest any of the specifically defined forms of *treifut*, according to those authorities, there is no basis for entertaining the notion that she was encompassed within that category.

3. The medical testimony before the Court reflected disagreement among physicians with regard to how long the twins might have survived without separation. When questioned in this regard one physician testified, ". . . it is very difficult to be precise . . . but I think three to six months is a reasonable guide of the kind of time we could be looking

at." However, another physician, a pediatric surgeon affiliated with London's Great Ormand Street Hospital, an institution that has had greater experience in separation of conjoined twins, testified that "my impression is they can live together for many months, or perhaps even a few years. . . ." The testimony of other physicians was rather equivocal. None was asked to quantify the probability of survival for a period of twelve months or longer.

In the case of the Philadelphia twins, Rabbi Povarsky suggested that the twin who was incapable of independent survival might have the status of a *nefel*, i.e., of an abortus or stillborn infant. The Gemara, *Shabbat* 135a, describes a nonviable neonate that has not yet expired as having a status comparable to that of a stone that cannot be moved on the Sabbath. A neonate incapable of survival for a minimum period of thirty days is deemed to be a *nefel*. It is arguable that, since a *nefel* does not have the status of a living person, it may be sacrificed to save the viable infant.

In his earlier-cited treatment of separation of conjoined twins this writer adduced a significant number of authorities who maintain that a neonate who survives for thirty days, even if its survival was possible only by virtue of the assistance of artificial life support systems, is not a *nefel*. Thus, even though Mary could not have survived without the assistance of the cardiopulmonary assistance of her sister's organs, nevertheless, having survived for more than the statutory thirty-day period, she was no longer a *nefel* and hence her life was entitled to the same protection as that of her sister.

III. DESIGNATION FOR DEATH

There is yet another provision of Jewish law that must be examined in seeking possible justification for sacrificing Mary in order to preserve the life of Jodie.

II Samuel 20:4–22 tells of how Joab, commander of King David's troops, had pursued Sheba the son of Bichri. The latter fled and sought refuge in the town of Abel. Thereupon Joab besieged the town and demanded that the fugitive be delivered to the king's forces. Joab threatened that, should the townspeople fail to comply, he would annihilate the entire populace. Scripture reports that the townspeople acceded to his demand: "And they cut off the head of Sheba the son of Bichri and threw it out to Joab."

The Palestinian Talmud, *Terumot* 8:10, assumes that the narrative concerning Joab and the delivery of Sheba the son of Bichri is recorded with approbation and cites the following *Baraita*:

> A group of people are traveling on a journey. [If] gentiles accost them and say, "Give us one of your company and we shall put him to death; but, if not, we shall kill all of you," even if all of them will be killed let them not deliver a single soul of Israel. [But] if [the gentiles] specified one [of the company], such as Sheba ben Bichri, let them deliver him and not be killed.

R. Simeon ben Lakish qualifies the latter ruling with the statement that the designated individual may be delivered to death "only if he is liable to the death penalty as was Sheba the son of Bichri." R. Yoḥanan disagrees and declares that specification, in and of itself, is sufficient to warrant delivery to the attackers even in the absence of any culpability on the part of the victim.

R. Simeon ben Lakish infers from the biblical narrative that acquiescence with such a demand can be sanctioned only in instances in which the victim's life is already lawfully forfeit, as was the case with regard to Sheba the son of Bichri who is described in II Samuel 20:1 as being guilty of *lèse majesté*. However, in instances in which the victim is not culpable, all must suffer martyrdom rather than become accomplices to murder. R. Yoḥanan maintains that the victim's guilt or innocence is irrelevant. Although members of a group dare not enter into collusion with a murderer by themselves selecting one of their company for death, nevertheless, once a person has been marked for death in any event, either alone if surrendered by his companions or together with the entire company if they refuse to comply, those who deliver him are not regarded as causing or compounding his misfortune; rather, they are engaged in the rescue of those threatened individuals whose fate has not been sealed.

Rambam, *Hilkhot Yesodei ha-Torah* 5:5, rules in accordance with the opinion of R. Simeon ben Lakish and sanctions the delivery of an already doomed victim only if the victim is guilty of a capital transgression[9] and adds the comment "*ve-ein morin ken le-khathilah*," i.e., that people should nevertheless not be directed or advised to deliver the victim even in such circumstances.[10] However, Rabbenu Shimshon, in his commentary on the Mishnah, *Terumot* 8:12, and Rabbenu Nissim, *Yoma* 82a, rule in accordance with the opinion of R. Yoḥanan and permit delivery of the specified victim in all cases in which the selection of the victim is determined by the perpetrator. Rema, *Yoreh De'ah* 151:7, cites both views without explicitly accepting one over the other.[11] *Taz*, *Yoreh De'ah* 257:7, citing an earlier decision of *Baḥ*,[12] rules in accordance with the more stringent position.

In the case of Mary and Jodie there was an inherent threat to the life of both in the sense that both twins would die if Mary were not "delivered" to death in the course of being separated from her sister. Thus, upon first analysis, the paradigm of the "group of gentiles" presented by the Palestinian Talmud as well as the attendant controversy between R. Simeon ben Lakish and R. Yoḥanan and its reflection in the opposing positions of medieval rabbinic authorities would appear to be the proper source for guidance with regard to the fate of Jodie.

To this one additional point must be added. The earlier-cited discussion of the Palestinian Talmud continues with a narrative concerning R. Joshua ben Levi that yields an additional perspective regarding delivery of an already specified victim. R. Joshua ben Levi and his compatriots found themselves in the position of harboring a fugitive in the city of Lod. The authorities besieged the city and, threatening the entire populace with death, demanded that the fugitive be turned over to them. R. Joshua ben Levi directed the populace to comply with that demand. The Palestinian Talmud further recounts that R. Joshua ben Levi had previously been privileged to have the prophet Elijah as a frequent visitor but subsequent to this incident Elijah ceased to reveal himself to R. Joshua ben Levi. The latter fasted many fasts until Elijah appeared to him and declared, "Shall I reveal myself to a betrayer!" When R. Joshua ben Levi protested, "Have I not acted in accordance with law?" Elijah dismissed his apologia with the words "Is this then the law of the pious?"

Put simply, the talmudic narrative teaches that delivery of a victim to death, even when halakhically defensible and motivated by an imperative to save others, is not consistent with piety. Although legally defensible, it is a course of action that a person possessing a keenly honed moral sensitivity should eschew as repugnant.[13]

In any event, in the case of Sheba ben Bichri, he and all of the inhabitants of the city faced imminent death by King David's forces. Consequently, even if specification of the victim by the perpetrator were sufficient to warrant delivery of one individual in order to save others, it is far from clear that such action would be permissible if the designated victim would otherwise be allowed to live for an unspecified or indefinite period of time before being put to death. In developing his more general thesis with regard to the law of the *rodef*, Rabbi Feinstein makes it clear that both R. Yoḥanan and R. Simeon ben Lakish permit delivery of an identified victim only because the victim is thereby deprived merely of *ḥayyei sha'ah*, i.e., the brief, ephemeral period of time that he would otherwise survive before being put to death together with the entire group. Thus, both R. Yoḥanan and R. Simeon ben Lakish would agree that if the victim might survive for an extended period of time, i.e., more than twelve months, if not delivered to the enemy, the specified individual may not be delivered to an earlier death.

The principle underlying permissibility of cooperation in cases of specification by the malefactor is not explicitly formulated by the Palestinian Talmud. It might be assumed that the rationale underlying R. Yoḥanan's position is that, in situations in which non-intervention will result in the death of all, delivery of a single member of the company cannot be sanctioned simply because no one is empowered to select one person over another. However, when the selection is made by the perpetrator of the heinous scheme, those who accede to his command are absolved from fault: it is the perpetrator who has first decreed death for all and it is the perpetrator who has then selected one for death and spared the others. Rabbi Feinstein, however, dismisses that analysis on the argument that the life of the person delivered to the perpetrator is surely foreshortened as a result of having been delivered. To be sure, were he not handed over, he, too, would be put to death together with the entire company, but his death would perforce be delayed for at least the limited period of time required to subdue and annihilate the entire group. Since hastening a person's demise by even a moment is a capital transgression, argues Rabbi Feinstein, those who deliver the designated victim cannot plead that they have caused him no harm.

In developing his analysis of the controversy between R. Yoḥanan and R. Simeon ben Lakish, Rabbi Feinstein introduces the novel concept that the specified individual is a *rodef* by virtue of his very existence.[14] That individual, once he has been designated for delivery to death, causes the others to be endangered simply by virtue of his continued presence among them. In delivering the designated victim to the perpetrator the rest of the company are indeed also *rodefim* with regard to the specified person. Nevertheless, the two acts of pursuit are qualitatively different. By his very presence among them the specified individual is passively engaged in "pursuit" of the normal longevity anticipation of the other members of the group; the others, however, are in "pursuit" of only the brief and ephemeral life expectancy of a person who is already marked for death and who faces imminent execution.

It is indeed the case that Jewish law does not distinguish between diverse quantitative life expectancies and hence the life of a newborn child who may anticipate living to the age of three score and ten is not more precious than the life of a frail and feeble octogenarian. However, for some purposes, e.g., for priority with regard to rescue, Halakhah does recognize a distinction between *ḥayyei sha'ah*, i.e., the brief and ephemeral residual life span of a terminally ill patient, and normal life anticipation. *Ḥayyei sha'ah* is defined by many authorities as an anticipated life span of less than twelve months.[15] Rabbi Feinstein asserts that R. Simeon ben Lakish sanctions the delivery of an already specified victim because the gravity of the consequence of his "pursuit" of the other members of the group is greater than the gravity of the act of those who, by virtue of their act of delivery, pursue him. The designated victim is engaged, albeit passively, in "pursuit" directed against a person or persons who would otherwise enjoy normal longevity; the others are engaged only in an act of "pursuit" *vis-à-vis* ephemeral, transient *ḥayyei sha'ah*. It is manifestly clear from Rabbi Feinstein's analysis that, in his opinion, specification of a particular victim does not warrant his delivery even according to R. Simeon ben Lakish in a situation in which, were the victim not to be delivered, his life would be prolonged for a period of twelve months or longer.

Applied to the case of Jodie and Mary, the consequence

of Rabbi Feinstein's thesis is that, although Mary was "specified" for death (in the sense that the sacrifice of her life would have preserved the life of Jodie, but not vice versa, and that failure to "deliver" Mary would result in the death of both infants), such specification did not warrant the sacrifice of Mary's life unless it was certain that, even absent intervention, her demise within twelve months was a matter of certainty or a matter that was close to certain (*umdena karov le-vadai*). And, apparently, that was a matter regarding which the babies' physicians disagreed.

IV. DECISION-MAKING IN CASES OF RISK

Unlike other legal systems, in Jewish law, as recorded by Rambam, *Hilkhot Roẓeaḥ* 1:6-9, elimination of a *rodef* in order to preserve the life of a putative victim is not only sanctioned but is mandated by the commandment "You shall cut off her hand, your eye shall have no pity" (*Deuteronomy* 25:12). Nevertheless, elimination of a *rodef* is similar to other *miẓvot* in the sense that self-endangerment is not required in fulfillment of a *miẓvah* and is not required even for the preservation of the life of another. Thus a person need not expose himself to possible gunfire in subduing a *rodef* in order to rescue another person who is endangered.

Another relevant principle associated with the notion of *ḥayyei sha'ah* is reflected in the case of a person suffering from an illness that, if left untreated, is terminal in nature but for whom a therapy is available. That therapy, however, may or may not be successful. If successful, it will cure his illness and allow him to live out his allotted life span but, if unsuccessful, it may prove to be toxic and cause him to die earlier than would have been the case had he been left untreated. The patient may avail himself of that therapy if he so wishes but he is not required to do so. Expressed in different terms, a patient may gamble the certainty of *ḥayyei sha'ah* in the hope that he will thereby achieve a cure and with it a normal longevity anticipation but no person is required to accept that gamble.

The physicians were in disagreement with regard to the gravity of the risk that Jodie would not survive surgical separation from her weaker twin. Some estimated the likelihood of mortality associated with the procedure to be 5 to 6%; others placed it between 1 and 2%. Elsewhere,[16] this writer has endeavored to elucidate the threshold of the halakhic category of danger and has sought to establish that, to a significant extent, the halakhic concept of danger reflects a sociological perception rather than a raw statistical quantification. Accordingly, virtually all forms of major surgery, and certainly the type of surgery contemplated in the separation of Jodie and Mary, are defined by Halakhah as hazardous procedures and hence are discretionary at best.

By the same token, a person need not accept the risk of losing *ḥayyei sha'ah* in order to eliminate a *rodef* despite the fact that elimination of a *rodef* constitutes fulfillment of a *miẓvah*. That is the case even in a situation in which it is the putative victim himself who seeks to thwart the *rodef*.

In the medical context, the decision to accept or to refuse the risk of forfeiting *ḥayyei sha'ah* in a failed attempt to achieve a cure rests with the patient. A human being is charged with the duties and responsibilities of a bailee *vis-à-vis* his body and his life; he is charged with assessing risks and benefits in making responsible choices. When the patient is not competent to make such decisions on his or her own behalf, the person or persons responsible for the patient's care and well-being, i.e., a member of the immediate family or, in the absence of family, the person denoted in legal terminology as the patient's "next friend," is duty-bound, and hence privileged, to make that decision.[17] In the case of a minor, the decision, so long as it is reasoned and rational, rests with the parents.

Assuming, *contra* the suggestion made earlier, that separation of the twins would not have been halakhically construed as the murder of Mary, the decision to expose or not to expose Jodie to the hazards of surgery rested with the parents. Thus, the decision of the Court of Appeal, based upon judicial precedents established by earlier decisions of British courts as well as upon its understanding of Great Britain's Children Act of 1989 as requiring the Court to substitute its assessment of the best interests of the child for the decision of the parents,[18] is not consistent with the principles of Jewish law.

NOTES

1. Case No: FDO0P10893, High Court of Justice, Family Division, 25 August, 2000.
2. Case No: B1/2000/2969, Court of Appeal (Civil Division), 22 September, 2000.
3. In order to mandate separation of the twins it was necessary for the Court of Appeal to make two separate determinations: 1) The surgical separation is lawful despite the certainty of the resultant death of one of the infants. 2) The separation, despite the attendant medical problems and risk to life, is in the best interest of the twins.

   The first issue is clearly the more formidable since common law does not recognize necessity as justification for homicide. Lord Justice Ward determined intervention to be lawful by virtue of the physicians' legal duty to each of the twins. Unfortunately, they cannot care for both equally and therefore must choose between them: "[T]he doctors cannot be denied a right of choice if they are under a duty to choose. They are under a duty to Mary not to operate because it will kill Mary, but they are under a duty to Jodie to operate because not to do so will kill her. It is important to stress that it makes no difference whether the killing is by act or by omission. That is a distinction without a difference." Applying the test of proportionality, he determined that the physicians' duty to Jodie outweighed their duty to the non-viable twin.

   Lord Justice Robert Walker incorporated that line of reasoning in his concurring opinion but relied more heavily on the notion that the separation is justifiable on the grounds that it will restore bodily integrity and autonomy to each of the twins. Even with regard to the weaker twin, "The operation will give her, even in death, bodily integrity as a human being. She will die not because she was intentionally killed but because her own body cannot sustain her life."

It is quite obvious that neither of those arguments is halakhically cogent. The third judge, Lord Justice Brooke, however, relied entirely upon his own formulation of what is, in effect, the "designation for death" (*yiḥduhu*) rationale presented herein in section III in conjunction with an analysis of the discussion of the Palestinian Talmud, *Terumot* 8:10.

4. See *infra*, note 18.
5. Common law extended the right of defense of a third person only if that person was a member of the intervener's family or stood in a special relationship with his or her protector. See Model Penal Code §3.05, comment 1 (1962 Proposed Official Draft with 1985 Revised Commentary). Primarily due to the impact of the Model Penal Code, forty-one states now have statutes regulating the defense of others. For a survey of the provisions of those statutes, see Marco F. Bendinelli and James T. Edsall, "Defense of Others; Origins, Requirements, Limitations and Ramifications," *Regent University Law Review*, vol. 5 (Spring, 1995), pp. 153–214. See also Paul H. Robinson, *Criminal Law Defenses* (St. Paul, 1984), vol. II §133.

   In Great Britain, the Criminal Law Act 1967, s. 3, provides that a person may use such force as is reasonable in the circumstances in order to prevent a crime and explicitly declares that this provision shall replace the rules of common law. Accordingly, it is likely that killing an aggressor would be justifiable to prevent unlawful killing or grievous bodily harm. See J. C. Smith and Brian Hogan, *Criminal Law*, 5th ed. (London, 1983), pp. 325-327. Cf., Glanville Williams, *Textbook of Criminal Law*, 2nd ed. (London, 1983), p. 501, note 1 and accompanying text.
6. See my *Contemporary Halakhic Problems*, IV (New York, 1995), pp. 84–86
7. See also *Ḥazon Ish*, *Hilkhot Ishut* 27: 3.
8. For a list of those authorities see *Encyclopedia Talmudit*, XXI, 4–7 and, in particular, *ibid*., p. 4, note 40. See also Abraham S. Abraham, *Nishmat Avraham*, *Yoreh De'ah* 29:1, note 1.
9. Cf., however, R. Shimon Efratti, *Mi-Gei ha-Hareigah*

(Jerusalem, 5751), p. 23, who presents a strained interpretation of Rambam based upon his own novel understanding of the *Tosefta, Terumot* 7:23. Rabbi Efratti's understanding of both the *Tosefta* and Rambam is at variance from that of all earlier halakhic scholars.

10. See *Taz, Yoreh De'ah* 257:7, who interprets this phraseology as connoting that wise and pious individuals should not become personally involved in delivering the victim but that they need not protest or interfere with the actions of others with the result that the populace will presumably accede to the demand. Cf., R. Moshe Feinstein, *Iggerot Mosheh, Yoreh De'ah*, II, no. 60, *anaf* 4.
11. Rema first cites the permissive view and then prefaces the restrictive view with the phrase "and some say." For canons of halakhic decision-making in such cases see *Shakh, Yoreh De'ah* 242: addendum, "*Kiẓur be-Hanhagat Hora'at Issur ve-Hetter,*" sec. 5. In this case both *Baḥ* and *Taz* rule in accordance with the stringent position.
12. See also R. Joel Sirkes, *Teshuvot Bayit Ḥadash* (*Baḥ*) *ha-Yeshanot*, no. 43. An English translation of that responsum was published by Elijah Judah Schochet, *A Responsum of Surrender* (Los Angeles, 1973).
13. Cf., however, this writer's explanation of the impious nature of such an act in *Be-Netivot ha-Halakhah*, I (New York, 5756), 111–115. According to that analysis, the reservation expressed in the Palestinian Talmud is a qualification of the opinion that requires that the specified party be guilty of a capital offense and is expressed only with regard to specification of a person guilty of *lèse-majesté*.
14. Cf., *Be-Netivot ha-Halakhah*, I, 109–111.
15. See *supra*, pp. 258–263.
16. See "Smoking," *Tradition* (Summer, 1977), pp. 121–123 and *supra*, pp. 239–246.
17. As recorded in *Shulḥan Arukh, Ḥoshen Mishpat* 235:20 and 285:2, the *bet din* is responsible for appointing a guardian for persons who are incompetent to manage their own affairs. See R. Eliezer Waldenberg, *Ẓiẓ Eli'ezer*, IV, no. 13, who, in a concluding statement, asserts that government officials are authorized to make such decisions on behalf of indigent patients confined in state-run mental institutions. It may be assumed that *Ẓiẓ Eli'ezer*'s assertion is not intended to apply in jurisdic-

tions in which decision-making authority of relatives or legal guardians is recognized even in such situations.

18. American courts do not adopt the notion that, when the matter is brought to their attention, they supplant the parents as the party endowed with decision-making authority. Rather, they regard the parents as empowered to make decisions on behalf of minor children and decline to contravene parental decisions unless the result is so egregious as to constitute child neglect or abuse. See, for example, *Newmark v. Williams*, 588 A.2d 1108 (Del. 1991). The American case most resembling the decision with regard to Jodie in the British case under discussion is *In re Phillip* B., 156 Cal. Rptr. 48 (Cal. Ct. App. 1979), *cert. denied*, 445 U.S. 949 (1980). A twelve-year-old boy afflicted with Down's syndrome suffered from a congenital heart defect that, if not surgically corrected, would ultimately lead to an early death. Because of problems resulting from the heart defect the mortality risk associated with the surgery was between 5 and 10%. Pointing, *inter alia*, to the hazardous nature of the proposed surgical intervention, the parents refused to grant consent for corrective surgery and the court upheld the parents' right to make that decision. For surveys of American case law and the legal theory governing those decisions, see Elizabeth J. Sher, "Choosing for Children: Adjudicating Medical Care Disputes Between Parents and the State," *New York University Law Review,* vol. 58, no. 1 (April, 1983), pp. 157–205 and Walter Wadlington, "David C. Baum Memorial Lecture: Medical Decision Making for and by Children: Tensions Between Parent, State, and Child," *University of Illinois Law Review*, vol. 1994, no. 2, pp. 311–336.

10

Autopsies to Substantiate Financial Claims

I. THE PROBLEM

Many life insurance policies are written with double indemnity clauses that provide for supplementary payment when death occurs in an untimely fashion as a result of an accident. Not infrequently, death occurs in circumstances in which there is genuine doubt with regard to whether the death was accidental or the result of natural causes. One case that was the subject of litigation a number of years ago involved a young man who went swimming in the ocean and drowned. The beneficiaries asserted that death was to be attributed to turbulent waters and hence was accidental. The insurance company countered that it was entirely possible that the swimmer suffered a heart attack and hence there was no liability on its part for double indemnity. Accordingly, the insurance company refused to honor a claim for double indemnity without an autopsy to determine the cause of death. Similar issues arise in automobile or industrial accidents in which heirs bear the burden of proof in a claim for tort damages. The relatively few discussions of the issue in rabbinic literature are cited and reviewed by Rabbi Menachem Slae in his well-researched *Ha-Bituaḥ be-Halakhah* (Tel Aviv, 5740).[1] However, many of the discussions in those sources are rather cursory and do not reflect the rigorous analysis that the topic requires.

Several writers note that many insurance policies contain clauses stipulating that the insurance company retains the right to require an autopsy as a condition of compensation for accident liability. The authors cite the opinion of a number of rabbinic authorities who maintain that post-mortem examinations performed pursuant to *in vivo* consent of the deceased are permissible. The issue involved in that controversy was examined in this column in the Winter-Spring 1972 issue of *Tradition*.[2] In point of fact, those clauses are not customarily couched in terms of consent of the insured but as a reservation to the insurance carrier. In practice, insurance companies do not require a post-mortem examination when the cause of death is indisputable and indeed they may not be able to enforce a demand for an autopsy when such a request is not deemed reasonable.[3] Courts have considered religious sensibilities as a factor to be considered in determining reasonableness.[4] Hence, there is no reason to construe acceptance of such a clause as indication of consent to an autopsy. Moreover, the weight of rabbinic opinion deems consent of the deceased to be irrelevant.[5]

Whether potential financial loss constitutes grounds for permitting an otherwise prohibited act of desecration of a corpse centers upon a discussion recorded in the Gemara, *Bava Batra* 154a. The Gemara relates that an incident occurred in Bnei Brak in which a young man sold a parcel of real estate and died shortly thereafter. His heirs sought to nullify the sale on the grounds that the seller was a minor who lacked halakhic capacity to effect a conveyance of property. Halakhic majority is contingent upon presence of pubic hair. Accordingly, the heirs demanded exhumation of the body in order to conduct a visual examination. The Gemara records that R. Akiva dismissed their petition declaring, "You are not permitted to defile him. Moreover, signs [of maturity] are likely to change after death." The ensuing discussion establishes that R. Akiva's response was appropriate only because burden of proof was upon the heirs. Were burden of proof, however, upon the purchasers claiming title, they would have been entirely justified in contending, "We have given him money. Let him be defiled!" *Tosafot* explain that the difference between the claims of heirs and those of purchasers is two-fold in nature: 1) Since they will not be able to recover the funds they have expended, purchasers seeking possession of property for which they have given valuable consideration face an out of pocket loss if they do not prevail whereas heirs will simply not realize a gain. 2) Relatives have an obligation to inter the deceased. *Tosafot's* reasoning in advancing the latter consideration seems to be that the obligation to bury the dead is essentially an obligation to prevent ignominy from occurring to the corpse. Relatives must assume the costs of burial; hence they must also bear the burden of unavoidable financial loss entailed in preventing untoward conduct *vis-à-vis* the corpse.

II. THE NONPERMISSIVE VIEW

The earliest rabbinic authority to address this question was R. Chanoch Ehrentreu, *Shiyarei ha-Minḥah*, no. 34. The responsum itself is undated but Rabbi Ehrentreu, who served as Chief Rabbi of Munich, died in 5685. *Shiyarei ha-Minḥah* was posthumously published by the author's son-in-law (Haifa, 5732). The case presented to Rabbi Ehrentreu involved a man who died suddenly despite the fact that he was vigorous and appeared to have been in good health. The widow sought compensation from an insurance company. Although the grounds for the conflicting claims are unclear, the insurance coverage was apparently limited to a work-related accident. Accordingly, the woman's claim was predicated on the allegation that, some time prior to his death, "one of [her husband's] internal organs became torn as a result of hard labor." The insurance company countered with a demand for exhumation of the body and a post-mortem examination to establish that this was indeed the case.

In an extremely cursory response, Rabbi Ehrentreu noted that, in view of the passage of time since the death of the husband and his apparent good health prior to his demise, it was highly unlikely that an autopsy would substantiate the widow's claim.[6] More significantly, Rabbi Ehrentreu declares that the question involved "a matter of money" and hence he could not sanction the procedure. Although Rabbi Ehrentreu does not cite the discussion in *Bava Batra*, he quite obviously equates the widow's position *vis-à-vis* the insurance company with that of an heir who cannot demand defilement of a corpse in order to substantiate a claim to property.

In a contribution to a rabbinic periodical that appeared in the early years following establishment of the State of Israel, *Ha-Torah ve-ha-Medinah*, vol. V–VI (5713–14), pp. 206–207,[7] R. Moshe Dov Welner presents an unequivocally negative view based upon a straightforward application of the talmudic sources. Drawing upon the discussion of *Bava Batra*, but without citing earlier discussions of the issue, Rabbi Welner notes that, in demanding payment of the proceeds of a life insurance policy, the beneficiaries seek financial benefit rather than avoidance of loss. He also points to *Tosafot*'s further comment to the effect that close relatives may not demand exhumation because they have an obligation with regard to burial of the deceased. The import of *Tosafot*'s comment is that the essence of the obligation to bury the dead is to spare the corpse the indignity associated with putrification. Since that duty carries with it a financial responsibility[8] it would be antithetical to fulfillment of that obligation to permit heirs to cause dishonor to the corpse for financial considerations.[9] Rabbi Welner cogently concludes that, just as relatives have an obligation to inter the remains, so do they have an obligation to prevent an autopsy if it is within their power to do so.

III. THE PERMISSIVE VIEW

The question of the permissibility of an autopsy to eliminate the possibility of suicide which would have served to debar collection of proceeds of a life insurance policy is addressed by R. Aaron Epstein, *Teshuvot Kappei Aharon* (Munkacs, 5693), no. 6. The situation involved a person who had insured himself for a large sum of money. The policy contained a clause disclaiming liability in case of death as the result of suicide. Subsequent to the death of the insured, payment was denied on the allegation that suicide was the cause of death. Although he expresses some hesitation in offering a definitive ruling, *Kappei Aharon* cites the distinction between heirs and purchasers of real estate drawn by the Gemara. Applying this distinction, it would appear that, as plaintiffs seeking their own financial advantage, beneficiaries of an insurance policy do not have a right to perform an autopsy in order to advance their claim. *Kappei Aharon*, however, asserts that the distinction drawn by the Gemara is not between pursuit of gain as opposed to loss of capital funds already expended or a distinction between the claim of a plaintiff and that of a defendant, but that the focal point of the distinction is "who performs the desecration, who seeks the desecration and to whom the benefit of desecration accrues." *Kappei Aharon* then asserts that "immediately upon the death of the insured, it is incumbent upon [the insurance company] . . . to pay the heirs the amount of the insurance and the heirs need bring no proof" as demonstrated by the fact that if the body is "lost or burned" with the result that there could be no proof of suicide the insurance company is held liable. Hence, the insurance company's demand for an autopsy is "for their benefit" and the heirs "are not obligated to protest [in order to prevent] the company from desecrating [the body]."

Even if *Kappei Aharon*'s analysis of the Gemara's distinction is to be accepted, his conclusion appears to be faulty. *Kappei Aharon* construes the situation as one in which the insurance company seeks proof in order to exonerate itself from payment of funds that are already due and owing. Technically, the allegation of suicide may well be an affirmative defense. However, when suicide is alleged, and the body is available for autopsy, the burden of proof shifts to the beneficiary. Thus, the autopsy is for the benefit of the beneficiaries who must prove their claim. Moreover, the insurance company is powerless with regard to compelling a post-mortem examination. Accordingly, the beneficiaries need not merely refrain from "protesting" in order to prevent the autopsy but must actively grant their consent for its performance.

R. Yekutiel Yehudah Grunwald, *Kol Bo al Avelut* (New York, 5716), p. 48, cites the comments of *Kappei Aharon* but signifies his agreement with that authority's permissive ruling on two entirely different grounds: 1) In executing the insurance contract, the insured agreed to an autopsy in circumstances in which there is suspicion of suicide. 2) The autopsy may be sanctioned on the grounds that it is being performed for the "honor" of the deceased[10] since it is undertaken in order to rebut a stigmatizing allegation of suicide.

Rabbi Grunwald's arguments are hardly compelling. As noted earlier, the permissibility of an autopsy pursuant to the consent of the deceased is a matter of considerable controversy. Moreover, acceptance of a standard form contract declining liability without an autopsy in cases of suspected suicide can hardly be construed as consent to the autopsy. It is at least as likely that acceptance of such a stipulation constitutes no more than a release and acknowledgment that the insurance company will not be held liable in circumstances in which an autopsy may legitimately be required. Assuredly, in inserting such a clause, the insurance company does not seek advance consent to an autopsy; it is certainly to the insurance company's advantage to disclaim liability. Accordingly, the insurance company seeks only a stipulation and acknowledgment that it will not be held liable in the absence of an autopsy. Rabbi Grunwald's second consideration is no more convincing. An allegation of suicide interposed by an insurance company in order to avoid payment may be legally cogent but should not give rise to actual suspicion. No rabbinic authority has been heard to argue that, in the absense of an insurance claim, an autopsy may be performed to dispel such rumors, or even to disprove a coroner's verdict of suicide. In light of the very strong halakhic presumption that the deceased did not commit suicide, an autopsy would appear to be redundant and quite unnecessary to preserve the honor and reputation of the deceased.

Other cases that resulted in lenient rulings were presented to both R. Eliezer Dunner, Chief Rabbi of Cologne, and to R. Ze'ev Zevi Klein of Berlin. Rabbi Dunner, *Zikhron Avraham Mosheh: He'arot al Talmud Bavli* (Jerusalem, 5705), *Sanhedrin* 68a, reports that an insurance company refused payment of a claim pending performance of an autopsy to determine if the insured, who had died suddenly, did indeed succumb "as a result of an illness covered by the insurance policy." Rabbi Klein, *Kahana Mesaya Kahana* (Berlin, 5698), no. 11, addresses the situation of a decedent whose insurance coverage was limited to accidental death. In that case the insurance company demanded an autopsy in order to determine that the death did not occur as the result of illness. Rabbi Klein describes the widow and children as living in abject poverty and in danger of starvation if they would not recover the proceeds of the insurance policy.

In the case presented to him, Rabbi Dunner permitted an autopsy on the basis of a line of reasoning that appears to be without parallel in the rabbinic literature devoted to this topic. His basic premise is that autopsies may be performed with the consent of the deceased. Although there is significant precedent for that position, Rabbi Dunner's justification is quite novel. R. Jacob Ettlinger, *Teshuvot Binyan Ẓion*, no. 170, who was the first authority explicitly to permit autopsies with consent of the deceased, maintains that the prohibition against desecration of a corpse constitutes a transgression against man, akin to theft and the like, rather than a transgression against God. As such, argues *Binyan Ẓion*, the prohibition does not encompass situations in which a person willingly consents to post-mortem dissection. Rabbi Dunner, however, presents a line of reasoning that is not predicated upon *Binyan Ẓion*'s analysis of the prohibition. Rabbi Dunner argues that since only "defilement" of the corpse is prohibited it follows that, "if [the autopsy] is in accordance with the intention of the deceased and for his honor, it is not defilement and is permitted."[11] In the case brought to Rabbi Dunner's attention, the insured had paid premiums for nineteen years. Rabbi Dunner assumes that the decedent would not have wished the rather large sum represented by the premium payments to have been wasted but would have preferred that his widow be able to improve her unfortunate situation.[12] Accordingly, Rabbi Dunner ruled that an autopsy performed with constructive consent of the deceased should not be construed as a prohibited ignominy.

As did Rabbi Dunner, Rabbi Klein finds entry into an insurance contract containing such terms to be tantamount to a grant of permission to perform a post-mortem examination. However, in sanctioning the autopsy, Rabbi Klein does not rely upon that position. He also dismisses the contention that an autopsy may be permitted when it is to be performed by a non-Jew. Rabbi Klein accepts the view that the rabbinic ban prohibiting a Jew from directing a non-Jew to perform a prohibited act is not limited to activities forbidden on *Shabbat*.[13] He does, however, cite the view of *Pri Megadim, Oraḥ Ḥayyim, Mishbeẓot Zahav* 307:4, who suggests that the prohibition may be limited to transgressions punishable by lashing[14] but advances the novel assertion that all authorities concede that the ban applies to prohibitions directed, not toward an act, but toward the result of the act, as is the case with regard to defilement of a corpse. It should be noted that *Teshuvot Noda bi-Yehudah, Mahadura Tinyana, Yoreh De'ah*, no.

210, expressly rules that surviving relatives are forbidden to grant consent for a post-mortem dissection with the comment that "since [the physicians] cannot do [so] without their consent, it is as if [the relatives] are the defilers." Nevertheless, in a line of reasoning echoing that of *Kappei Aharon*, Rabbi Klein argues that since it is not the heirs who must bring proof by performing an autopsy, but rather it is the company that has the prerogative of demanding a post-mortem examination, "the heirs need not forgive their claim."

In an article appearing in *Ha-Torah ve-ha-Medinah*, vol. VII–VIII (5716–5717), pp. 323–326, Rabbi Issachar Levine expresses a position that is essentially identical to that of Rabbi Dunner. As expressed by Rabbi Levine: "The crucial factor is the intent. If the intent is for a pressing matter . . . it entails no defilement."

IV. RE-EXAMINATION OF THE TALMUDIC SOURCE

R. Nathan Natte Leiter, in a responsum included by his son, R. Ze'ev Wolf Leiter, in the latter's *Teshuvot Ẓiyun le-Nefesh Ḥayah* (Jerusalem, 5724), no. 16, discusses the case of a person who was killed as a result of the negligence of another party in an accident involving a "carriage," presumably a horse-drawn coach. The family wished to engage in legal proceedings in order "to punish [the owner of the carriage] in accordance with the punishment he deserves and to obtain a sum of money as would be determined by the court. . . ." The problem confronting the members of the family was that it was likely that they would be asked to consent to exhumation of the body and an autopsy.

Rabbi Leiter rules that it is forbidden for relatives to consent to an autopsy in virtually all circumstances. Moreover, he argues that purchasers of property and creditors also have no right to demand the disfigurement and mutilation of a body that occur in the course of an autopsy. Rabbi Leiter notes that *Shulḥan Arukh, Ḥoshen Mishpat* 97:15, rules that a debtor cannot be compelled to hire himself out to perform any form of labor in order to satisfy a debt and that any contractual agreement to that effect is not enforceable. The creditor certainly has no claim upon the debtor for "a pound of flesh." On what basis then, queries Rabbi Leiter, can the claimant demand mutilation of a corpse in order to prevent a loss to himself? He further notes that Rema, *Ḥoshen Mishpat* 107:2, grants a creditor only the right to delay burial in order to exact payment but does not grant him any proprietary interest in the debtor's remains.

Accordingly, Rabbi Leiter declares that the discussion in *Bava Batra* should not at all be construed as permitting mutilation or even exhumation of the corpse. Troubled as well by the fact that the Gemara speaks only of defilement but not of the "fear of judgment" associated with exhumation, Rabbi Leiter asserts that the discussion is limited to uncovering the body for an examination *in situ*. Since in simply uncovering the corpse the repose of the body is not disturbed, a mere visual examination entails no actual violation of the corpse. The text of Rema's ruling similarly speaks only of delay of burial that entails no violation of the corpse. Nevertheless, asserts Rabbi Leiter, the Gemara regards even such noninvasive measures to be forbidden to close relatives since such acts are antithetical to the honor relatives owe the deceased as is reflected in their obligation to inter the remains.

Rabbi Leiter further considers the argument that punishment for negligent manslaughter in the form of payment of compensatory damages may be an "honor" to the deceased. *Teshuvot Noda bi-Yehudah, Mahadura Tinyana, Yoreh De'ah*, no. 210, does indeed permit a post-mortem examination designed to bring a murderer to justice on the grounds that punishment of the perpetrator is an "honor" to the victim. Nevertheless, asserts Rabbi Leiter, it may be the case that only capital punishment in cases of willful homicide, i.e., punishment in kind, represents an "honor" to the murder victim. If lesser punishments are not to be construed in that manner, a post-mortem examination that will not lead to execution of the murderer remains an ignominy that cannot be sanctioned.

The most negative position with regard to performance of autopsies for financial considerations is presented by R. David Shapiro, *Or Ha-Mizraḥ*, vol. V, no. 3-4 (Elul 5717). The case presented to Rabbi Shapiro involved a double indemnity provision in a life insurance policy. The insured's motor vehicle plunged into a river and he was drowned. The insurance company sought an autopsy to determine if death was actually caused by drowning and not by a heart attack. Unlike Rabbi Leiter who understood the Gemara as referring to removal of earth covering an already interred body, Rabbi Shapiro asserts that the discussion recorded in *Bava Batra* does not refer to exhumation (or, presumably, even uncovering) of the corpse but to pre-burial examination of the body. Thus, the distinction between heirs and purchasers is limited to examination for the presence of pubic hair, an act that is inconsistent with the dignity due the deceased but which falls well short of gross defilement of the corpse. Accordingly, exhumation or anatomical disfigurement, argues Rabbi Shapiro, are forbidden even in face of actual out-of-pocket loss.[15] In point of fact, Rabbi Shapiro's interpretation of the discussion in *Bava Batra* appears much earlier in *Teshuvot Knesset Yeḥezkel, Yoreh De'ah*, no. 44.[16]

Although the arguments supporting the analyses of the discussion in *Bava Batra* advanced by Rabbi Leiter and Rabbi Shapiro are quite engaging, those interpretations are impliedly rejected by the host of rabbinic decisors who do draw a distinction between heirs and others who face a potential loss and apply that distinction to actual dissection of the corpse. Moreover, in a parallel incident recorded in *Semaḥot* 4:12, the text spells out that the Sages refused to permit disturbing the repose of the dead after burial. Similarly, in codifying the relevant halakhic provisions, *Shulḥan Arukh, Yoreh De'ah* 363:7, rules that heirs are not permitted to open the grave in order to determine the status of the deceased. The clear implication is that creditors may order the opening of the grave. By the same token, visual examination prior to burial would appear to be permissible under all circumstances as evidenced by the terminology of *Shulḥan Arukh, Yoreh De'ah* 363:7, which speaks only of a prohibition attendant upon exhumation of the body.[17]

V. A FINAL COMMENT

Although a significant degree of controversy exists with regard to the permissibility of autopsies in order to support insurance claims as they are presented in the vast majority of such cases, it seems to this writer that, in some limited circumstances, such autopsies would be sanctioned by all authorites other than *Knesset Yeḥezkel*, Rabbi Leiter and Rabbi Shapiro. It would seem that, if the decedent has not left an estate of sufficient value to satisfy the widow's *ketubah*, her standing is no different from that of any other creditor. It then follows that, if a creditor may demand exhumation in order to be able to collect his debt, the widow (who has no halakhic obligation to inter her husband's remains) may do so as well.

NOTES

1. An English translation by Bracha and Menachem Slae titled *Insurance in the Halakhah* (Tel Aviv, 1982) was published by the Israel Insurance Association, as was the original Hebrew volume.
2. That material is reprinted in this writer's *Contemporary Halakhic Problems*, I (New York, 1977), 125–126.
3. See *Atkins v. Medical Examiner of Westchester County*, 100 Misc.2d 296, 418 N.Y.S.2d 839 (1979); *Weberman v. Zugibe*, 90 Misc.2d 254, 394 N.Y.S.2d 371 (1977); *Matter of Wilensky v. Greco,* 74 Misc.2d 512, 344 N.Y.S.2d 77 (1973).
4. See *Saperstein v. Commercial Travelers Mutual Accident Association,*

36 N.Y.2d 79, 324 N.E.2d 539, 365 N.Y.S.2d 154 (1975).

5. See sources cited in *Contemporary Halakhic Problems*, I, 125-126. See also R. Chaim Eleazar Shapira, *Teshuvot Minḥat Elazar*, IV, no. 28; R. Meir Shapiro, *Teshuvot Or ha-Meir*, no. 74; R. Abraham I. Kook, *Da'at Kohen*, no. 199; R. Moshe Feinstein, *Iggerot Mosheh, Yoreh De'ah*, III, no. 140 and *Yoreh De'ah*, IV, no. 59; R. Ovadiah Yosef, *Yeḥaveh Da'at*, III, no. 85; and R. Isaac ha-Levi Herzog in an article serialized in various issues of *Kol Torah*, vols. I through III (5707–5709), and reprinted in *idem, Pesakim u-Ketavim*, V (Jerusalem, 5750), no. 148.
6. Cf., *Teshuvot Shivat Ẓion*, no. 65, who opines that desecration of the corpse that is a certainty, even when permitted on behalf of a claimant, cannot be permitted if the financial benefit is not certain but merely doubtful.
7. This material is reprinted in Rabbi Welner's *Teshuvot Ḥemdat Ẓevi, Yoreh De'ah*, no. 20.
8. See *Teshuvot Maharam Minẓ*, no. 53, cited by *Bet Shmu'el, Even ha-Ezer*, 118: 20; *Eshel Avraham, Yoreh De'ah* 348; and R. Shlomo Kluger, *Teshuvot Tuv Ta'am va-Da'at, Mahadura Telita'a*, part 2, *Yoreh De'ah*, no. 216. See also *Teshuvot Ḥakham Ẓevi*, no. 48.
9. See Rema, *Ḥoshen Mishpat* 107:20.
10. See R. Ezekiel Landau, *Teshuvot Noda bi-Yehudah, Mahadura Tinyana, Yoreh De'ah*, no. 210, who appears to regard an autopsy designed to bring a murderer to justice as being performed for the purpose of "honoring" the deceased. See also *Teshuvot Me'orot Natan, Yoreh De'ah*, no. 79. Cf., however, *Teshuvot Aryeh de-Bei Ila'i, Yoreh De'ah*, no. 19, who, upon analysis of the discussion of the Gemara, *Ḥullin* 11b, asserts that the Gemara considers and rejects the notion that dissection may be undertaken for the honor of the deceased. From the context of his discussion it appears that *Aryeh de-Bei Ila'i* does not permit an autopsy even for purposes of facilitating the execution of the victim's murderer.
11. In a particularly strained analysis of the discussion in *Bava Batra*, Rabbi Dunner asserts that purchasers may demand examination of the body, not because of their potential financial loss, but because the deceased would have wished his transfer of title to be confirmed. The thesis presented by Rabbi Dunner is based upon that analysis.
12. It should be noted that R. Abraham Benjamin Samuel Sofer,

Teshuvot Ketav Sofer, Yoreh De'ah, no. 174, discusses exhumation of a body for purposes of establishing the identity of the deceased in order to permit the wife to remarry. Although he does not rule permissively (other than when identification is necessary for purpose of *ḥaliẓah,* which is regarded as a benefit to the deceased in that *ḥaliẓah* contributes to the repose of the husband's soul), *Ketav Sofer* does note in a parenthetical comment that preventing the wife from remaining a life-long *agunah* redounds to the merit of the decedent and hence it is arguable that exhumation might be permitted on those grounds. [A permissive view is expressed by *Teshuvot Shivat Ẓion*, nos. 64–66, in opposition to the restrictive view of R. Eleazar Fleckles. A similar permissive view is espoused by *Teshuvot Knesset Yeḥeskel, Even ha-Ezer*, no. 46. See also sources cited by *Sedei Ḥemed, Asifat Dinim, Ma'arekhet Aveilut,* no. 137.] Although in that comment *Ketav Sofer* employs terminology indicative of a theory of constructive consent, it is clear from the context of the responsum that *Ketav Sofer* deems an act that redounds to the merit of the soul, by definition, as not constituting a prohibited act of desecration. A similar argument might be made if, absent the insurance proceeds, the widow and orphans would be impoverished, as distinct from a situation in which such funds would only serve to enhance their standard of living.

13. See sources cited in *Encyclopedia Talmudit*, II, 44–45 and *Sedei Ḥemed, Kuntres ha-Kelalim, Ma'arekhet ha-Alef*, no. 172.
14. *Pri Megadim* expresses doubt with regard to this matter because the discussion of the question of directing a non-Jew to perform a forbidden act is presented by the Gemara, *Bava Meẓi'a* 60a, in the context of directing a non-Jew to muzzle an ox while it is threshing. That act, for a Jew, is a violation of a negative commandment punishable by lashing. *Pri Megadim*, however, does not distinguish between negative prohibitions punishable by lashing and negative commandments that do not carry that penalty (e.g., desecration of a corpse) but between acts that are forbidden by a negative commandment and those prohibited by virtue of a positive commandment, e.g., directing a non-Jew to purchase *ḥameẓ* on the afternoon of the day preceding *Pesaḥ* according to the authorities who maintain that the negative commandment prohibiting ownership of *ḥameẓ* is limited to ownership on *Pesaḥ* but that ownership on the afternoon preceding the festival is forbidden solely by

virtue of the positive commandment to destroy *ḥamez*, a commandment that effectively bars ownership of *ḥamez* as of midday of *erev Pesaḥ*. For sources that disagree with *Pri Megadim* and prohibit directing a non-Jew to perform any forbidden acts, see *Sedei Ḥemed, Pe'at ha-Sadeh, Kelalim, Ma'arekhet ha-Alef*, no. 16.

15. R. Moshe Dov Welner, *Ha-Torah ve-ha-Medinah*, vol. V–VI (5713–14), pp. 206–207, asserts that desecration of a corpse by Jewish claimants themselves is always forbidden and that, accordingly, the reference in *Bava Batra* is to an examination carried out by non-Jews. However, heirs, who have an obligation of burial and hence of assuring proper honor to the deceased, must prevent even non-Jews from subjecting the corpse to indignity. Cf., however, R. Eliezer Deutsch, *Teshuvot Duda'ei ha-Sadeh*, no. 76, who writes, " . . . and, if so, the Jew does not cause him defilement since, in any event, [the non-Jews] will defile him," and thereby seems to imply that, if capable of doing so, even a non-relative should prevent defilement by a non-Jew.
16. Rabbi Shapiro himself cites *Teshuvot R. Akiva Eger, Mahadura Tinyana*, no. 17, in support of his position. R. Akiva Eger does understand *Bava Batra* as referring to examination prior to burial. However, it is evident from R. Akiva Eger's entire responsum that he understands the discussion as applicable to exhumation as well.
17. See also *Bet Hillel, ad locum* and *Teshuvot Kappei Aharon*, no. 6. Cf., however, *Teshuvot R. Akiva Eger, Mahadura Tinyana*, no. 17 and R. Issachar Levine, *Ha-Torah ve-ha-Medinah*, vol. VII–VIII (5716–5717), p. 322.

11

Medical Malpractice: A Thumbnail Sketch

Medical malpractice has received scant attention in rabbinic literature of the modern period. One significant reason for the paucity of such material is that, at least in Western countries, physicians are covered by malpractice insurance. Hence physicians are seldom called upon to compensate victims with the result that rabbinic decisors are not called upon to determine the justiciability of such claims.

The enforceability of an insurance contract providing malpractice coverage presents an extremely interesting issue, as does the enforceability of any contract providing indemnity against unanticipated financial loss. In terms of Jewish law, there is a significant question with regard to whether any insured individual can demand indemnification on the basis of such a contract because of the problem of *asmakhta*, roughly translated as a financial undertaking that the obligee does not really believe he will be called upon to satisfy. The physician does not expect to commit malpractice; the company cer-

This paper was originally delivered at the "Second International Conference on Medicine, Ethics and Jewish Law," in Copenhagen, Denmark, January 2001, and is presented, with revisions, as published in the conference proceedings, *Selected Topics in Jewish Medical Ethics*, ed. by Fred Rosner, Henri Goldstein and Edward Reichman (Denmark: Hojers Forlag, 2003), pp. 100–111.

tainly hopes that he will not. But, more significantly, insofar as each individually insured physician is concerned, the insurance company does not anticipate that it will be called upon to satisfy a malpractice claim against him. Yet, on the basis of statistical probability, the insurance company may be able to predict rather accurately how much of every dollar collected in premiums it will pay out in claims. Does a malpractice insurance policy constitute a valid and actionable contract in terms of Jewish law, or does is it not?[1]

Although the issue is of significant theoretical interest, it would be quite surprising to discover that any insurance company is interested in the answer. The reason for such lack of interest is very simple. An insurance company that seeks totally to avoid enforcement of its policies will not remain in business very long. No client will continue to pay premiums to a company that refuses to honor any and all legitimate claims. So whether or not an indemnity contract is halakhically enforceable turns out to be a rather moot question. Insurance companies will continue to pay valid and legitimate malpractice claims for the very simple reason that insurance companies want to remain in business and wish to continue to collect premiums.

The issue of medical malpractice itself, i.e., the question of halakhic liability for misfeasance, is relatively uninteresting simply because there is relatively little controversy among contemporary authorities regarding such liability. The absence of controversy, however, is rather surprising because, as everyone knows, wherever there are two Jews, there are three opinions. The corollary to that proposition is that, wherever there are two rabbis, there are four opinions because each one of the rabbis says, "Maybe one can say this—and perhaps one can say the opposite." That does not by any means mean that each of the contradictory opinions held by the same individual is valid. The absence of controversy is even more remarkable because, at first glance, the view of contemporary decisors appears to be at variance with the black-letter law formulated by early-day scholars.

A story is told about the famous artist Pablo Picasso. The story is probably apocryphal, but, as the story goes, one day, in the company of a friend, Picasso visited an art gallery. The proprietor of the art gallery had on display a painting by Picasso that he was offering for sale. The artist examined the painting, approached the proprietor and said, "You are a thief! You are trying to sell a painting that is a fraud. That painting is not a Picasso!" Picasso's friend looked at him in amazement and exclaimed, "What do you mean? Of course it is a Picasso. I was in your studio the day you painted that picture!" Whereupon Picasso turned to him and calmly replied, "Don't you know that I sometimes paint fakes?"

It is necessary to understand that Halakhah, quite like medicine, is as much an art as it is a science. Not everyone who puts the brush to canvas, much less everyone who takes a brush in hand, is necessarily an artist. And even Picasso sometimes changes his mind with regard to the artistic merit of his work. In every intellectual discipline, it sometimes turns out that what at one time was thought to be correct turns out either not to be correct or not at all applicable in light of changed circumstances. Turning to the topic at hand, assessment of negligence in medical treatment is dependent upon the state of medical knowledge and accepted procedures at a particular time. Apparent discrepancies in determination of negligence disappear upon recognition that any such determination is based upon a particular assessment of the nature of the physiological process involved and of the appropriate remedy.

With regard to the basic notion of malpractice liability, the liability of the practitioner falls under the general category of "*adam ha-mazik*—man, the tortfeasor," a phrase that embodies the halakhic concept that every human being is financially responsible for the consequences of his bodily acts. In Jewish law, a person who does damage to another person's property is held to a very strict standard of liability. There is some controversy with regard to the extent and parameters of that liability. Ramban, *Milḥamot ha-Shem*, *Bava Kamma* 29a and in his commentary on *Bava Meẓi'a* 82b,[2] maintains that such liability is absolute, i.e., that there are virtually no circumstances in which a tortfeasor will be excused from liability for damage that he has caused even if he has committed no act of negligence whatsoever.[3] *Tosafot*, *Bava Kamma* 27b, espouse a somewhat different position in maintaining that a person who is an *ones gamur*, i.e., a person who performs an act that causes damage of a nature that is totally unforeseeable and hence unavoidable, is not liable. However, even according to *Tosafot*, an individual is held liable for all other damages, even if there is no negligence whatsoever.[4]

In light of that fundamental principle of tort liability, one is almost astonished to read the comment of the medieval Spanish authority, Rabbenu Nissim of Gerondi, *Sanhedrin* 84b, who, in discussing liability for malpractice, declares that the physician enjoys absolute immunity with regard to any inadvertent act that he may commit because "*be-reshut hu merape*," i.e., the physician heals with authority, with specific license and dispensation granted by Scripture. That authority is formulated by the Gemara, *Bava Kamma* 85a, in the statement: " '*ve-rapo ye-rape*,' *mi-kan she-nittnah reshut le-rofe le-rapot*." That talmudic passage is generally, but inaccurately, translated: " 'And he shall surely heal' (Exodus 21:19)—From here it is derived that the physician has permission to heal." However, that translation is imprecise because the connotation of "*reshut*" is much stronger than "permission." The word "*reshut*" in this context has the same meaning as it has in the dictum recorded in *Pirkei Avot* 1:10, "*Al titvada le-reshut*—Do not become overly familiar with the government." In that statement the term refers to the governing authority. Similarly, in *Bava Kamma* 85a, the term has the connotation of "authority." In recording the phrase "*ve-rapo yerape*—you shall surely heal," the Torah grants the physician authority to heal and therefore, declares Rabbenu Nissim, if he harms rather than heals, the physician is subject to no liability whatsoever because he practices medicine with divine license. Elsewhere,[5] in a legalistic context, I have referred to the license conferred upon the physician as, in effect, establishing the practice of medicine as a privileged battery. A physician is granted a privilege to perform acts of battery and that privilege carries with it immunity from liability in cases of misadventure.

Rabbenu Nissim, however, adds another comment that is highly significant. He declares that it is only in cases in which *libeih onseih*, i.e., the error that was committed was born of rational misconception, that the physician is exonerated. At the time that the physician performed the procedure that resulted in misadventure, he believed that he was acting in accordance with accepted medical standards and practice, that what he was doing was appropriate and would benefit the patient. The physician made a simple error of judgment. The physician's judgment in any particular case is determined by his knowledge, skills and experience and thus, in a fundamental sense, is preordained. Since the physician could not with integrity have acted otherwise his action is deemed to be "coerced." To be sure, the physician was not deprived of free will, but the manner in which that freedom is exercised is shaded by antecedent causes that can be thwarted only by conscious intervention of an autonomous will. The concept expressed by Rabbenu Nissim is akin to what philosophers term "soft determinism."[6] According to Rabbenu Nissim, the physician is not liable because he acted out of intellectual duress that he had no cause to resist.

However, when the error is not intellectual or a matter of medical judgment, when the error is what we would describe as a mistake that did not have to happen, when the untoward result would not have occurred had the physician been vigilant in exercising due care and prudence, it is apparent from the comments of Rabbenu Nissim that the physician is to be held liable. Malpractice of that nature constitutes a tort that is fully actionable before a *bet din*.

Rabbenu Nissim expresses a position that is extremely favorable to physicians. Rabbenu Nissim's position is more favorable to physicians than is the position of other medieval authorities, and indeed is more favorable than the doctrine applied in common law jurisdictions. Nevertheless, Rabbenu Nissim's position confers only a limited immunity upon the physician. When the physician acts in good faith in accordance with his own knowledge, talent and skill and has been careful and vigilant in his treatment of the patient, Rabbenu Nissim maintains that he is to be exonerated totally and completely; he incurs no liability even in the eyes of Heaven. The standard to which the physician is held is not some form of an objectively determinable community standard of medical practice, as is the standard applied in American law, but a standard based entirely upon the particular physician's knowledge and skill. Nevertheless, if the physician has been negligent in any way, if the harm caused by the physician is the result of an avoidable accident, if the damage is the result of something that the physician himself, had he been properly vigilant, would have recognized as inappropriate, according to Rabbenu Nissim, his conduct is tortitious and is actionable before a human court.

However, the view of Rabbenu Nissim is not the position of normative Jewish law. The normative position of Halakhah reflects the view first enunciated by Ramban in his *Torat ha-Adam* and later incorporated in *Shulḥan Arukh*, *Yoreh De'ah* 336:1. Ramban declares that, if the physician errs and causes damage, he is *patur be-dinei adam* but he is *ḥayyav be-dinei shamayim*, i.e., he is not held liable by a terrestrial court but he is liable in the eyes of the Heavenly Court.

According to Ramban, a physician is held to a standard of

strict liability; the physician is an *adam ha-mazik*, a tortfeasor pure and simple, at least in the eyes of Heaven. The physician cannot plead that "*libeih onseih*," that "his heart compelled him" and hence that he acted out of "intellectual duress." A human being is unreservedly liable for his actions and hence, if the physician commits an error, even if he does so without negligence and entirely in good faith, he will be held liable at least in the eyes of Heaven.

Ramban's view, in turn, is based upon a statement of the Tosefta, *Gittin* 3:13, that declares: "If a proficient physician who practices with licensure of the *bet din* [causes harm] inadvertently, he is to be exonerated; if he acts knowingly he is to be held liable for reason of perfection of the universe." It is the final phrase, "*mipnei tikkun ha-olam*—for reason of perfection of the universe," that is problematic. Ramban and those who follow in his footsteps understand the explanatory phrase, "*mipnei tikkun ha-olam*," as serving to elucidate the reason for the exoneration of the physician who errs inadvertently. It is self-evident that a physician who acts willingly and knowingly or who wantonly harms his patient must be held liable. Liability for willful malpractice needs no explanation; willful malpractice is a simple battery and liability is obvious. The physician who commits a battery is liable, not "for reason of perfection of the universe," but because the victim of a tort must be made whole. Moreover, applying general principles of tort liability, the physician who causes harm unintentionally should also be liable *be-dinei adam*, at the hands of man—and not merely at the hands of Heaven. Consequently, in conformity with general rules of jurisprudence, the human court should assess penalties against the physician who is guilty of malpractice even if he errs inadvertently. Hence it is exoneration of the physician in instances of non-negligent harm that requires explanation. Thus, the phrase "*mipnei tikkun ha-olam*" employed by the Tosefta is to be understood as referring back to the earlier clause that declares that a physician who causes harm inadvertently is to be exonerated. The Tosefta explains that, in such cases, the physician is exempt, at least *be-dinei adam* only *mipnei tikkun ha-olam*, i.e., because of a need to promote the perfection and benefit of the universe.

And how does granting a physician immunity from malpractice liability promote the perfection and betterment of the universe? In our day, a student does not need any inducement to motivate him to enroll in medical school or to seek the practice of medicine as a profession. Today, the fear of a malpractice suit does not deter physicians from practicing medicine if for no other reason than that insurance coverage for medical malpractice is readily available. To be sure, in some specialties, premiums for such coverage, at least in some locales, can be in excess of a hundred thousand dollars per year. Nevertheless, physicians are able to pay such high premiums because their fees are high enough to enable them to do so.

In ancient times, such fees would have been unthinkable. In those days physicians were compensated in exactly the same fashion that rabbis were compensated. As a result, both rabbis and physicians were as poor as—let us not say as poor as church mice—but as poor as synagogue mice. According to Jewish law, the standard of compensation for both a physician and a rabbi is no higher than *sekhar battalah*—the fee or wage the physician or rabbi would have commanded had he not allowed performance of medical or rabbinic duties to interfere with his pursuit of some other gainful occupation for which he is qualified and in which his skills are readily marketable. The physician who treats a patient is not at all paid for his services; the physician is paid for loss of income and for nothing more than loss of income. But if the physician's compensation is limited to an amount equal to the loss of income he might have earned by devoting the same amount of time to some other gainful pursuit and if, by practicing medicine instead of pursuing some other career, the physician exposes himself to the prospect of a malpractice suit, why should any prudent person enter the practice of medicine? He might as well become a rabbi; if he chooses the rabbinate rather than medicine he will receive the same income and will avoid malpractice problems. The physician could certainly engage in whatever other activity he is being paid to abjure and receive the identical compensation without fear of being separated from his earnings as a result of malpractice proceedings. Therefore, in order not to discourage aspiring physicians from the practice of medicine, there had to be rabbinic legislation conferring upon them immunity from malpractice liability.

The disincentive posed by potential malpractice liability could be remedied only by rabbinic legislation providing immunity for the physician at least in instances of *bona fide* error. The motivating principle underlying this rabbinic enactment is the concept of *tikkun ha-olam*, i.e., "perfection of the universe." Protection and benefit of mankind required that the physician be exempted from malpractice liability in order not to discourage individuals from embarking upon the practice of medicine. However, that exemption applies only to liability as assessed by the *bet din*. The consideration of *tikkun ha-olam* is invoked to establish an exemption only insofar as "the laws of man" are concerned. The Sages of the period of the Mishnah either were unable or, more likely, unwilling to exonerate the physician from any and all liability and hence he remains liable "at the hands of Heaven."

The Tosefta's announcement of liability "at the hands of Heaven" is not a hortative declaration or an expression of pietistic sentiment. An individual may technically be liable at the hands of Heaven and not at the hands of man, but the *bet din*, if it chooses to do so, has ways and means of enforcing even "heavenly" obligations. To be sure, when an obligation exists only "at the hands of Heaven," the *bet din* does not have the authority to send a marshal to seize the tortfeasor's property but imposition of a *ḥerem*, or excommunication, is an appropriate measure that may be employed in order to force such a person to satisfy an obligation that exists in the eyes of Heaven. Moreoever, there are authorities who maintain that an individual who fails to fulfill such an obligation, even though it is enforceable solely by the Heavenly court, is nevertheless disqualified from serving as a witness in a terrestrial Jewish court. Those are rather significant sanctions, not to speak of the consideration that obligations recognized by the Heavenly court should not be taken lightly because of the fact that the Heavenly court can avail itself of manifold means of enforcement. The Heavenly court is always in a position to enforce its judgment and there is no way to avoid its reach.

Be that as it may, the normative rule as enunciated by Ramban and followed by *Shulḥan Arukh* and later authorities, is that the physician, unless he acts wantonly and willfully, is not directly liable at the hands of a human court. That is what lawyers would call "black letter law." However, when one reads the comments of more recent authorities and peruses the responsa literature a different picture emerges. The first significant elaboration appears in the writings of R. Chaim Joseph David Azulai, a late eighteenth-century Sephardic authority commonly known by the acronym "Ḥida" formed from the intial letters of each of his names. Ḥida incorporates a very cryptic and unamplified remark in his work *Tov Ayin*, no. 9, sec. 8. Ḥida declares that if a physician who has failed to recognize the nature of an illness because "*lo hitbonnen*," i.e., he did not reflect sufficiently or did not pay sufficient attention to the symptoms presented by the patient, and therefore made an incorrect diagnosis and, as a consequence of his erroneous diagnosis, he prescribed the wrong medication or performed an improper or unnecessary surgical procedure, the physician, according to all authorities, will be held liable and judgment will be enforced by the *bet din*. On first reading, Ḥida's statement is quite remarkable since it appears to stand in stark contradiction to the rule formulated in the

Tosefta. The physician described by Ḥida acted *be-shogeg*, inadvertently and in good faith; he certainly did not cause harm wantonly or even knowingly. The Tosefta declares that the physician who commits malpractice inadvertently is *patur bi-yedei adam*, exempt from liability "at the hands of man," yet Ḥida tells us that he is liable even at the hands of a human court.

It is basically Ḥida's position that is adopted by at least two later authorities, although the comments found in those sources do not relate directly to the statement of Ḥida. *Misgeret ha-Shulḥan*, cited by R. Eliezer Waldenberg, *Ramat Raḥel*, no. 23, addresses the case of a physician who has erred and there exists an *umdena de-mukhaḥ*, i.e., it is immediately recognizable, that the error occurred because the physician was a *to'eh be-dvar mishnah*. To the rabbinic ear, the term "*to'eh be-dvar mishnah*" has a certain resonance. Literally, the reference is to an error with regard to recorded information. In the context of Ḥida's discussion, the connotation of that phrase is that the physician made an elementary mistake, not an error of judgment but a mistake with regard to facts and information readily available to any medical practitioner. The physician erred because he did not master the available medical information. He did not fully master the corpus of the "medical *mishnah*;" he either did not read the relevant medical literature or did not master what he read. In situations in which everyone recognizes that the error would not have been made by a physician who had been a diligent student and who had assiduously pursued the type of ongoing medical education in which members of the medical profession customarily engage, *Misgeret ha-Shulḥan* declares that the physician is to be held liable even by a human court.

On first impression, and taken by itself, *Misgeret ha-Shulḥan*'s position seems quite remarkable. The harm caused by the physician is neither willful nor wanton. It would seem that the harm arising from his conduct is in the category of the inadvertent harm with regard to which the Tosefta rules that the physician is *patur be-yedei adam*, i.e., the act entails no liability in terms of a human court, but *ḥayyav be-yedei shamayim*, i.e., the physician is liable only in the eyes of Heaven. Yet *Misgeret ha-Shulḥan* declares that error of such nature results in an actionable claim and that the *bet din* will award damages.

Much in the same vein is a ruling issued by Rabbi Eliezer Waldenberg, *Ramat Raḥel*, no. 23, and endorsed by Rabbi Samuel ha-Levi Woszner, *Teshuvot Shevet ha-Levi*, IV, no. 151, with regard to a physician who inoculated a patient with a harmful drug.[7] The physician believed that he was administering the proper medication but it turned out that the medication was inappropriate and proved to be toxic to the patient. In failing to read the label the physician clearly committed an act of malpractice. Both Rabbi Waldenberg and Rabbi Woszner rule that, in such an instance, the physician is to be held liable even by a human court. Again, we are confronted by the same question: Why should the physician be held liable for damages? To be sure, the physician was negligent, but the resultant harm was inadvertent; ostensibly, the applicable rule is that the physician is *patur be-yedei adam*, i.e., insofar as the *bet din* is concerned the physician should be exonerated, and should remain liable only in the eyes of Heaven.

Although none of these authorities cite Ramban in justifying their ruling, it appears to this writer that their rulings flow directly from the comments of Ramban in his *Torat ha-Adam* and that by carefully examining the comments of Ramban one can understand how the rulings of these latter-day authorities were derived. The Gemara, *Bava Kamma* 85a, declares, " '*Ve-rapo ye-rape*—and he shall surely heal'—from here it is derived that the physician has authority to heal." Why is it necessary for explicit biblical dispensation to practice medicine? Why would anyone presume that medical ministration is prohibited? *Tosafot, ad locum*, explain that, in the absence of divine license, in practicing the healing arts a medical practitioner "would appear to be contravening the decree of the King." Or, as Rashi and Rashba, in their respective commentaries *ad locum*, put it, biblical authority to practice medicine is required because otherwise such action would be objectionable on the grounds that "God afflicts and [the physician] heals?" The concern is clearly theological in nature. After all, sickness is a physiological process and God is the author of that process. Thus, the practice of medicine is sheer audacity on the part of man. If so, how dare man intervene? It is therefore necessary for the Torah to declare explicitly that the physician is granted authority to practice medicine. In that declaration the physician is granted divine dispensation to practice the healing arts. Such is the explanation of Rashi, *Tosafot* and Rashba.

Ramban offers an entirely different resolution to the question of why the Torah must explicitly declare "*ve-rapo ye-rape*." Ramban explains that the physician has every reason to shun the practice of medicine for fear of misadventure. If he commits an error and the patient dies, the physician is guilty of manslaughter; if the physician commits an error but the patient survives, he has violated the prohibition against mayhem. Moreover, if the physician causes harm he will be held financially liable as well, at least in the eyes of Heaven. Accordingly, declares Ramban, the import of the dictum "*nittnah reshut le-rofe le-rapot*—authority was given to the physician to heal" is that the Torah tells the physician not to be concerned with regard to inadvertent transgression. The physician need not fear that he will tarnish his immortal soul with sin. The Torah grants the physician authority to practice medicine and assures him that in doing so he is an agent of divine providence rather than a potential transgressor. However, Ramban adds a caveat: "*ve-hu she-nizhar kemo she-ra'uy lizaher be-dinei nefashot ve-lo yazik be-peshi'ah*;" the physician is exonerated from sin and liability on the condition that "he is scrupulous and vigilant in the manner in which it is proper for a physician to be vigilant and that he not cause harm through negligence."

If we take this comment of Ramban and place it next to the words of the Tosefta, we immediately understand that Ramban posits a limitation upon the ambit of rabbinic legislation enacted for the benefit of society (*mipnei tikkun ha-olam*). The Sages of antiquity had a problem. They sought to encourage individuals to study medicine and to enter upon the practice of medicine. But they did not want to grant physicians license to commit malpractice knowingly and wantonly. As a result, determined Ramban, they exonerated the physician "for the perfection of the universe" (*mipnei tikkun ha-olam*), i.e., for the benefit of society, only if a physician is prudent to the extent to which a physician ought to exercise prudence; however, if the physician is negligent in his practice of medicine, he enjoys no immunity whatsoever. The Sages conferred only limited immunity upon the physician. They granted the physician immunity from liability as *adam ha-mazik*, i.e., as "man the tortfeasor," but they limited that immunity to liability for damages arising from non-negligent acts. Accordingly, the physician remains liable even *be-yedei adam* for damage born of medical negligence. Ramban understands the Tosefta as exonerating the physician only in instances of inadvertent non-negligent harm.

Thus it turns out that what at first appeared to be a significant controversy between Ramban and Rabbenu Nissim is a very limited controversy indeed. Rabbenu Nissim regards the physician as having been exonerated totally and completely when *libeih onseih*, i.e., when he has made an honest error of judgment, but not in any other situation. Ramban declares that, if the physician has been negligent, he is liable *be-yedei adam*, even insofar as the human court is concerned. Accordingly, in instances of negligent conduct, there is no conflict at all between the position of Ramban and Rabbenu Nissim; both regard negligent malpractice as an actionable tort. The only controversy between them is with regard to liability in the eyes of Heaven in instances of non-negligent conduct. According to Rabbenu Nissim, absent negligence, there is no liability even in the eyes of Heaven; according to Ramban and *Shulḥan Arukh* liability exists in the eyes of Heaven even in the absence of negligence.

There is one other highly significant limitation upon the liability of physicians. In declaring the physician's liability, the Tosefta employs the term "*rofe uman*." Ostensibly, that term should be translated as "a skilled physician." The word "*uman*" is generally employed as a reference to an artisan, i.e., a skilled craftsman; hence "*rofe uman*" would then be translated as "a skilled physician." A fifteenth-century authority, R. Simon ben Ẓemaḥ Duran, *Tashbaẓ*, III, no. 82, defined that term rather differently. The term "*uman*" is the Gemara's appellation for a *mohel*, a person who performs circumcision. The term *uman*, opines *Tashbaẓ*, connotes a person who uses a metal knife, i.e., a surgeon, and hence a "*rofe uman*" is employed to designate "a surgeon-physician." Consistent with his definition of the term "*rofe uman*," *Tashbaẓ* maintains that the Tosefta declares that it is only a surgeon who is liable for malpractice but that other medical practitioners are not liable. Why is the surgeon liable whereas other physicians are not liable? Because, explains *Tashbaẓ*, a surgeon employs a knife or a scalpel while all other physicians heal by means of medications, salves, ointments, or *merḥaẓa'ot*, therapeutic baths of one kind of another. With regard to treatment carried out without use of a metal implement, declares *Tashbaẓ*, if the physician errs, he is not liable even in the eyes of Heaven.

However, *Tashbaẓ*' analysis of the term "*rofe uman*" might appear to involve a distinction without a difference. *Tashbaẓ* fails to explain the rationale for applying a standard to a surgeon that is different from the standard applied to other physicians. Indeed, Rabbi Waldenberg, *Ẓiẓ Eli'ezer*, IV, no. 13, sec.1, cites the words of *Tashbaẓ*, and exclaims in wonder: "*Atu im adam mashkeh le-ḥaveiro sam u-memito mi-kakh, lo yitḥayyeiv mi-shum reẓiḥah*?—If a person gives his fellow a poisonous potion and kills him, will he not be liable for murder?"

Rabbi Waldenberg's astonishment is somewhat misplaced. We eagerly anticipate the rebuilding of the Temple and with it the restoration of the Sanhedrin to its chambers in the *Lishkat ha-Gazit* within the Temple precincts. Then, if, Heaven forfend, an individual shall stand trial for capital homicide committed by poisoning, an advocate will surely appear to plead on behalf of the defendant and will cite a long line of authorities who, although they affirm that causing of death by means of poison is indeed a form of homicide, nevertheless maintain that poisoning a victim does not constitute capital homicide in Jewish law. Why? Because, according to Halakhah, there cannot be capital punishment without proximate cause.

The concept of proximate cause exists in common law as well and figures prominently in determination of tort liability. But it is extremely difficult to define proximate cause as the concept is understood in common law or in the American legal system. This writer fears that he once offended a law school colleague by casually remarking that proximate cause is what the court finds it to be. To be fair to the American legal system, that may have been a slight overstatement. But the fundamental point is quite clear: Despite a significant body of case law devoted to the formulation of a definition of this legal notion, the concept of proximate cause remains elusive and imprecise.

It is much easier to define the notion of proximate cause in Halakhah. In Halakhah, proximate cause is narrowly defined and, absent proximate cause, there is no capital punishment. Similarly, an *adam ha-mazik*, i.e., a person who performs a physical act that causes property damage, is held liable only if he is the direct cause of the resultant harm. If a person seizes a stone or a rock and throws it at someone else's Ming vase, he can expect to be held responsible both by an American court and by a *bet din*. If he takes the same rock and throws it at the chandelier and as a result the chandelier comes crashing down and shatters the Ming vase, no American court will exonerate the tortfeasor for absence of proximate cause. However, from the vantage point of Halakhah, this individual has committed an act in the nature of *gerama*; the vase was destroyed not by the projectile set in motion by the tortfeasor directly, but by an object set in motion by that projectile. The motion of the chandelier is only indirectly attributable to the person who threw the rock. The force of the chandelier is a *ko'aḥ sheni*, i.e., a new force generated by the force of the rock and hence not directly attributable to the tortfeasor. A person who caused damage by means of *gerama* will not be found liable by a *bet din* (*be-yedei adam*) but is liable in the eyes of Heaven (*be-yedei shamayim*). In such a situation, a *bet din* will not seize the tortfeasor's property in order to collect assessed damages but the tortfeasor will be held liable at the hands of the Heavenly court.

What, then, is the difference between a surgeon who makes a lethal incision and a physician who prescribes a toxic medication? The difference is that a surgeon who performs chest surgery and nicks the aorta is directly responsible for the death of the patient. If, however, he administers a drug, arguably even by injection, the drug works its way through the body and produces various chemical reactions. A chain of multiple causes and effects is set in motion that ultimately culminates in the death of the patient but the act of administering poison is not the direct and immediate cause of death.

The earliest formulation of that distinction is based upon an inference from a statement of Rambam in the context of his formulation of the prohibition against abortion and of an exception to that prohibition in certain cases posing a threat to the life of a pregnant woman. Rambam, *Hilkhot Roẓeaḥ* 1:9, rules that, in the case of a hydrocephalic fetus having a head with a circumference that is too large to pass through the birth canal, an abortion must be performed because the child is a *rodef*, a "pursuer" or aggressor, who, absent intervention, will cause the death of the mother. Rambam adds the comment that the abortion may be performed "*bein be-yad bein be-sam*—either physically or by means of a drug." Why does Rambam find it necessary to describe the various methods that can be employed in performing an abortion? R. Judah Eiyush, *Teshuvot Bet Yehudah, Even ha-Ezer*, no. 14, explains that an abortion performed by chemical means involves only a rabbinic infraction because there is no proximate cause, whereas if the abortion is performed by the physician with his own hands, there clearly is proximate cause and, consequently, the infraction is biblical in nature. Thus Rambam found it appropriate to state that the *rodef* may be eliminated by any means necessary, either by means of *gerama* or, if necessary, directly.

It is precisely this distinction that is reflected in the words of *Tashbaẓ*. *Tashbaẓ* states that the physician can be held liable only in instances in which he is the proximate cause of the harm; however, when there is an intermediate cause with the result that the physician is not the direct cause of the untoward effect, there is no liability, at least not at the hands of a human *bet din*.

However, *Tashbaẓ* makes the rather astonishing statement that the physician who merely prescribes medication will be held liable neither by a human court nor by a heavenly court. The problem is that *gerama be-nizakin*, i.e., inadvertent non-proximate cause of a tort, does occasion liability in the eyes of Heaven. Yet, surprisingly, *Tashbaẓ* declares that the physician is exonerated even in the eyes of Heaven. This difficulty is noted by R. Yitzchak Ya'akov Weisz, *Teshuvot Minḥat Yiẓḥak*, III, no. 104, sec. 1.

R. Chaim Joseph David Azulai, *Birkei Yosef, Yoreh De'ah* 336:7, notes that, in affirming the physician's liability in the eyes of Heaven, both Ramban and *Shulḥan Arukh* do not qualify that statement in any way. Thus, those authorities are apparently in disagreement with the position of *Tashbaẓ* and maintain that a physician is liable in the eyes of Heaven even in instances of *gerama*. Moreover, some authorities, including *Imrei Binah*, *Hilkhot Dayyanim*, no. 30, and *Ẓiẓ Eli'ezer*, IV, no. 13, sec. 2, apparently maintain that harm caused by administration of medication must be regarded as the result of a direct act rather than as the product of *gerama*. Nevertheless, *Shevet ha-Levi*, IV, no. 151, remarks that "it is difficult to rule contrary to the position of *Tashbaẓ*."[8]

NOTES

1. For a discussion of the problem of *asmakhta* with regard to insurance indemnification see Menachem Slae, *Ha-Bituaḥ be-Halakhah* (Tel Aviv, 5740), pp. 79–81.
2. See also the comments of Ramban as cited in *Shitah Mekubbeẓet, ad locum*.
3. For sources concurring in and elucidating Ramban's opinion see *Oẓar Mefarshei ha-Talmud, Bava Kamma*, II (Jerusalem, 5745), p. 33, note 123.
4. For a detailed discussion of the position of *Tosafot* and concurring authorities see *ibid.*, pp. 31–36 and accompanying notes.
5. *Contemporary Halakhic Problems*, IV (New York, 1995), pp. 302–309.
6. The concept of soft determinism is probably best formulated by C. Arthur Campbell, *In Defense of Free Will: An Inaugural Lecture* (Glasgow, 1938) and *idem*, "Is 'Free Will' a Pseudo Problem?" *Mind*, vol. 60, no. 4 (October, 1951), pp. 441–465.
7. See also R. Eliezer Waldenberg, *Ẓiẓ Eli'ezer*, IV, no.13, sec. 1.
8. The foregoing is but a survey of the sources and issues pertaining to liability for medical malpractice in Jewish law. A fuller and more detailed analysis may be found in this writer's "Medical Malpractice in Jewish Law," *Tradition*, vol. 39, no. 1 (Spring, 2005), 72–117.

12

Moral Debate and Semantic Sleight of Hand

If there is to be any meaningful discussion concerning public policy, it must begin with the most basic moral value—truth. So fundamental is truth that no moral system, and indeed no cognitive discipline, would be conceivable without the basic premise that truth be assumed as a meta-principle.

The term "truth" is used in this context, not in the sense of truth-telling, but in the sense of truth-recognition. Every moral system recognizes that, under certain conditions, communication of a falsehood is not only devoid of odium but constitutes a moral imperative. A maniac wishes to know which button, when depressed, will release a nuclear device. In that case, the morally mandated response is self-evident; in other situations the same clarity may not obtain. Truth-telling in the physician-patient relationship is a case in point. Curiously, or perhaps not so curiously, it is usually the physician who advocates full disclosure, while the ethicist may be quite prepared to clothe the lie with moral sanction. Although communication of a falsehood to another individual may

This paper was originally delivered at an international symposium on "Law and Science at the Crossroads: Biomedical Technology, Ethics, Public Policy and the Law," sponsored by Suffolk University Law School in Boston, Massachusetts, October 1993, and is presented as published in *Suffolk University Law Review*, vol. 27, no. 4 (Winter 1993), pp. 1173–1193.

be justifiable or even commendable at times, self-deception ought never be condoned. Consequently, recognition and acknowledgement of factual verities must constitute the first step in the formulation of public policy.

Organ transplants and fetal tissue research designed to preserve human life are themselves entirely unobjectionable. Yet each involves an ancillary issue posing a significant moral problem which, in current debate, has become obfuscated by confusion with regard to matters that are entirely factual in nature.

I. LEGAL DEFINITIONS VS. COMMON PARLANCE

Organ transplants, including the heart, lung, and pancreas, cannot be successfully performed if removal of the donor organ is delayed until cardiac arrest occurs as the culmination of physiological deterioration. Under these conditions, tissue degeneration seriously compromises chances for successful transplantation of those organs. Transplantation of such organs is feasible only if the time at which the patient is presumed dead can be advanced to an earlier point in time. Employment of neurological criteria of death enables the patient to be pronounced dead while the heart still beats. Adopting a "brain death" standard makes transplantation of such organs possible.

The ongoing debate concerning adoption of so-called "brain death" criteria involves absolutely no controversy with regard to either factual or ontological matters. Definitions, by their very nature, are tautologies. The common-law definition of "death" as the "total stoppage of the circulation of the blood, and a cessation of the animal and vital functions consequent thereupon, such as respiration, pulsation, etc."[1] does little more than provide verbal shorthand for statements affirming or negating the presence of those phenomena. The criteria articulated in this definition simply establish the truth—conditions which must exist in order to render the proposition "X is dead" a true statement. The truth of the statement lies in the satisfaction of the criteria, nothing more and nothing less.

The term "death" does not denote a state or a phenomenon semantically distinguishable from the criteria in its definition. The term itself is descriptive, rather than prescriptive, and hence its use is entirely a matter of convention.

The theologian may speak of death as occurring upon departure of the soul from the body. If so, the theologian is making a highly significant ontological statement. If he further employs the common-law definition of "death" he, in effect, declares that "total stoppage of the circulation of blood, and a cessation of the animal and vital functions consequent thereupon" are merely the physical symptoms of a metaphysical event which cannot be perceived directly. Since metaphysical events are not subject to empirical verification or refutation, our hypothetical theologian's assertion cannot become a subject of scientific dispute. Indeed, a logical positivist adopting the verification principle of meaning would say that the theologian's assertion is neither true nor false, but bereft of meaning. Certainly, the clinical physician, in urging adoption of neurological criteria of death, does not pretend to possess some esoteric knowledge of the perambulations of the soul which is denied to the theologian. Indeed, the physician in question may deny the existence of the soul. Whether he commits a theological, metaphysical or lexicographical error in doing so is open to debate, but he surely does not commit the fallacy of self-contradiction.

The theologian, if he is inclined to make a statement equating death with departure of the soul from the body, understands the terms in question in precisely the same manner as they are understood by ordinary mortals. The theologian makes an additional assertion, however, which is neither empirical nor descriptive in the physical sense, but which is causal in nature. The theologian asserts the existence of a causal connection between the physical events denoted by the term "death," *viz*., "total stoppage of the circulation of blood, and a cessation of the animal and vital functions consequent thereupon" and the metaphysical phenomenon of the soul's departure from the body. I do not know whether our theologian intends to assert that the metaphysical event causes the physical effect or, conversely, that the physical phenomenon causes the metaphysical event. We may presume that there is little theological import in resolving the question of "Which came first, the chicken or the egg?"

The association of chickens and eggs, however, has profound import in fowl husbandry, and one may similarly presume that the putative departure of the soul from the body at the time of death is not without theological ramifications. Thus, one understands why, for the theologian, use of the term "death" involves more than a mere convention. To be sure, the theologian well recognizes that words derive meanings through common consensus. However, were the term "death" to be used in common parlance solely as a synonym for the onset of rigor mortis, the theologian would be constrained to coin his own term (perhaps "meta-death" or "soular death") for use as a needed verbal shorthand in theological and moral discourse. In the process, the theologian would perforce augment the esoteric jargon of his discipline.

The foregoing is intended neither as a theological excursus, nor as a tongue-in-cheek manner of exposition by means of trivialization. The point is clear: definitions are tautologies. Definitions are conventions. Hence, definitions are not subject to dispute other than in the purely lexicographical sense of dispute with regard to how words are actually used in common, scholarly or scientific parlance.

Definitions do little more than facilitate communication. Having agreed to use certain words to denote certain persons, places, things, or phenomena, we must then decide what we want to say about them. A "table" is defined as a "smooth, flat slab . . . fixed on legs."[2] Nothing in that definition, however, compels anyone to place food upon the table at meal time, or to use the table as a surface to support writing materials. Assuredly, knowledge of the meaning of the word "table" does not dispatch any person to a furniture store to buy a table posthaste. Man is defined by Aristotle as a rational animal. Yet acceptance of that definition does not compel the conclusion that cannibalism is odious or that carnivorous behavior is morally acceptable. The moral judgment that homo sapiens should be accorded certain privileges and immunities must be established on other than semantic grounds.

Let us assume, arguendo, that dolphins are rational creatures. Would it then follow that dolphins are human beings? Neither the zoologist nor the man in the street would answer in the affirmative. Would dolphins be entitled to non-discriminatory treatment along with fellow rational creatures, i.e., homo sapiens? An Aristotelian moralist might answer this question in the affirmative. It would turn out that, for him, rationality is not the definition of humanity, but the sufficient criterion for certain treatment. The question of dignity, privileges, and immunities to be accorded members of various species within the animal kingdom is a matter falling within the province of moral philosophers, theologians, legislators, and jurists. Pinpointing the physical or cerebral attributes which distinguish various species from one another is the task of the zoologist. Reporting how words are used in either common or scholarly discourse, whether such words are used with precision or imprecision, is the task of the lexicographer whose conclusions constitute a non sequitur insofar as scholars in other disciplines are concerned.

The definition of the term "death" is no different from the definition of any other term. The task of defining the term properly belongs to a lexicographer whose findings are essentially reportorial in nature. Other than in an Orwellian 1984 society, definition by means of legislative fiat is nonsensical. More significantly, the act of definition provides no basis whatsoever for moral conclusions of any nature. To be sure, common usage, which serves as the progenitor of any formal definition, reflects a *vox populi* moral stance which influences language usage. It can hardly be claimed, however, that a necessary causal connection must exist that mandates the inference of a moral cause from a semantic effect. Moreover, even if that was the case, such *argumentum ad gentium* would be subject to scrutiny through the prism of moral theory.

There is nothing mysterious or mystical about the use of most words in human discourse. Nor, with regard to most words, is there anything arcane about the parameters of usage—and hence the definition—of any given term. The common-law definition of "death" is nothing more than the adoption, for legal purposes, of the term as it was—and continues to be—used in common parlance. To be sure, that definition is a tautology—as is every definition. But words are assigned certain meanings because they are needed as a form of verbal shorthand for the communication of concepts. The term "death," particularly as applied to human beings, was made synonymous, not with decomposition of the body, the onset of putrefaction, or with rigor mortis, but with the cessation of respiration and cardiac function precisely because it is at that stage that the human organism is beyond medical treatment. As such, it is no more than an empirical statement devoid of any value judgment. Moralists of bygone ages were perfectly capable of debating the issue of euthanasia, both active and passive, despite this definition—or better, because of the definition. It is precisely because death is defined in terms of criteria which reflect the empirical impossibility of continued medical treatment that there is room for debate concerning withholding of treatment (passive euthanasia) or overt "negative treatment" (active euthanasia) at a stage prior to death when treatment, both positive and negative, is yet efficacious.

Time of death statutes are not lexicographical exercises. Any attempt to categorize them as merely legislative reflections of more precise language usage is an act of either intellectual or moral dishonesty, and possibly both. Nor is it correct to state that such statutes reflect advanced scientific knowledge and expertise. It must be emphasized that there is absolutely no medical, scientific, or factual issue involved in the "time of death" controversy. Newly formulated criteria of death are no more and no less than determinations of who shall be accorded, or better, who shall be denied, standing as a member of the human community with its attendant rights, entitlements and claims. Such a determination is a moral, philosophical, religious and legal issue. Most emphatically, it is not a scientific issue.

Definitions for legal purposes do not, and need not, reflect common usage. A definition for statutory purposes is designed to influence conduct, not speech. Adoption of neurological criteria of death for legal purposes generates a legal state in which a patient manifesting such criteria enjoys the rights, immunities, and privileges, not of a human being, but of a corpse. It is a statement, not of ontological fact, but of how society wishes to treat a human being in that particular physiological state. That, in turn, constitutes no more than the legislative embodiment of a value judgment. Essentially, a legal definition of death represents a decision to withhold treatment from a person manifesting a given clinical profile. It is not a judgment that further medical treatment will be of no avail. No principle, legal or moral, requires a physician to employ therapy which is nothing more than an exercise in futility. It is precisely because the patient is not beyond medical treatment that a determination not to employ treatment is advocated, i.e., it is precisely because bodily functions, including, but not limited to, cardiac activity and body metabolism, can be preserved by continued medical treatment that a decision not to treat is advocated.

II. "BRAIN DEATH": EMPIRICAL REALITY OR MEDICAL MYTH?

"Brain death" represents neither the destruction nor dysfunction of the brain in its entirety. Currently accepted neurological criteria of death, singly or in combination, demonstrate only that specific neurological activities have ceased. For example, absence of elicitable reflexes confirms just that phenomenon and nothing more; absence of reflex activity does not demonstrate that all electrical activity has ceased. Even a flat EEG—which is not regarded as an absolute requirement for establishing brain death—demonstrates only the absence of elicitable brain waves. A flat EEG does not, however, rule out the possible presence of electrical activity below the sensitivity threshold of the apparatus. A British physician has candidly stated that "in the usual clinical context of brain death there is no certain way of ascertaining (other than by angiographic inference) that major areas of the brain such as the cerebellum, the basal ganglia, or the thalami, have irreversibly ceased to function."[3] Other medical researchers report that hypothalamic-pituitary function is maintained after the diagnosis of "brain stem death."[4]

The hypothalamus, a structure that is part of the brain stem, regulates body temperature. It has been shown that hypothalamic activity persists, at least for a time, even in patients in whom "brain death" has been diagnosed.[5] There is also evidence that posterior pituitary function, specifically antidiuretic hormone secretion, persists in "brain dead" patients. Persons in whom the hypothalamus and neurohypophysis are nonfunctional should develop central diabetes insipidus because of the lack of antidiuretic hormone regulation. A number of studies have demonstrated, however, that many "brain dead" patients do not develop such a disorder.[6] One group of researchers reported that only eight and one-half percent of their patients showed clinical manifestations of diabetes insipidus.[7] Recent commentators have noted that the demonstrated phenomenon of residual neurological regulation represents not merely the presence of brain activity, but also brain function in the sense of "organized and directed cellular activity."[8]

Thus, "brain death" criteria are not sufficient for the diagnosis of permanent and irreversible cessation of all brain stem function. Certainly, total neurological dysfunction is entirely compatible with continued cellular metabolism. Unless metabolism has ceased, the tissue perforce remains alive. Theoretically, blood flow studies and radioisotope scanning might be employed to show that perfusion of the brain has ceased. However, although cellular decay of the brain does indeed commence upon cessation of blood circulation, an indeterminate period of time is required for decay of the brain to become complete. Cessation of the flow of blood to the brain cannot in itself be equated with total cellular destruction of the brain. At present, there is no scientific method that serves to establish how much time must elapse following cessation of perfusion for total cellular decay to result. Moreover, it is entirely likely that, physiologically, cardiac activity must cease well before this phenomenon could possibly occur.[9]

Even more significant is the fact that these techniques, in their current state of refinement, simply do not demonstrate that even perfusion of the brain has totally ceased. Researchers responsible for the development of these techniques claim only that such methods may be used to indicate cessation of circulation to the cerebrum, the seat of the so-called "higher functions" of the human organism. They are careful to describe the phenomena which they report as "cerebral death" rather than as "brain death."[10]

These phenomena are entirely compatible with some degree of continued circulation and perfusion of the medulla and the brain stem. In fact, in the original studies, radioisotope techniques did not demonstrate total cessation of circulation to the cerebrum, but only that circulation had decreased below the level necessary to retain its integrity. The scanning methods employed in the original studies did not indicate that all circulation to even a part of the brain, that is, the cerebrum, had been interrupted, but indicated only that the rate of flow was below that necessary to maintain functional integrity. Thus, in a summary of findings which form part of one of the original studies, these techniques are described as "indicative of significant circulatory deficit to the cerebrum."[11] Those studies indicated the presence of up to approximately twenty-four percent of normal predicated blood flow.[12]

More recently, one researcher, claiming that the isotope angiography which he employed was capable of showing termination of carotid circulation at the base of the skull,[13] frankly conceded that posterior circulation may continue with the result that "persistent perfusion and survival of the brain stem" remains a distinct possibility.[14] Another study, involving a small number of pediatric patients, utilized both the isotope bolus technique and cerebral angiography and somewhat surprisingly demonstrated persistent EEG activity despite negative blood flow studies.[15] The authors of that study candidly acknowledged that some circulation, either supplied by the external carotid system or in the form of limited cerebral perfusion, must have been present, albeit undetected, by blood flow studies.[16] Yet another recent study reported that spontaneous respiration was observed in two patients in whom cerebral blood flow studies demonstrated no cerebral perfusion.[17] That finding is truly remarkable and demonstrates the inherent compatibility of negative blood flow studies with even the classic indicator of life.[18] Moreover, it must be emphasized that blood flow studies are neither a legal requirement for pronouncing a patient dead on the basis of neurological standards, nor are they routinely performed as a matter of medical practice.[19]

A neurologist who accepts brain death criteria, Dr. James

Bernat, has candidly conceded that: "[T]he bedside clinical examination is not sufficiently sensitive to exclude the possibility that small nests of brain cells may have survived . . . and that their continued functioning, although not contributing significantly to the functioning of the organism as a whole, can be measured by laboratory techniques."[20] The Uniform Determination of Death Act, however, does specify that a person is dead only if he has sustained "irreversible cession of all functions of the entire brain."[21] Quite apart from ongoing hypothalamic-pituitary function in patients manifesting clinically accepted criteria of "brain death," it is well-established that clusters of brain cells may be perfused and continue to function on the cellular level. As Robert Veatch has noted: "[T]he law does not grant a dispensation to ignore cellular level function, no matter how plausible that may be."[22] Reliance upon neurological criteria of death in jurisdictions that have enacted a statute incorporating the language of the Uniform Determination of Death Act is in violation of the plain meaning of the statute.

The term "brain death" carries with it a certain emotional cachet and appeal. In fact, "brain death" is a misnomer: "brain death" criteria establish irreversible neurological dysfunction, not cessation of metabolic functions; "brain death," when confirmed by blood flow studies, represents the onset of metabolic dysfunction, not necessarily "death" of the neural tissue; and, even when supported by blood flow studies, "brain death" represents confirmed metabolic dysfunction of only a portion of the brain, not of the brain in its entirety. "Brain death" criteria are not designed, properly speaking, to serve as clinical criteria of death, but as proposed criteria for withholding further treatment and for withdrawing life-support systems. This is recognized and acknowledged by physicians who are sensitive to the ethical issues contingent upon this distinction. In a submission to the Working Party on Donor Organs of the Royal College of Physicians, two

British physicians correctly urged that a term such as "mortal brain damage" be substituted for "brain stem death."[23]

None of this is at all novel. The chairman of the Ad Hoc Committee of the Harvard Medical School to Examine the Definition of Brain Death candidly acknowledged:

> I was chairman of a recent committee at Harvard composed of members of five faculties in the university who tried to define irreversible coma. We felt we could not define death, I suppose you will say that by implication we have defined it as brain death, but we do not make a point of that.[24]

Consistent with that view, the Harvard Committee's report setting forth clinical criteria of "brain death" was published under the title "A Definition of Irreversible Coma."[25] Similarly, the statement concerning brain death issued in Great Britain by the Conference of Royal Medical Colleges in 1976 noted that "brain-stem death" is indicative of a hopeless outcome for patients and recommended utilization of such criteria for the purpose of removing patients from a respirator to allow patients to die.[26] Only in 1979 did the Conference of Royal Medical Colleges declare that "brain stem death" may be equated with the death of a person. In a Supplementary Statement for the R.C.P. Working Party on Donor Organs, Dr. David J. Hill stated: "The motives for this change are ethically questionable, as is the logic upon which it is based — *viz.*, the assumption that 'all functions of the brain have permanently and irreversibly ceased.' This statement is, to say the least, doubtful . . . ."[27]

Even though it is a misnomer, medical scientists employ the term "brain death" because laymen comprehend it to mean a physiological state in which any further treatment is not only contraindicated, but ludicrous. Introduction of the term "brain death" is a thinly veiled attempt to justify withholding medical treatment under the guise of redefinition of terms. The purpose of this lexicographical exercise is to secure moral and emotional approbation for a policy that would otherwise be greeted with repugnance and even indignation.

It is the deeply held conviction of many, and probably of the majority, that all human life is sacred and inviolate. Withholding of treatment has the effect of snuffing out human life. Any ad hoc decision to withhold treatment from a dying relative involves a great deal of soul-searching, and frequently engenders feelings of guilt. On the other hand, no one advocates medical treatment or continuation of life-support systems for a corpse. Pronouncing a person dead has the emotional effect of removing any aura of further moral responsibility. Such a process is, however, intellectually dishonest. In a less than fully informed world, semantic sleight of hand may affect popular perception, but it should not be permitted to affect the universe of moral discourse.

III. CONFLICTING VALUE SYSTEMS AND MORAL AUTONOMY

The term "Time of Death Statute" is a misnomer; the only accurate term is "Withholding of Treatment Statute." The sole question worthy of debate is whether treatment should be provided for an irreversibly terminal patient who manifests clinical symptom x, y, or z. This question poses a moral issue, not a question of medical fact or judgment. The physician is uniquely qualified to diagnose illness, describe the physical damage suffered by the patient, make a judgment with regard to the probable prognosis, and assess available modes of therapy. Subsequent to determination of those clinical matters, the decision to treat or not to treat, however, is a value judgment, not a medical decision. Adoption of a brain death statute is nothing other than a moral judgment to the effect that there is no human value which augurs in favor of the preservation of the life of an irreversibly comatose patient.

The argument in favor of withholding treatment from the irreversibly comatose patient can be formulated in one of two ways. It may be asserted that such life is entirely devoid of value and of no moral significance. Those who espouse this position bear the burden of formulating, in a clear and precise manner, the necessary attributes of humanhood which are correlative with human life endowed with value and moral significance. There is surely no reason for accepting neurological dysfunction as the sole point of demarcation between life which is morally significant and life which is devoid of value. It is no accident that many of those who adopt the radical "no value" approach are quite willing to accept other quality of life tests and to adopt the position that absent a certain quality threshold, preservation of life is not a value and generates no imperative. Advocates of the "no value" approach then differ among themselves only with regard to the nature or threshold of the quality of life which constitutes the dividing line.

If moral traditions exercise any meaningful role in the formulation of public policy, it is in the presentation of a value system against which to evaluate proposed policies. It would, of course, be incorrect to assume that all moral and religious traditions speak with one voice with regard to every aspect of any broad moral issue. Nevertheless, universal affirmation of the sanctity of human life in all of its guises is the cornerstone of all moral teaching. Notwithstanding the isolated utterances of some theologians which may lend themselves to such interpretation, it is difficult to find a religious figure of standing who would accept the thesis that any human life is utterly devoid of value. Were adoption of the policies under discussion possible only if predicated upon a value judgment negating the sanctity of such life, those policies would be in opposition to the traditions and values the world's major religions have propagated over a period of millennia.

The argument in support of withholding treatment from

an irreversibly comatose patient, however, may be formulated in an entirely different manner. It is unnecessary to deny the moral value of human life even in a moribund and non-sentient state in order to advocate, in a morally cogent manner, a policy of non-treatment. Arguably, such a policy might be justified on the grounds that it is designed to further other values that, at least under the given circumstances, are more compelling.

By its very nature, a moral system must posit a set of values. Yet no moral system can demand that its adherents promote each and every value in every conceivable situation. Truth-telling is a value. But, surely, all ethicists would agree that not only is telling a lie in order to conceal the location of a dangerous weapon from a madman not a violation of any moral code, but such a lie is morally mandated. Every moral maxim must be understood as qualified by a *ceteris paribus* clause. The posited value is clearly a moral *desideratum* and, in a utopian universe, would always be achievable. In the real world, however, moral values frequently conflict with one another because not all moral values can be pursued or achieved simultaneously. With regard to the example of the madman and the dangerous weapon, both truth-telling and preservation of life are values which should be promoted. But it is impossible to have one's moral cake and to eat it too. Truth-telling in that situation results in loss of human life. Preservation of life will entail a lie.

What does a moral agent do when two values come into conflict with one another? Every system of ethics must either establish a hierarchical ranking of the values it posits or must formulate canons for decision-making which enable a moral agent to adjudicate between competing values. When a conflict exists between truth-telling and preservation of life, the dilemma is easily resolved. Assuredly, in a system of weighted values, a white lie pales in comparison when measured against the value of human life.

In other situations the resolution of conflicting claims that arise from competing values is far less obvious. The Declaration of Independence speaks of men endowed by their Creator with certain "unalienable rights," a phrase synonymous with philosophers' "principles of natural law." The underlying notion is that every individual is created by God and endowed by Him with certain prerogatives which are inalienable in nature. In the eyes of our founding fathers, those rights included "life, liberty and the pursuit of happiness." The philosopher John Locke phrased this notion differently, speaking of life, liberty, and the enjoyment of property. To the American mind, the concept of happiness is apparently reducible, at least in part, to enjoyment of property. The "unalienable rights" of which the Declaration of Independence speaks represent fundamental values. Individuals are endowed with life and have a God-given right to have that life safeguarded and protected. Individuals are endowed with liberty, and no person should interfere with the personal autonomy of any other human being. Individuals are entitled to the pursuit of happiness and to the undisturbed enjoyment of their property.

In the real world, however, the value known as preservation of life frequently comes into conflict either with happiness or with its analogue, preservation of property. After all, society has access to only a finite amount of material resources, or so we are told. What happens when preservation of life simply costs too much? Preservation of life may be deemed too expensive in terms of the expenditure of resources and services in prolonging that life. Alternatively, preservation of life may cost too much in emotional coin because the patient is in pain, the family is in a state of anguish, or the physicians experience frustration because, their diligent ministrations notwithstanding, they are incapable of effecting a cure. What happens when a conflict arises between preservation of life and promotion of happiness? Happiness and elimination of pain are, after all, but two sides of the same coin. In the real world, such values often come into conflict with one another.

Well-intentioned individuals may differ with regard to the proper resolution of such dilemmas. Different moral and religious traditions have certainly presented diverse answers. A moral system distinguishing between "ordinary means" versus "extraordinary means," or which sanctions the withholding of "heroic measures," has not decided that preserving human life with heroic measures or extraordinary means is of no moral value. Rather, it has recognized that certain factors render the mode of treatment heroic or extraordinary because they represent other values which must be compromised or sacrificed to preserve the life in question. The pain and suffering, or even the inconvenience involved, may constitute such a conflicting value. Similarly, the sheer cost of treatment may constitute such a value. The emotional distress and suffering caused to others may also be such a value. Further, a position stating that a woman suffering from cervical cancer need not submit to a gynecological examination at the hands of a male physician asserts that preservation of feminine modesty is such a value. In each instance, the sanction provided for withholding treatment involves a decision that preservation of life simply represents one value among many. Hence, under certain circumstances, preservation of life is rendered subservient to preservation of other values.

It is clear that the Catholic tradition, which posits a distinction between ordinary versus extraordinary means, asserts that preservation of life represents but one value among many. That tradition has, in turn, profoundly influenced the development of Western societal mores and of societal attitudes regarding withholding of treatment. Jewish tradition, on the other hand, teaches that preservation of life is of paramount value and that virtually all other values are rendered subservient to the transcendental value of preservation of human life.

Certainly, public policy should recognize that different moral and religious systems resolve moral dilemmas in different ways. It is established public policy in the United States that diverse systems of moral and religious values be recognized and accommodated. Indeed, heretofore such accommodation was regarded as constitutionally mandated save in the face of a compelling state interest. In manifold areas pertaining to employment, education and family law, legislative fiat and/or judicial mandate require such accommodation. Diverse value systems certainly are entitled to the same recognition and accommodation in matters pertaining to bioethical issues.

Recognition of the claims of diverse moral and religious traditions is essentially a matter of civil liberty. For this reason, it is certainly arguable that the state should not interfere with an individual's right to treatment as a living human organism, even if in a comatose or so-called vegetative state. Similarly, the state is under no parallel obligation to force treatment upon such persons against their previously announced intentions. Nor is the state necessarily compelled to treat the termination of such a person's life as an act of homicide, punishable in the manner set forth in the penal code. The state need merely acknowledge that it respects and accommodates the religious and moral beliefs of all of its citizens and will not treat a person, or allow him to be treated, in a manner which is repugnant to him.

Of course, one who interferes with the legally protected civil liberties of another breaks the law. But society may well declare the appropriate punishment to be that prescribed for violation of civil liberties, rather than that provided for homicide. Thus, no anomaly exists between adoption of neurological criteria of death in a criminal code and incorporation of a so-called "religious exemption" provision in other areas of law. The same principles of liberty and personal autonomy, as well as the provisions of the Free Exercise Clause of the First Amendment, should serve to guarantee that even when statutes provide that neurological criteria may be employed for purposes of pronouncing a patient dead or, more accurately, for purposes of withholding further treatment, such criteria should not be utilized to remove or deny life-support mechanisms in violation of a patient's religious or moral convictions.

To be sure, the First Amendment has long been understood as providing absolute immunity regarding matters of religious belief, but not as providing absolute license in matters of religious practice. As early as 1878, the Supreme Court of the United States ruled that a free exercise claim could not be asserted as a defense against prosecution for violation of statutes which prohibit the practice of bigamy.[28] Not every state interest or concern, however, can justify placing a burden or restriction upon the right to practice one's religion freely. Thus, over sixty years later, the Supreme Court ruled that the state's interest in preventing the littering of public streets could not justify a municipal ordinance which would effectively ban dissemination of religious literature.[29]

More recently, the Supreme Court ruled that a state must ordinarily grant exemption from provisions of law in order to permit the free exercise of religion.[30] Once claimants demonstrate that the challenged regulation imposes some significant burden upon the free exercise of their religion, the burden of proof shifts to the state to demonstrate that the regulation, or the denial of an exemption, is necessary to protect a compelling state interest.[31] Such accommodations can be denied only in the face of "some substantial threat to public health, safety, peace or order."[32] The Supreme Court effectively overturned those decisions in *Employment Division v. Smith*.[33] As indicated by the title of the subsequently enacted Religious Freedom Restoration Act, it may be presumed that Congress has legislatively restored the earlier enunciated standards of free exercise.[34]

It is quite difficult to identify a state interest that is so compelling as to warrant application of neurological criteria of death in violation of a patient's free exercise rights. It must be remembered that the harvesting of organs even in order to save the life of others, laudable as that purpose may be, is not legally permissible unless sanctioned by the deceased or the next of kin. Consequently, the need to preserve the life of another person cannot constitute a compelling state interest under such circumstances since, in matters pertaining to organ transplants, that goal may readily be thwarted. It may also be contended that allowing a patient to occupy a bed in an intensive care unit (ICU) renders that bed unavailable for another patient for whom such a bed may literally be a matter of life or death. Assuredly, the state does have a compelling interest in preserving life and in restoring its citizens to good health. Yet, as applied to the matter under discussion, this argument is entirely specious. Nothing in current law or administrative regulations prevents hospitals or health care professionals from exercising their own judgment in deciding how to allocate scarce medical resources or in deciding which patient to treat when all patients cannot be treated: It is tragic that triage decisions must ever be made, yet emergency room personnel are not infrequently called upon to make such decisions and to do so in accordance with their own best medical judgment. Similarly, patients may be removed from the ICU and placed elsewhere when other patients have a greater need for, or may derive greater benefit from, the ICU facility. It is not at all argued that a free exercise claim can be asserted when doing so would prevent the exercise of sound medical judgment and thereby redound to the detriment of others.

Moreover, the law has long recognized that, even when a free exercise claim cannot be asserted in order to compel privileged treatment, a "zone of permissible accommodation" exists within which the law may legitimately accommodate religious practices. Thus, a school may institute a program of released time in order to facilitate religious instruction,

Sabbath observers may be exempted from restrictions against commercial activity on Sunday, and conscientious objectors may be exempted from military service. In a pluralistic society, recognition and respect for the religious convictions and practices of others is a social value of the highest importance. It may cogently be argued that exemption from a requirement that death be pronounced on the basis of neurological criteria, when such determination would violate an individual's sincerely held religious convictions, is a constitutionally protected right. Even if not constitutionally mandated, such religious convictions are no less deserving of accommodation than are matters of far less pressing concern.

IV. SEMANTIC CONFUSION AND THE ABORTION DEBATE

To a somewhat lesser degree, the same type of semantic obfuscation distorts the debate regarding fetal tissue experimentation. Few moralists, if any, find the actual experimentation problematic in itself. They base their concern upon the fact that the fetal organs necessary for such experimentation are obtained as the result of abortion. Some opponents maintain that the inherent immorality involved in the destruction of the fetus renders any benefit derived from such an act *malum per se*. Hence, public funding of such research constitutes collusion in the antecedent abortion, regardless of whether the abortion would have been performed absent the existence of a research program requiring the abortus.

Many who oppose such research generally, or specifically oppose public funding of such research, focus upon the contention that fetal tissue research, or government endorsement implied by public funding of such research, will inextricably lead to at least a marginal increment in the performance of nontherapeutic abortions. The research proposals under discussion, if successful, will yield therapies designed to cure or to prolong the lives of countless individuals afflicted with life-threatening illnesses. The potential for preservation of life through the intermediacy of abortion must perforce diminish the odium associated with that procedure. As an instrument for good, the act of abortion cannot be perceived as an unmitigated evil. A torn, tormented, and guilt-ridden young woman struggling with the moral dilemma associated with the question whether "to abort or not to abort" will now have forced upon her one additional consideration to be added to the potpourri of social, economic, and moral forces already pushing and tugging in opposite directions. In addition, the involvement of prestigious institutions and respected members of the scientific community, coupled with implied governmental approval evidenced by public funding of research utilizing the aborted fetus, endow the abortion procedure with an aura of moral acceptability. Surely in at least some instances, these factors will tip the decision-maker's scales against preservation of the fetus.[35]

Thus, the debate focuses upon the morality of abortion rather than on the morality of fetal research *per se*. This debate revolves, at least in part, upon whether the fetus is a "person" or a person "in the full sense" of the term. "If this suggestion of personhood is established," reads the majority opinion in *Roe v. Wade*, "the fetus' right to life would then be guaranteed specifically by the [Fourteenth] Amendment."[36]

Curiously, in other contexts, courts have ruled that a fetus does have a "juridical personality." In a unanimous decision of the Supreme Court of New Jersey, Chief Justice Weintraub wrote: "We are satisfied that the unborn child is entitled to the law's protection and that an appropriate order should be made to ensure blood transfusion to the mother."[37]

In *Roe*, the Court recognized that, apart from the semantics of the Fourteenth Amendment, the state has a compelling interest in preserving human life.[38] It is that recognition that gives rise to a particularly troublesome issue. The Court's reasoning is troublesome precisely because the Court conceded that it was not capable of resolving the semantic issue for the simple reason that medicine, philosophy, and theology have not been able to define the moment of the beginning of human life.[39] Since it cannot be demonstrated that the fetus is endowed with human life, the Court concluded, it cannot be accorded the protection of the Fourteenth Amendment.[40]

Whether the protection of the Fourteenth Amendment is limited solely to beings who are indubitably "persons" or whether it extends also to beings whose personhood is more questionable, such as Martians, humanoids, and fetuses, is a matter of constitutional jurisprudence and is certainly debatable. Morally, the matter is analogous to the following scenario: A hunter deep in the woods sees a shadowy figure at some distance. It is unclear whether the figure is a bear or a human being. Fellow hunters are consulted and are equally doubtful. An optical physicist and an ophthalmologist are summoned. They bring prisms, light meters and measuring tools. Upon concluding their examination of both the figure and the environs, they declare that, at the given level of illumination, the human eye cannot make a definitive determination. Thereupon, the hunter fires his rifle and scores a direct hit.

In the unfortunate event that the "shadowy figure" was indeed a person, can there be any question that the hunter manifested depraved indifference to human life and should be prosecuted to the fullest extent provided by law? But what if the body of the "shadowy figure" is never recovered? Granted, for purposes of criminal law, in the absence of a *corpus delicti*, it will be impossible to prove that a crime has been committed. But, morally, does such a person not stand condemned as being at least a "doubtful" murderer? Indeed, even if the bullet struck a bear and not a human being, would the hunter be morally exculpated? Elemental considerations of morality should serve to establish a compelling state interest in the protection of the life represented by a shadowy figure that is possibly human, possibly beast; elemental considerations of morality should serve to establish a compelling state interest in preservation of life that is even possibly human. Assuming that the definition of the beginning of human life is forever beyond resolution, with the result that the fetal corpse is forever buried in the quagmire of scientific ignorance so that evidence of its personhood can never be presented in a court of law, has the moral question been resolved? If not, does public policy not cry out for plugging any semantic loophole that may exist in the legal corpus governing our society?

Some time ago, an eminent scientist and Nobel laureate, Dr. James Watson, made the startling proposal that "birth" be defined not as parturition or emergence of the baby from the womb, but as occurring some seventy-two hours after this event. Consequently, if a baby is not yet "born" and is found to be physically or mentally defective, it could be destroyed with impunity up to the moment of "birth."[41] As a result of lexicographical sleight of hand, infanticide within seventy-two hours of parturition would be relabeled as feticide; since abortion no longer carries with it opprobrium, unwanted babies could be readily (and morally) disposed of in this manner.

In a similar vein, England's Nobel Prize-winning biologist, Dr. Francis Crick, has advocated legislation under which newborn babies would not be considered legally alive until they are two days old and certified as healthy by medical examiners.[42] Michael Tooley, professor of philosophy at Stanford University, would grant even greater latitude. He argues that human babies, even after birth, are no more than kittens and cannot bear rights until they have awareness of themselves as persons.[43] Accordingly, he finds no reason to view with disapprobation the killing of any child within the first two weeks of life.[44]

It is instructive to note, however, that on purely medical grounds, it is difficult to sustain the argument that the fetus is not a human being. Essential criteria of life can be ascertained in the womb even in early stages of pregnancy. The presence of heart function and brain activity has been documented in embryos at six to eight weeks. The most recent investigations disclose that a formed cortex can be perceived visually in the fetal brain on the fortieth day of gestation and that brain waves can be discerned by an EEG by the forty-third day. According to the criteria for the establishment of time of death proposed by the Harvard Ad Hoc Committee, one may conclude that death has occurred only if the patient is unresponsive to external stimuli, if reflexes are absent, if there are no spontaneous movements or respiratory efforts, and if an EEG reveals the absence of brain activity. If any of these criteria are manifest, life must be present. Paul Ramsey and others have argued quite cogently that since the fetus responds to pain, makes respiratory efforts, moves spontaneously, and manifests electroencephalographic activity, it must be deemed a human life even on the basis of the very liberal views of the Harvard Committee.

V. CONCLUSION

The discussion has now come full circle. Neither the determination of the beginning of human life nor the cessation of human life is within the province of the lexicographer. In point of fact, human life is a broad continuum beginning with the formation of germplasm within the gonads and ending only with decomposition of the body in the grave. Between which points on that continuum we choose to assign the appellation "person" to the organism is entirely a matter of convention. How we should relate to the organism at any given point on the continuum is a matter for legal, theological, and moral determination. Each of these disciplines must deal with questions of that nature on the basis of its own axioms, principles, concerns and considerations. Debate may turn upon the relevance of particular physiological phenomena, analogy to antecedent determination of other issues or an appeal to a proof-text regarded as authoritative. The one argument that is entirely irrelevant is an appeal to a definition since definitions are merely conventions. Worse still is an endeavor to change the definition in order to silence the moral debate. Redefinition is nothing other than semantic sleight of hand. Logically, it is as uncompelling as any circular argument; morally, manipulation of definitions, regardless of the morality of the end it is designed to achieve, is itself an odious means and has no place in moral discourse.

To be sure, in a pluralistic society, disparate value judgments with regard to both old and novel questions of moral concern should be anticipated. In a democratic society, public policy must be formulated within broad parameters of social morality to allow for diversity within unity. The strength of American democracy lies in its system of law which reflects a keen sensitivity for the accommodation of diverse value systems in forging "one nation, under God, with liberty and justice for all."

NOTES

1. Black's Law Dictionary 400 (rev. 6th ed. 1990).
2. Webster's New Collegiate Dictionary (1961).
3. Christopher Pallis, *Defining Death*, 291 Brit. Med. J. *666,* 666 (1985).
4. G. M. Hall *et al.*, *Hypothalamic-Pituitary Function in the "Brain-Dead" Patient*, Lancet, December 6, 1980, at 1259; see also *infra,* notes 5-7 and accompanying text (providing further research supporting theory that hypothalamic activity persists after death of brain stem function).
5. Hall, *supra,* note 4, at 1254. Respiration is controlled by the vagus nerve whose nucleus is located in the medulla. Respiratory activity, therefore, cannot continue after destruction of the brain stem or cessation of brain stem activity.

   The beating of the heart is autonomous, although the rate of the heartbeat is controlled by the sympathetic nervous system. In theory, cardiac activity may continue indefinitely, even subsequent to destruction of the brain. Nevertheless, survival of the sympathetic nervous system is probably dependent upon cerebral influences. Hypothermia, which serves to counteract the stimulatory effect of the central system, has been reported in brain dead patients prior to cardiac arrest. Body temperature is regulated by the hypothalamus within the brain. Thus, it is quite possible that *total* cessation of all brain function, including hypothalamic functions, rapidly leads to cardiac death and, conversely, cardiac activity may persist for a relatively short period in brain dead patients only because the patients are not truly "brain dead," i.e., some residual brain functions have not ceased. Cf. David R. Field, *Maternal Brain Death during Pregnancy,* 260 JAMA 816, 818 (1988).

6. Kazunori Arita *et al.*, *Hypothalamic Pituitary Function in Brain Dead Patients*, 16 NOO SHINKEI GEKA 1163, 1171 (1988); Debra H. Fiser *et al.*, *Diabetes Insipidus in Children with Brain Death,* 15 CRITICAL CARE MED. 551, 553 (1987); M. Hohenegger *et al.*, *Serum Vasopressin (AVP) Levels in Polyuric Brain-Dead Organ Donors,* 239 EUR. ARCHIVES PSYCHIATRY & NEUROLOGICAL SCI. 267, 269 (1990); Kristan M. Outwater & Mark A. Rockoff, *Diabetes Insipidus Accompanying Brain Death in Children,* 34 NEUROLOGY 1243, 1246 (1984).
7. A. Grenvik *et al.*, *Cessation of Therapy in Terminal Illness and Brain Death,* 6 CRITICAL CARE MED. 284, 291 (1978).
8. Amir Halevy & Baruch Brody, B*rain Death: Reconciling Definitions, Criteria, and Tests*, 119 ANNALS INTERNAL MED. 519, 520 (1993).
9. See *supra,* note 5, and accompanying text (discussing necessity for cardiac activity to stop before cellular decay of brain can occur).
10. P. Braunstein *et al.*, *A Simple Bedside Evaluation for Cerebral Blood Flow in the Study of Cerebral Death: A Prospective Study on 34 Deeply Comatose Patients,* 118 AM. J. ROENTGENOLOGY, RADIUM THERAPY & NUCLEAR MED. 757, 767 (1973); Julius Korein *et al.*, *Radiotsotopic Bolus Technique as a Test to Detect Circulatory Deficit Associated with Cerebral Death*, 51 CIRCULATION. 924, 924–39 (1975).
11. Korein *et al.*, *supra,* note 10, at 924.
12. See Julius Korein *et al.*, *Brain Death: Angiographic Correlation with*

the Radioisotope Bolus Technique for Evaluation of Critical Deficit of Cerebral Blood Flow, 2 ANNALS NEUROLOGY 1505, 1505–10 (1977).

13. Julius M. Goodman *et al.*, *Confirmation of Brain Death with Portable Isotope Angiography: A Review of 204 Consecutive Cases,* 16 NEUROSURGERY 492, 492 (1985).
14. *Id.* at 496.
15. Stephen Ashwal & Sanford Schneider, *Failure of Electroencephalography to Diagnose Brain Death in Comatose Children,* 6 ANNALS NEUROLOGY 512, 517 (1979).
16. *Id.*
17. Madeleine Grigg *et al.*, *Electroencephalographic Activity after Brain Death,* 44 ARCHIVES NEUROLOGY 948, 948–49 (1987).
18. There have been at least two reported cases of the birth of live babies subsequent to brain death resulting from natural causes. Field, *supra,* note 5, at 816; William P. Dillon *et al.*, *Life Support and Maternal Death during Pregnancy,* 248 JAMA 1089, 1090 (1982). In a third case, the patient satisfied generally accepted criteria of brain death although electroencephalograms showed some slight, unspecific intermittent activity. J. E. Heikkinen *et al.*, *Life Support for 10 Weeks with Successful Fetal Outcome after Fatal Maternal Brain Damage,* 290 BRIT. MED. J. 1237, 1237 (1985). The extensive brain damage evident upon post mortem examination, however, was compatible with clinical findings showing no detectable brain stem functions. *Id.* The spectre of a cadaver producing offspring induces a measure of intuitive skepticism and should certainly give pause in accepting any novel theory defining the mother as a cadaver.
19. Additionally, although patients have manifested commonly accepted "brain death" criteria and their physicians were prepared to rely upon such criteria, the patients subsequently recovered. William D. Goldie & Robert H. Price, *Recovery from "Brain Death" with Absent Evoked Potentials*, 5 J. CLINICAL NEUROPHYSIOLOGY 354, 354 (1988); A. Ogunyemi *et al.*, *Generalized Convulsive Seizure in a Patient with Clinical Features of Brain Death*, 29 EPILESIA 673, 673 (1988). Three patients recovered from apneic coma accompanied by absent brain stem reflexes. Amer SN Al-Din *et al.*, *Coma and Brain Stem Areflexia in Brain Stem Encephalitis (Fisher's Syndrome)*, 291 BRIT. MED. J. 535, 535–36 (1985). The authors cited brain stem encephalitis as the cause of the neurological phenomena manifested in

those patients. *Id.* at 536.

20. James L. Bernat, *How Much of the Brain Must Die in Brain Death?* 3 J. Clinical Ethics 25 (1992).
21. Unif. Determination of Death Act §3, (U.L.A. 1980).
22. Robert M. Veatch, *The Impending Collapse of the Whole-Brain Definition of Death*, 23 Hastings Center Rep., July–Aug. 1993, at 18.
23. Drs. D. Wainwright Evans & David I. Hill, submission to the Working Party on Donor Organs of the Royal College of Physicians, Jan. 23, 1987.
24. Henry K. Beecher, *Definitions of 'Life' and 'Death' for Medical Science and Practice*, 169 Annals N.Y. Acad. Sci. 471, 471 (1971).
25. See *A Definition of Irreversible Coma*, 205 JAMA 337, 340 (1968) (stating clinical criteria of brain death). Criticism that use of this term "perpetuates confusion in the medical field between the state of being permanently unconscious, as are patients in a persistent vegetative state, and that of being dead" is unwarranted. *Deciding to Forego Life-Sustaining Treatment, A Report on the Ethical, Medical and Legal Issues in Treatment Decisions,* Report of the President's Commission for the Study of Ethical Problems in Medicine and Biomedical and Behavioral Research, at 173 (Mar. 1983). The distinction between irreversible coma and systemic death is clear and precise. Moreover, the persistent vegetative state is readily distinguishable from irreversible coma.
26. Christopher Pallis, *ABC of Brain Stem Death,* 286 Brit. Med. J. 209, 210 (1983). This is the purpose for which neurological criteria are recognized in Sweden and Poland. *Id.* In those countries, manifestation of brain death criteria is not unequivocally equated with death, but is accepted as warranting withdrawal of ventilating support. *Id.* Consequently, organ removal is prohibited in those countries for transplantation purposes while the heart is still beating. *Id.*
27. Dr. David J. Hill, supplementary Statement for the R.C.P. Working Party on Donor Organs, Jan. 23, 1987.
28. Reynolds v. United States, 98 U.S. 145, 162 (1878).
29. Schneider v. State, 308 U.S. 147, 163 (1939).
30. Sherbert v. Verner, 374 U.S. 398, 403 (1963).
31. *Id.* at 407.

32. *Id.* at 403.
33. 494 U.S. 872, 882–89 (1990).
34. Pub. L. No. 103-41, 107 Stat. 1488.
35. It is certainly not uncommon for women generally disposed against abortion to decide to terminate an unwanted pregnancy. Such women experience a significant degree of cognitive dissonance. Michael B. Brachen, *The Stability of the Decision to Seek Induced Abortion*, RESEARCH ON THE FETUS: APPENDIX, HEW Publication No. (OS) 76-128, at 16-15. Thus, it is not surprising that conflict during decisionmaking is prevalent. *Id.* at 16-16. The percentage of women who undergo at least one change of decision regarding abortion is reported to be approximately one-third. *Id.* at 16-2, 16-16. Given the vacillation which exists, any relevant factor may become decisive in reaching a decision. Without statistical data, it is impossible to predict the percentage of women for whom the deciding factor would be the beneficial aspects of participating in fetal tissue transplantation projects and for whom the absence of such projects would induce a decision not to abort. It is certain that for at least some women, this will be the deciding factor.
36. Roe v. Wade, 410 U.S. 113, 156–57 (1973).
37. Raleigh Fitkin-Pollak Morgan Memorial Hospital v. Anders, 42 N.J. 421, 423, 201 A.2d 537, 538 (1964).
38. *Roe*, 410 U.S. at 154.
39. *Id.* at 159.
40. *Id.* at 158.
41. A Prism Interview: Nobel Laureate James D. Watson: Children from the Laboratory, 1 PRISM 13 (May, 1973).
42. *Id.*
43. Michael Tooley, *Abortion and Infanticide*, 2 PHIL. & PUB. AFF. 37, 60-61 (1972).
44. *Id.* at 61–62.

Index of Biblical and Talmudic Sources

BIBLE

MISHNAH AND TALMUD

General Index

C

G

U